Badgers

Badgers

Ernest Neal & Chris Cheeseman

Illustrated by
John Davies
and
Michael Clark

T & A D
POYSER
NATURAL
HISTORY

© T & A D Poyser Ltd

First published in 1996 by T & A D Poyser Ltd
24–28 Oval Road, London NW1 7DX

Typeset by Phoenix Photosetting, Chatham, Kent
Printed and bound in Great Britain by
the University Press, Cambridge

A catalogue record for this book
is available from the British library

ISBN 0-85661-082-8

Contents

The colour plate section can be found between pages 146 and 147.

List of Colour Plates

1. Sow (at back) with two well-grown cubs, still suckling after summer drought, July.
2. Part of a very large social group. Essex. Photo Don Hunford.
3. Albino. Note pink eyes and lack of melanin in hair and claws. Photo Gordon Burness.
4. An erythristic and normally-coloured cub from the same litter. Photo Michael Morgan.
5. Adult boar setting scent on sow.
6. A sow gripping cub by neck prior to dragging it down the entrance. Photo Jill Hutchinson.
7. Badgers at entrance leading to a coal mine. Northumberland. Photo Jill Hutchinson.
8. Foraging in a bluebell wood. Photo Ted and Glen Coleman.
9. Climbing wire netting (see p. 10). Photo Ted and Glen Coleman.
10. Yawning. Note dentition. Photo Jill Hutchinson.
11. Sow bringing back a bundle of green grass as bedding.
12. Grooming session. Photo Don Hunford.
13. Badger asleep in couch. Photo C. Cheeseman.
14. Sow suckling well-grown cubs. Photo Eric Ashby.
15. A litter of five cubs, estimated 3–4 days old, discovered in a large heap of hay in a barn. Somerset. 30 January.
16. Cub aged about 8 weeks by sett entrance.
17. Woodland sett showing the ground outside hard and smooth, caused by cub play. Mud marks may be seen on the scratching tree.
18. Badger nest in hollow tree with bedding overflowing. Sweden, August.
19. An 'up-and-over' made by badgers when crossing a hedgebank bordering a Somerset lane; March.
20. Remains of a wasps' nest dug out the previous night. September. Photo Frank Hawtin.
21. American badger, *Taxidea taxus*. North America. Photo Pat Morris.
22. Hog badger, *Arctonyx collaris*. S.E. Asia. Photo Ardea Photographics.
23. Honey badger, *Mellivora capensis*. North Kenya.

Acknowledgements

We would like to express our great thanks and indebtedness to all those whose writings we have consulted and the many correspondents who over the years have shared their experiences of badgers and provided much valuable data. In particular we would like to thank Dr Rosie Woodroffe and Dr David Macdonald for recent data, some of it unpublished, on social and reproductive aspects; Keith Neal and Dr Roger Avery who made available the results of four years' observations at a sett in Somerset; Chris Ferris for allowing us to quote from her remarkable diaries; Dr Tim Roper for the use of figures and data concerning sett excavations and with Jude Moore for unpublished data of atmospheric conditions within a sett; Dr Warren Cresswell for providing data on badger weights in the south-west; Dr Julian Brown for recent data and figures of spool-and-line tracking; Professor Poul Valentin-Jensen for permission to use diagrams related to locomotion; George Barker and the late Dr Keith Bradley for unpublished data on diet; Dr Herbert Hofer for the use of graphs showing variation of diet with habitat, and Dr Hugh Griffiths for maps concerning population densities in Europe.

We also thank Dr Lucy Rogers (CSL) for help over analysing data and commenting on the manuscript; Peter Mallinson (CSL) and Judi Ryan (CVL) for help with data analysis; Dr Richard Clifton-Hadley (CVL), Neil Curwen (farmer), Andrew Turnbull and other MAFF colleagues for comments on the TB chapter; Elizabeth Pointer and colleagues at the Department of Transport for provision of figures on the cost of badgers on roads; Dr Mike Swan (Game Conservancy Trust) for information and comments on badgers and game rearing, and Paul Butt (ADAS) for details of Kent County Council's problem sett on Romney Marsh.

We also thank most warmly members of the Mammal Society and Badger Groups all over the U.K. who supplied data of sett distribution and habitat, and in particular, Clem (E.D. Clements), who took endless trouble co-ordinating their efforts, analysing the data and producing the invaluable table of over 23,000 setts for this book. Many other people have helped us in a great variety of ways and we apologise if we have unwittingly omitted those we should have included.

Last but not least, we would like to express our warmest gratitude to our wives for their invaluable support and in particular, the enormous help given by Gill Cheeseman in the preparation of the manuscript.

Many of the photographs in this book were provided by Ernest Neal. Others have allowed us to use some of their finest badger pictures for which we are very grateful. We also thank our two artists: John Davies, who so skilfully provided sketches which add so much to the attractiveness of the book, and Michael Clark for outstanding drawings made for previous editions.

Foreword

Since writing *The Natural History of Badgers* (1986) much research has been done which has added considerably to our understanding of the badger, particularly concerning the social behaviour, ecology and population dynamics of the Eurasian species. A high proportion of this research in Britain was initiated through the need to assess scientifically the possible implication of badgers in transmitting bovine tuberculosis to cattle and provide the necessary understanding for controlling the disease. It is ironical that much of this excellent work might never have been attempted but for this complex and distressing problem.

This book is a major revision of the 1986 edition. I greatly welcome Dr Chris Cheeseman's contribution as co-author. He has been in charge of badger research authorised by the Ministry of Agriculture and Fisheries at Woodchester Park, Gloucestershire since its inception and is responsible, along with his co-workers, for much new understanding of the badger's world. This book, in order to be comprehensive, inevitably contains much factual material which was present in the previous edition. However, there has been so much new material to add, more evidence to submit and exciting new discoveries to include that many chapters, the later ones in particular, have been altered considerably. We have also changed the sequence of chapters and amalgamated some of them; bovine tuberculosis has been dealt with fully in a separate chapter, a number of illustrations and tables have been added or substituted and new artwork incorporated.

Between us, Chris and I have studied badgers for over 80 years; it has been very rewarding to see from those early beginnings how many other scientists and naturalists have caught the badger-watching bug and contributed so greatly to the understanding of these animals. It is the aim of this book to attempt to synthesise the extensive knowledge which now exists and make available to the general reader a summary of what has previously only been obtainable from scientific papers.

We make no apology for including what has been described as 'anecdotal' material. Most examples included have been the result of correspondence received over many years from responsible badger watchers whose observations in many instances have been as reliable as those contained in scientific papers. It has been our experience that such material often stimulates further research which either contradicts, confirms or extends our understanding of the behaviour described. We have selected this material with care and the reader is left in no doubt whether such inclusions are 'anecdotal' or substantiated and can be judged accordingly.

Badgers have now acquired a special place in the affections and interest of a much wider spectrum of people than ever before. Through television their charming and intriguing behaviour has been enjoyed by millions thanks to the patience and skill of such outstanding cameramen as Eric Ashby. Many viewers will also have nostalgic memories of the series of programmes, *Badger Watch*, when, thanks to the sophisticated techniques of the BBC, badger behaviour was shown 'live' using remotely controlled infra-red cameras. Other programmes such as *Brockside* have almost literally brought badgers into our homes. But many people have not been content with arm-chair viewing and have gone out of the way to watch badgers for themselves. In this way they have discovered the thrill of watching wild mammals at night and experienced the deep satisfaction of making intimate contact with the natural world.

Nevertheless, while badgers have given such pleasure to many, others have continued to persecute and molest them. Now, at last, in this country, legislation affords them and their setts protection from cruelty and unwarranted interference. However, it is one thing to have legal protection, quite another to see that it is enforced. It is encouraging that all over the country a remarkable network of badger groups has been formed which, apart from studying, enjoying their watching and helping with local problems, co-operate with the police as guardians of the badgers and their setts in their areas.

The world of badgers is in some ways analogous with the human world. It is made up of large numbers of individuals grouped together in discrete social groups, each badger having its own distinctive personality and temperament. Like us, their behaviour is greatly influenced by their need for homes and living space, and being social creatures like we are, they too have their problems of learning how to live together . . . and with us.

Ernest Neal (Bedford, 1995)

CHAPTER 1

Introduction

BADGERS are members of the weasel family, the *Mustelidae*, a group of mammals, typically with rather long bodies carried on short legs. They all possess musk glands which produce secretions, usually strong smelling and often used defensively, for communication, or both. This very successful family of small to medium-sized carnivores contains a number of familiar species which illustrate very well the evolutionary principle of adaptive radiation. Thus the ancestral forms were less specialised forest dwellers, but during the course of evolution they diversified greatly into highly specialised species now exploiting a wide range of habitats.

Living in Western Europe today, the more typical mustelids are terrestrial, such as the weasel (*Mustela nivalis*), stoat (*Mustela erminea*) and polecat (*Mustela putorius*) which show a progression in size and so fill different niches because the size-ranges of their prey are different. A less familiar terrestrial species, the much larger wolverine (*Gulo gulo*) has become adapted to the more severe conditions of Northern Europe and America.

By contrast the pine marten (*Martes martes*) has become largely arboreal. It is a marvellous climber and acrobat, being beautifully adapted to life in the trees of the more northern forests. In Britain, however, it appears to be quite as much at home in rocky and more open habitats. The very similar beech marten (*Martes foina*) has very comparable adaptations but does not compete much with the pine marten as it favours deciduous woodland and more cultivated land, and even urban areas. Although its range overlaps the pine marten's, it tends to have a more southerly distribution; it does not occur in Britain.

Another highly specialised mustelid is the otter (*Lutra lutra*) which has become largely aquatic. Although quite at home on land it is only when seen in water that one appreciates how perfectly it is adapted for its mode of life.

Finally, there is the Eurasian badger (*Meles meles*) which has many adaptations for a fossorial life, spending long periods below ground in an extensive burrow system it has excavated. Feeding largely on invertebrates and being much more omnivorous than other mustelids, it competes very little with them for food.

Thus, through this considerable diversity, a number of closely related species can live together in the same region by exploiting different niches.

The Mustelidae is divided into five subfamilies: the Mustelinae which includes the stoats, weasels, polecats, martens and wolverines; the Mellivorinae with a single species, the honey badger or ratel; the Melinae which contains the true badgers; the Mephitinae, the skunks; and the Lutrinae, the otters.

THE EURASIAN BADGER

The name badger is probably derived from the French word *bêcheur*, a digger (Harting 1888). However, it has not been in use for very long because up to the middle of the 18th century, the names 'brock', 'pate', 'grey' and 'badget' were used in parts of England, particularly the former which has given rise to many place names. Others include 'brochlach' (Scottish Gaelic) and 'broc' (Irish Gaelic). In southern Ireland it is sometimes referred to as 'earth dog' and in China 'the sweet-potato pig'.

The first badgers Ernest ever saw in the wild was in 1936 (Neal 1977). He was returning from a mothing expedition in a wood in the Cotswolds and was quietly wandering down one of the rides when he heard a great commotion going on in the wood to his right. Obviously several sizeable animals were rushing about among the dry beech leaves, occasionally making high-pitched yelps similar to those made by puppies when playing together boisterously. He tried to get near, but in spite of the noise they were making they heard him and all he managed to obtain was a fleeting glance of several badgers stampeding for home. Approaching the spot, all he could see were the gaping holes of a large sett. He vowed he would try to see them properly the next night! That occasion turned out to be a red-letter day in his life as it started him off on a study of these intriguing animals over more than 50 years. The following account is based on the field notes Ernest wrote up afterwards.

> I set out in high hopes about an hour before dusk. Approaching up-wind as quietly as possible, I crept under a box bush and lay down on the ground some 8 metres from the main holes. It was not a good vantage point as there was a ridge which obscured my view of the larger entrances, but I dared not go closer as the light was still good. Everything was quiet except for a few birds returning to their roosting trees. A persistent cuckoo stuttered as it flew over the wood 'cuck-cuckoo', 'cuck-cuckoo', and a pair of carrion crows noisily advertised their return to a fir tree.
>
> Dusk was deepening when my attention was riveted by a loud scratching noise going on just over the ridge. It was the unmistakable reaction of an animal to its parasites and I knew that at any moment I should get my first proper sight of a badger.

Within a minute or so the scratching ceased and a grey form came into view. The badger was clearly visible as it set off at a steady trot towards its feeding grounds.

I hoped this was not the end, so I kept quite still and before long had my reward. A little striped face looked over the ridge, and then another, then both disappeared again to the accompaniment of a loud yelp as one cub playfully bit the other. As it was now nearly dark, I cautiously came out from under my bush and carefully raised myself on to a bough about a metre up a lime tree. This gave me a good view of the sett, and with my back to the trunk I was not noticed. I shall never forget that scene! Instead of seeing two cubs as I expected, there were five, and soon they were all romping around the entrances of the sett and tumbling over each other as they bit and growled. They were quite small, no bigger than large cats and as playful as kittens. An adult was there too, probably the mother; she sat on one side as the cubs played together. I presumed it had been the boar that I had previously seen going off. A new noise broke out when one cub found an old treacle tin in which a stone had become lodged; for a long time they pawed and leapt on it, fighting hard for possession and giving out a series of excited yelps.

Then the noise subsided and the work of the evening commenced. They left the vicinity of their home and rooted among the leaves and stones for food. They seemed to be everywhere; I wondered what they would do if they came my way. It was not long before I knew, as one inquisitive cub came snuffling in my direction pushing its sensitive snout into every patch of leaves. I held my breath as it passed immediately below my feet without an upward glance — its head no more than 60 cm from my shoes. But finding it was on its own, it ran off towards the others. Gradually the noises grew fainter as all the badgers moved off through the wood. It was now possible to relax; I came off my perch and left them to their feeding.

Since that time, we have watched badgers many hundreds of times, occasionally together, more often under very different circumstances. We have learnt much more about the best techniques for watching them — these will be described in detail later in the book. However, all badger watchers will agree from their own experiences that when they saw badgers in the wild for the first time it was a very special and memorable event and for many the start of a long association with these intriguing animals.

CHAPTER 2

General Characteristics

EXTERNAL FEATURES

BADGERS spend much of their time underground and are phenomenal diggers; many of their characteristics are adaptations to this fossorial mode of life.

A badger is very powerfully built. It has rather a small head, thick, short neck, long and wedge-shaped body and a very short tail. The body is carried on short, but extremely strong limbs and the feet are armed with strong claws. These characteristics all help to make the animal a very efficient digger capable of working heavy material in confined spaces.

The badger has a rather elongated snout which it uses when rooting, much in the same way as a pig. The end of the snout (rhinarium) has an almost rubbery texture, and being flexible, the badger is able to peel it back away from the upper jaw when probing for food or digging in the ground. This lessens the risk of injury to this very sensitive area and prevents particles getting up the nostrils.

It would appear from its anatomy that the badger is capable of closing the nasal canal by muscular action about 5 mm from the openings of the nostrils. It is not easy to see if this happens in a live badger; but if it does, it would certainly serve a very useful purpose during digging operations. However, under dusty conditions, a badger will repeatedly blow out air through the nostrils, so the mechanism does not appear to be wholly effective.

Vibrissae (whiskers) are present on the snout. These are long, stiff, black hairs with a supply of nerve endings at the base. They act as tactile sense organs. In the badger they are shorter and far less conspicuous than those of the otter, cat or rabbit. As with other animals that pick their way through narrow spaces and thick vegetation, the vibrissae probably help the badger gauge the width of an opening. This applies especially to those which project sideways and arise from a region near the front end of the facial stripe. However, the four which project in various directions from above each eye probably warn the animal of anything near enough to damage that organ.

FIG 2.1   *Head of an old boar showing rhinarium and whisker pattern.*

The eyes are small in comparison with the size of the head and appear to be of far less importance than the other sense organs.

The ears, like those of many other animals which do a lot of digging, are small and lie close to the side of the head. They are tipped with white. Although they are almost rigid, badgers can move the posterior ridges forwards, thus closing the aperture. This happens automatically when digging in loose soil — a useful adaptation which helps to keep the ears clean.

The limbs are extremely efficient digging tools. Fore and hind limbs are of comparable size and their musculature is exceptionally well developed, especially in the former. A badger's immense strength was demonstrated when Chris saw one tip up a huge stone weighing 25 kg in order to get at food placed underneath it!

FIG 2.2   *Badger about to tip up a stone weighing 25 kg in order to get at food placed underneath it.*

The feet are broad and strong and have five digits, the hind feet being smaller. Both are protected on the underside by a very thick cornified layer. There are also special pads of dense connective tissue which form cushions over those joints where most pressure is borne when digging and running. These pads make the characteristic impressions of a badger's spoor and consist of five separate digital pads near the tip of each toe and a broad plantar pad which covers the joints between all the toes and the metapodials. When walking, the wrist and heel, which are behind the plantar pad, are kept slightly off the ground in the digitigrade manner so they only appear in the spoor in soft mud and snow.

The claws, unlike the cat's, are non-contractile, those of the fore feet being much longer and stronger than those of the hind. It is surprising that with so much digging, the front claws become far less worn than the hind. Only in very old animals is wear in the fore claws noticeable but wear is seen in the hind claws in quite young animals. A possible explanation could be that the claws of the front feet grow faster than the hind ones to compensate for greater wear; this happens in mongooses and other carnivores that dig a lot. However, it may partly be due to the different manner in which the fore and hind feet are used in digging (p. 44).

The claws are not only used for digging but are useful when grooming; they also act as defensive weapons. In this connection, J. MacNally (1970) writes:

> I wondered how injuries, sustained by terriers when badger digging, could be caused, until by chance I saw a boar fighting off three terriers in a cairn. He came time after time up to the rocky threshold of the cairn, driving the dogs out with lightning slashes

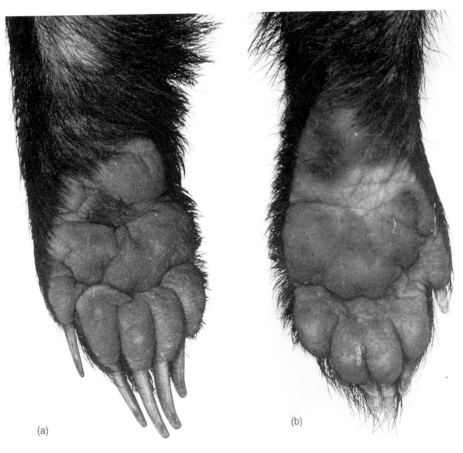

FIG 2.3   *Fore foot (a) and hind foot (b) of the same badger.*

to right and left with his long-clawed front feet. I no longer wondered how a terrier could have hair, skin and flesh torn off its head and left dangling.

LOCOMOTION

A badger's movements are related to its size and shape. It is a moderately heavy animal (p. 12), with a rather long back, so the spine is kept fairly rigid to give the body sufficient support. It is therefore unable to arch its back as much as shorter animals, or pounce like a fox or cat. As the limbs are of comparable length, the back is kept horizontal during locomotion, and having short legs which move quite rapidly, it sometimes appears to glide along.

FIG 2.4   *Footprint of fore foot in soft mud showing heel marks.*

When walking slowly, there are usually three legs supporting the body at any one time. The legs are moved symmetrically, with the left ones repeating those of the right half a stride later. When the trail of a walking badger is followed, you can see that the tracks of the smaller hind feet are often superimposed on those of the front but they do not always register exactly. The tracks are placed near to the median line but not so completely as a fox.

When a badger trots, its body is supported by two diagonal legs at any one time. This is the most common form of locomotion when a badger is moving fairly rapidly, as when going from one sett to another or to its feeding grounds. When trotting, the head is held low down and moves gently from side to side, the hind quarters swaying in sympathy but in a more pronounced manner. However, trotting is not continuous as badgers stop at frequent intervals to listen. The trail made when trotting shows the pad marks further apart than when walking; they are usually not registered.

When a badger is really in a hurry it will gallop. It does this when badly frightened or in pursuit of another during a territorial fight. When galloping, the legs are moved asymmetrically and at times the body may be completely unsupported. The trail made when galloping shows the tracks well spread out and not registered. A badger galloping in front of a car kept up a speed of 25–30 km h^{-1} (E, Neal, pers. obs.). They cannot keep up a gallop for long, as mentioned in a letter to *The Field* (Mallinson 1954):

At about 22.30 on a moonlight night I suddenly became aware of a most extraordinary noise. At first I thought it was an engine with a leaky boiler on the distant railway line, but I quickly realised it was close and drawing near. Then into view came two badgers, one behind the other. They were running as hard as they could, wheezing and blowing as if in the last stages of exhaustion. They pounded past me and through a wire fence. Badger number one continued on into the wood, but badger number two suddenly collapsed. He stretched and rolled from side to side in the dewy grass, exactly like a dog, puffing and wheezing all the time. I slipped through the fence and turned a powerful torch on him, but he continued to roll about until I was ten feet from him, when he stopped blowing, stared at me intently, scrambled to his feet and after a moment's hesitation, lumbered away.

When interpreting badger tracks it should be borne in mind that the prints of the fore feet are at least 5 mm broader than the hind and that in the former the inner toes are set further back. The marks of the claws are often conspicuous, especially in the fore foot, and their impressions are further away from the digital pads than in the hind. The width of the fore foot of an adult male of about 12 kg is around 50 mm compared with 45 mm in an adult female of about 10 kg. However, much larger prints do occur, up to about 65 mm for a very large boar.

Climbing takes place occasionally although badgers are not the best build and weight to climb well. Their usual reason for climbing trees appears to be to find slugs. On wet nights slugs often browse on algae and lichens on the trunk, and if the bark is rough enough, as in elders, a badger will climb like a bear, clasping the trunk with both fore and hind feet, getting a grip with its claws. The mud from the feet and the marks of its claws may sometimes be seen to a height of about 5 m, but this usually happens only if the trunk is sloping. A vertical trunk is seldom climbed successfully, and then only when the bark is rough. Chris Littlejohn was able to film a badger climbing a vertical birch tree to a height of 5 m to reach

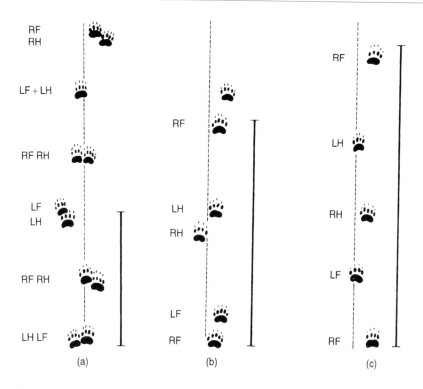

FIG 2.5   *Tracks of badgers when (a) Walking (hind foot may sometimes register completely with fore); (b) Trotting; (c) Galloping, showing stride length (the fifth toe does not always show). Source: after Jensen (1959).*

food placed on a bird table. Also, Glen Coleman successfully photographed badgers climbing wire netting erected to keep rabbits out of a field. They chose a place near a stile using their claws to get a grip. When they reached the stout wooden bar at the top, they balanced on it for a while using all four feet and had a good sniff before descending vertically down the other side, completely ignoring the horizontal foot rest of the stile (Plate 9). When playing, badgers will clamber over logs and fallen trees and sometimes use the latter as a bridge to get across a stream or ravine.

Occasionally badgers have been known to fall into swimming baths which have been emptied for the winter. M.R. Dunwell describes such an incident which occurred one February. The badger was found one morning curled up in a pile of leaves in one corner of the pool. Some rough planks which had been nailed together were placed up the side as a ramp but the badger could not be persuaded to use them; instead it used one corner and tried to climb the vertical wall. Slipping back, it tried the reverse procedure, standing on its front legs with its underside facing the corner and trying to climb up backwards. It even stood on one front leg so as to have three legs working at the wall. It could not quite manage it, and when left alone, retired to its nest of leaves. It later escaped unseen, presumably with the help of the planks.

There was a rather similar instance when two children discovered a badger in an empty swimming pool at Pill, Avon. Although the pool had been drained, it had up to 150 mm of water and ice over three-quarters of its floor. The badger was found curled up in the driest corner. A long plank was arranged as a ramp and the boys tried to encourage the badger to freedom. Its first approach to the ramp was in reverse and it backed up about a metre before losing its footing. Eventually, induced to use a more orthodox direction, it went trundling up the plank and away. A short film of this saga was shown on television by the BBC after the news. It is interesting that in both these instances the badger tried to go up backwards. This appears to be the usual method when climbing is difficult.

FIG 2.6 *Badger climbing an elder tree after slugs.*

Badgers can swim well, although they usually prefer to cross a stretch of water by other means. Badgers which occupied a sett near the River Yeo in Devon would regularly come out at dusk, make their way to the river, 'belly flop' into it and swim across to the other side where there were good foraging grounds.

Mark Fisher (pers. comm.) described how his tame badger swam across a tarn in the Lake District, Cumbria, at a point where it was about 40 m across. It held its head high, snorting quite a lot and swimming with the usual dog-paddle technique. Others who have kept badgers as pets have commented on their liking for water and their ability to swim well.

Sylvia Shepherd (1964) related how her tame badger 'Brocky' took a bath most nights in hot weather. It would lie on its back across the beck, damming it up until the water flowed over its stomach. It used the same place each evening but would never use the lake for that purpose.

Major Seale, the Coastal Warden for the National Trust at Newquay, Cornwall, had a tame badger which was a marvellous swimmer. It loved swimming in the sea and became quite a local tourist attraction.

WEIGHTS AND MEASURES

The average size of adult badgers varies considerably throughout their range. A sample of 31 males from south-west England which were measured (Neal 1977) gave an average head–body length of 753 mm (range 686–803) and average tail length of 150 mm (range 127–178). In females the corresponding figures were 72 mm (range 673–787) and 150 mm (range 114–190). The average total lengths came to 903 mm for males and 874 mm for females. From another sample from south-west England (Fargher & Morris 1975), one male measured 880 mm plus a tail of 160 mm, total 1040 mm, and a female, 880 mm with a 330-mm tail, total 1010 mm. However, some much smaller animals had much longer tails than the above, including a male and female both with tails of 200 mm.

Badgers are heavy for their size, but weights vary considerably according to the time of year and the food available. For 16 years, Chris has regularly live trapped and weighed badgers from Woodchester Park, Gloucestershire. The comprehensive data from this exercise demonstrate the seasonal change in weights of adult males and breeding and non-breeding females (Fig 2.7; unpubl. data). Males were almost exactly 1 kg heavier than females throughout the year. All animals were heaviest in the October–December period, illustrating the effect of fat deposition during the late summer and autumn. Lowest weights occurred between April and June following the utilisation of this stored fat when food is more difficult to obtain. Breeding females were significantly lighter than non-breeding ones during the latter period owing to the prolonged lactation.

The loss of fat during the spring period varies according to the severity of the winter. In mild damp winters in south-west England badgers are active on most nights except for a brief spell, usually in December, when they feed very little (p. 97). Under these conditions they use up less fat as more food is available. But when winters are cold and/or springs dry, food is scarce and weights drop to very low levels. One sow suckling cubs at the time of her death weighed only 6.7 kg. In Fig. 2.7 these yearly variations average out as the data cover so many years.

Average weights vary considerably according to the available food in the territory. Woodchester Park has the highest known badger density anywhere, and it is not surprising that figures are lower here than for some other areas. Thus for the whole year the average weight for adult males was 9.3 kg and for females, 8.09 kg (non-breeding, 8.23 and breeding, 7.97). In a sample of 117 animals mainly from Somerset (Neal 1986), the average for adult males was 11.6 kg (range 9.1–16.7) and for females, 10.1 (range 6.5–13.9). In a large sample from south-west England with a bias towards Cornwall and Gloucestershire (W.J. Cresswell, pers. comm.) the average weight for adult males was 11.1 kg, and for adult females, 10.2 kg. In Speyside, Scotland (Kruuk 1989) adult males averaged 10 kg and females, 9 kg. However, Kruuk showed that over 8 years these average weights went down about 1 kg owing to a change in farming practice and pasture deterioration. Near the west coast of Scotland weights were lower than those in the east by about 25%. Low weights are

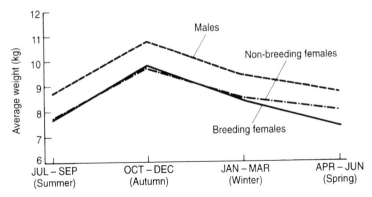

FIG 2.7   *Average body weights of adult males and of breeding and non-breeding females 1976–1992 at Woodchester Park, Gloucestershire. Source: C. Cheeseman (unpubl. data).*

also characteristic of Scandinavian badgers although they tend to put on more weight in the autumn than in Britain (P. Skoog, pers. comm.).

It is interesting to note the variation in Russian badgers. Although their head–body lengths are comparable with those in Britain, they put on so much fat in summer and autumn that they become as round as a barrel and may reach phenomenal weights. In Moscow province (Ognev 1935) the average autumn weight was 20 kg, but one killed on 23 September weighed 34 kg. That must have been quite a badger!

However, exceptionally heavy badgers are not confined to Russia, since in Britain a number of very heavy animals have also been recorded. These include one of 23 kg which was trapped at Uckfield, Sussex and another of 25 kg killed near Folkestone, Kent in February 1949. Brian Vesey-Fitzgerald (pers. comm.) gave details of three badgers taken from a sett in Durham, a boar of 27.7 kg and another boar and a sow approaching that weight. One killed near Rotherham, Yorkshire in December 1952 weighed 27.3 kg; it was weighed by the Scouts under the supervision of the local vicar (A. Bramble, pers. comm). To what extent these exceptional weights are due to heredity or environment cannot be assessed but food supply clearly plays a major part. This is evident from the large weights attained by badgers in captivity when given plenty of food and insufficient exercise. One such, at 9 months, weighed 16 kg!

Although much of the variation in average weights from different regions also strongly suggests a nutritional explanation, recent work on genetic variation in badgers in certain parts of Britain, Ireland and Continental Europe shows that badger populations may be morphologically and genetically distinct. Hence a genetic component in weight differences may also be involved (Lynch *et al.*, 1992).

THE SKIN AND PELAGE

A badger's skin is remarkably tough and extremely loose. It has aptly been described as 'rubbery' in texture. These properties make it extremely difficult for an attacker to grip any part of the body without being badly bitten in return. Today, in Europe, there are few animals apart from dogs and the occasional fox defending cubs that would attack a full-grown badger. Only dogs which are large and strong can inflict much damage as the teeth of smaller ones cannot penetrate the skin at all. In fact the skin is so loose that if a terrier does get a hold, its teeth merely grip a fold of the badger's skin.

Badgers when playing together often bite hard enough to cause a yelp but they do not damage the skin. However, when adults fight, the strength of their bite is enough to make a nasty wound, often in the region of the rump.

The pelage in winter consists of long guard hairs 90–100 mm in length and a felt-like underfur. The guard hairs are pigmented with melanin which shows as a dark band about 20 mm long rather nearer the tip than the base. The overall effect is to give the badger a greyish look. The underfur is light in colour and contains no melanin, so when the guard hairs are disturbed by wind, or when the animal is very wet, light patches show through and disturb the greyish look of the dorsal and lateral regions.

On the limbs and the ventral side of the neck, chest and abdomen the hairs are shorter and dark all over except in some places where there is a short lighter region at the base. There is far less hair on the abdomen than elsewhere, the guard hairs being short and the underfur sparse. In some lactating sows the abdomen is almost denuded of hair.

In parts of Aberdeenshire seven badgers killed in road accidents have had white patches on the paws; two had all four feet showing this feature, three had both fore feet marked, one with one front and one rear and one with two front and one rear (M. Harris, pers. comm.). Paul Patchett reported a similar variation in Yorkshire.

The hairs of the head and neck are short and white except those which form the characteristic dark stripe on each side. This starts behind the ear, passes through the eye region and turns down slightly towards the jaw about 20 mm from the black tip of the snout. The ears are also tipped with white hairs, although badgers have been reported without these, possibly as a result of fighting. A strange variation in facial pattern was described by Michael Picken (pers. comm.); in addition to the two facial stripes, there was a thin dark band like a bridge between them in the region above the eyes giving a somewhat triangular pattern of dark. This badger was seen several times at a sett in the Mendips.

The hairs of the tail are lacking in melanin. This is worth remembering, because on one occasion, having found some long white hairs incorporated in lumps of clay at the sett entrance, Ernest thought he had discovered where an albino was living. When he watched, it was disappointing to see perfectly normal badgers emerge . . . but they had white tails!

When hairs develop in a badger's skin their hair follicles do not occur singly, but the primary one gives rise to secondary follicles surrounding it. The major follicle forms a guard hair and the subsidiary ones the finer hairs of the underfur. The latter are arranged like the pappus of hairs on a thistle fruit.

Badgers moult once a year. Novikov (1956) describes the process as follows:

The moult begins in the spring, the underfur falling out first, then the guard hairs. The process begins on the withers and shoulders spreading to back and flanks. The guard hairs are also shed gradually from the beginning of summer in the same sequence as the underfur. New guard hairs grow in the late summer followed by the underfur. The process continues in the reverse order from the spring moult, i.e. from the posterior part of the neck to the head. The growth of the pelage ends in the autumn.

In the late summer and autumn when fat is laid down, some is stored in the mesentery, particularly around the kidneys, but most is stored in the skin. The latter is deposited in layers between muscles, so in section it looks like streaky bacon.

It has long been thought that badger fat had therapeutic properties, especially for the cure of rheumatism, strains and sprains. It certainly has excellent penetrating powers if rubbed into the skin. Analysis of the fat by Dr I. Macdonald of Guy's Hospital in London, did not highlight any substances which might be curative, although it did show that much of it was derived from the fat of earthworms, the badger's favourite food. However, the following story is related for the sake of the record (Neal 1977). An old lady living in a village in Somerset had a badly swollen hip joint. A bone-setter told her that the only possible cure was badger grease as it was a long-standing injury. Davies, who heard of the lady's plight, tried everywhere to find some grease, without success, but eventually phoned Ernest and told her story. Ernest had no fresh grease but did have some about 3 years old which was very rancid and almost orange in colour. He hardly liked to offer it, but Davies thought it worth trying. She rang up a fortnight later to say that the day after the first application the skin went very red and started to draw; later, the swelling went down, and by the time she phoned, the lady was completely cured and was overjoyed. Ernest has often wondered since whether it was faith healing, or perhaps the action of substances formed by the bacterial action making the fat rancid. It would be interesting to know!

THE SIGNIFICANCE OF THE COLOUR AND PATTERN

The colour and pattern of an animal are always of some significance. In some, cryptic colours play a major role in survival, others have colours and patterns which warn predators not to attack as they may be poisonous, distasteful or have some potent means of defence. Again, they may be used as social signals or recognition marks between members of a species; the white patches on the rump of deer or the tails of rabbits are examples. In some, the colours and patterns show a compromise between two essential requirements, protection and recognition, in others between warning colours and protection. In the light of this diversity of function how can the colour and pattern of a badger be explained?

Many nocturnal animals are cryptically coloured, the majority being brown or grey; this certainly applies to the body of a badger, but not its head. When you can see anything at all in a wood at night you can see a badger's head very plainly. There are circumstances, as when moonlight produces a dappled effect, when the head pattern makes a badger quite difficult to see, but this is no argument for calling the head cryptic. However, on one occasion (Neal 1977), Ernest was watching a sow with her two small cubs playing near a sett in a slight hollow. Suddenly, a dog barked loudly, and although out of sight, it could not have been far away. The cubs reacted by going down below, but the sow, which was standing at the time, flattened herself on the ground by the entrance and partly covered her face with her fore paws. The camouflage was perfect. This type of behaviour, more often seen when under attack, demonstrated very well how a badger can under some circumstances make itself inconspicuous.

It was R.I. Pocock (1911) who first suggested that black and white patterns of mammals could act as warning signals. He pointed out that animals which had these patterns were nocturnal or crepuscular and usually had a very potent method of defence such as the powerful bite of the badger or the nauseating stink of the skunk. He also pointed out that these animals fed mainly on small prey which did not move fast, rather than on agile animals which would be forewarned by the obvious nature of the animal's colouring. He also noted that these animals made little attempt to conceal themselves but shuffled about noisily while foraging. This explanation of the badger's conspicuous head seems highly likely.

However, Maurice Burton (1957) argued that if this is warning coloration, what enemies has the badger to warn off? One could reply that badgers have been around for a long time and an animal such as the wolf could at one time have been a possible aggressor. Foxes too have been known to attack them, although they normally keep out of each other's way unless disputing a refuge or defending cubs. But what of the cubs? Surely it is they who need the warning colours. Cubs certainly have their enemies, particularly foxes, and foxes and badgers often live in the same burrow system. It is most significant that cubs acquire the same pattern as the adults almost from birth, because by this means they are able to share to some extent the advantage the adult enjoys. A fox, having once had a painful encounter with an adult badger, would associate this with the conspicuous facial pattern and might well think twice before attacking a cub showing the same markings. The situation is comparable to the advantage shown by some insect mimics, which although harmless themselves, resemble those which have stings or a noxious taste.

This hypothesis is also supported by a cub's reaction to attack. It at once turns to face the aggressor, showing the facial markings to best advantage, and at the same time fluffs up its coat making it look much larger than it really is. It also makes a series of most menacing noises. The effectiveness of this behaviour was well demonstrated when Ernest was watching a cub digging for pig-nuts (Neal 1986). The cub was quite oblivious of his presence, and on coming to within a metre of where he was standing, it suddenly caught his scent, made an explosive snorting sound and erected its fur like a bottle brush as it faced him. Some of the fur seen from in front looked like a circular ruff surrounding the head as the pale underfur showed up conspicuously. It certainly succeeded in making itself *appear* formidable.

The pattern may also serve as a warning to other badgers to keep their distance when feeding. Although they usually forage independently, when the cubs are young they often keep within a short distance of one another. However, if one finds a sizeable food item such as a dead bird and another approaches, it will at once display its head pattern by facing the trespasser and make a warning sound.

There is little doubt that the pattern also serves as a recognition signal. A badger's eyesight is not very good (p. 30) but the white pattern is effective even in poor light. David Humphries (pers. comm.) describes how, when he held a badger's mask in front of his face, the badgers appeared to accept him as one of them if he crawled about on the ground nearby, but down wind. Ernest's own experience using a stuffed badger confirmed that other badgers recognised the pattern at once. They also reacted to their own image in a mirror as if they recognised it as a badger.

So to understand the coloration of a badger it is best to consider it in terms of its reaction to possible aggression. It has three alternatives. First, it can turn and face the aggressor; it then displays its full warning colours. Second, rather unusually, it can flatten itself and blend as well as possible with its surroundings, hiding its face with its paws. Third, it can run away with its head held low and thus less visible with the body relatively inconspicuous at night against most backgrounds.

VARIATION IN HAIR COLOUR

In many mammals hair colour is very variable and its genetic control complex. In badgers there are at least three easily recognisable colour variations: melanistic, albino and erythristic, but there are also intermediates between these three caused by varying amounts of melanin deposited in the guard hairs.

No badger has been recorded as totally melanistic, but extremely dark animals have been seen, the white facial stripes being normal (Neal 1977). One of these was described as a 'jet black' badger which was seen near Dursley, Gloucestershire, by P.J. Prosser (pers. comm.).

True albinos are seldom pure white, although when very young they approach this condition. Usually they are more of a cream or biscuity colour. Much depends on the colour of the local soil as the hairs are liable to get stained. Albinism is due to the almost complete absence of melanin so the facial stripes are usually invisible, although in some you can just make them out. The hair on the underside of the body may appear slightly darker as these are more likely to be stained. The claws and the tip of the snout also lack pigment, and the absence of melanin in the cells behind the retina allows the blood supply to show up making the eyes appear pink.

Albinos are homozygous with recessive genes, so when an albino mates with a pure-breeding, normally coloured animal the cubs will all appear normal. However, these cubs will all carry the recessive gene for albinism. With a rather limited dispersal range and somewhat restricted mating possibilities (p. 170), a higher proportion of animals carrying this gene is likely to be present in some populations. This is borne out by clusters of records, particularly from Dorset, Kent, Berkshire and Essex, suggesting that it is a fairly local phenomenon.

In some places, accounts of white badgers are almost legendary and certain ancient setts are associated with their appearances. One such area is near Dorchester in Dorset, where albinos have been well documented. Here an adult albino was killed by a car in February 1962 and later that year a young albino sow was found dead in the same locality. Three years later, D.H.B. Brown (personal communication) photographed a very large albino boar in the same area and later that year saw a family of cubs at a place a few kilometres away, one of which was an albino. Then in 1979 a local farmer disturbed some badger-diggers who were about to shoot an albino they had just dug out, and in 1980 he also found two albino cubs at the same sett; they too had been shot. On the same farm another albino was seen in 1983/4 and Ernest watched there himself. The site was difficult for watching owing to much vegetation so the entrances were obscured, but this made the appearance of the animal more dramatic. One moment there was nothing, the next, there it was, large, conspicuous, pale biscuit-coloured and almost unreal, staring in his direction with pink beady eyes. It was a strange and memorable experience.

The most complete account of an albino badger was given by G. Burness (1970a, b). It represented a remarkable piece of sustained field work over more than 9 years with the help of two enthusiastic badger watchers, Gary and Philip Cliffe. This albino boar was seen on more than 200 occasions and its life history documented.

This badger, aptly named 'Snowball', was born as one of a litter of three in 1961. The other two cubs were normally coloured. The albino was treated in the same way as the others although in play there were slight signs of persecution. As Burness wrote, 'he always seemed in the front of every chase'. By the autumn he became rather less sociable, emerging at a different time to the other cubs and going off to forage on his own. He remained in the parental sett for his first winter, which was a very severe one, and did not leave it until the following June when a new family was much in evidence at a sett in the same hedgerow. He could not be found for a month or so and was at one time thought to have died because an albino boar was reported killed by a car not far away. However, this turned out to be another animal. Snowball was eventually located at a sett about 400 m away from his original home. He was living amicably with a large, very old boar and a small sow, both of usual colour.

By his second winter he was mature and was seen to mate with the small sow in February. Four cubs were born to this sow the following year, all normally coloured, and

FIG 2.8 *Semi-albino: note indication of darker colour in eye-stripe and body. Photo G. Burness.*

in succeeding years when she had litters the cubs were always normal. Snowball was seen quite often at the same sett with her, but in later years less frequently. He was last seen by Burness in 1971.

Semi-albinos have their pigmentation greatly reduced. They appear very pale with a yellowish or brownish tinge, looking much like albinos, but the facial stripes are easily seen and the hairs on the abdomen and legs are rather darker; the eyes are pink and the nose pale brown. W.W. Page (pers. comm.) describes a semi-albino boar in Essex which he saw many times between 1964 and 1966. In 1963 a true albino cub was born at the same sett and was presumed to have been sired by the semi-albino.

Erythristic badgers have a distinctive gingery appearance on back and sides, while the normally black underparts and legs are a sandy red. The colour is due to a different pigment, phaeomelanin, in contrast to the eumelanin found in normally coloured badgers. The density of the pigment in the guard hairs and its reddishness vary slightly amongst erythristics. The eye colour appears to vary from pale brown to red. Erythristics have been recorded from many counties, but like albinos they are more common in some localities where, presumably, the relevant genes (which are also recessive), are more frequent in the population.

In addition to the colour varieties described so far, Ernest described a badger seen in the Cotswolds (Neal 1948) as 'a bright sandy yellow, more yellow than a sandy cat'. This sow was seen in 1945. In the summer of 1957, D.A. Humphries (pers. comm.) watched many times in the same wood and saw 'a fairly yellow boar and a very yellow sow'; they were seen several times in good light. The sow had two cubs which were normally coloured. The yellowness of these animals was due to the non-melanic parts of the guard hairs, the dark parts being normal.

It is important to distinguish these genetically controlled colour forms from local variations due to distinctive soil staining. For example in the Brendon district of Somerset, all the underfur and the lighter areas of the guard hairs are reddish due to the local red sandstone soil. In another area where badgers are living in an ironstone deposit they have been described as 'positively scarlet'. No doubt the Durham badgers that tunnelled into a coal pit could be described as pseudo-melanic!

There is also variation with age. By the time the cubs come above ground (if their colour is typical) they are silvery grey, although there may be staining of the hairs in some areas. By the autumn of their first year they appear slightly less silvery and when they acquire their winter coat in the autumn of their second year they are darker grey. With very old animals there is a tendency to become lighter again due, probably, to the decrease in length of the dark band in the guard hairs.

THE DIFFERENCES BETWEEN THE SEXES

There are no differences in colour or pattern between the sexes, so identification is often difficult under field conditions. However, there are certain characteristics which, taken together, can be helpful.

An adult boar is more heavily built, and, when seen head-on, shows a distinctly broader head with fuller cheeks. The region between the ears is also slightly more domed. When seen from the side the nose appears blunter, the head shorter and the neck thick. A very

FIG 2.9   *Old adult boar.*

much more variable, but nevertheless useful, characteristic is the tail which in many males is thinner and whiter. An adult sow is a sleeker animal with narrower head and neck; her head is flatter and narrower between the ears; the tail is typically more tufty and less white dorsally, but there is much variation.

Although the width of the head is probably the best indicator of sex in the field, as R.W. Howard (personal communication) showed by skull measurements, only those with particularly broad or narrow heads are true to sex and there is a grey area of overlap where this criterion is unreliable. However, width is not only a product of skull proportions but also musculature which is greater in adult boars.

Very occasionally you can see the genitalia of a badger when it sits up and scratches itself; in adult males the scrotal sacs are prominent, but not so in immatures. In females, absence of scrotal sacs and more prominent nipples (three pairs in both sexes) make identification of adults easy; immatures are much more difficult. In the male, the penis is not visible as it lies under the skin in a forward-projecting position, and when in use, protrudes through an aperture in the skin.

One skeletal feature which is characteristic of most carnivores is the baculum or os penis. This is a rod-like bone with a groove ventrally for the passage of the urethra; it has an expanded head and supports the penis. Its length and weight usually attain adult proportions towards the end of the second year of life, but as the time of puberty varies considerably the baculum is an unreliable indicator for age determination (Graf & Wandeler 1982). Incidentally, in south-west Scotland the bacula of badgers were once polished and used as brooches which were given by a lad to his lassie.

FIG 2.10 *Adult sow.*

Immediately below the tail and above the anus in both sexes there is a large pouch, the sub-caudal gland, which secretes a cream-coloured, fatty substance with a faint musky smell. Its function will be discussed later (p. 139).

THE SKELETON

A badger's skeleton endorses much of what has already been said about the fossorial adaptations of the species (p. 4). It has the general mustelid proportions, being low slung and rather elongated, but it gives the impression of great strength with its rather rigid spine and short but very strong limb bones. The general arrangement may be deduced from Fig. 2.11. For details of some of the individual bones the book by Lawrence & Brown (1973) can be recommended.

The characteristic shape of a badger's skull is best understood by considering its main functions. Primarily it has to house and protect the brain, accommodate the organs of special sense — eyes, ears and olfactory — and deal with the intake and mastication of food. The strength, size and shape of the skull are therefore a reflection of how a badger carries out these functions and the proportional importance of each.

The large brain case, small eye orbit placed rather far forward and the somewhat elongated nasal apparatus all reflect the relative importance of the structures they protect. But the median sagittal crest, position and strength of the articulation of the lower jaw and the comparative size of the zygoma are adaptations related to the tremendous strength of the bite and the type of dentition (see Fig. 2.12).

A badger's bite should never be underestimated as many who have handled these animals can testify. It used to be said that if caught in a spring trap, the marks of its teeth on the iron could sometimes be detected!

The closure of the jaw is brought about by three sets of muscles, temporalis, masseter and pterigoideus. In the badger it is the temporalis which is extremely well developed and does most of the work. This muscle arises mainly from the lateral surface of the brain case and the fibres are inserted on the upper projecting portion of the mandible (see Fig. 2.13). From the region of insertion, the fibres fan out in dorsal and posterior directions giving great leverage to the jaw. To increase the surface area for the attachment of this great temporalis muscle the median sagittal crest has evolved. It forms the chief distinguishing feature of a badger's skull.

The point of articulation of the lower jaw is further forward than in other mustelid skulls giving more room for those temporalis muscle fibres which run backwards horizontally. These are the ones which are so important when the jaws are nearly closed and hence when the bite is strongest. Because of this great pressure exerted by the temporalis

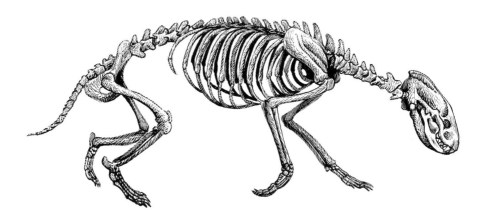

FIG 2.11 *Skeleton of badger.*

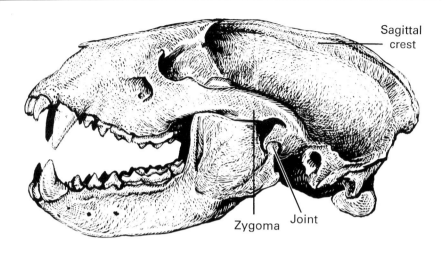

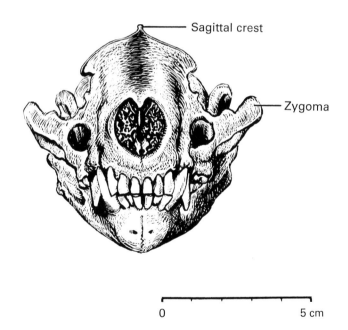

FIG 2.12   *Skull of adult boar: lateral and anterior views.*

the joint with the mandible needs to be strengthened to prevent dislocation. This is achieved by enlargements of the bones of the socket both in front and behind to form a groove. The jaw fits into this so completely that with an adult's skull, dislocation is impossible and only a fracture will allow the jaw to come away from the skull. However, it is possible that this type of articulation may be as important for accuracy of bite as for strength.

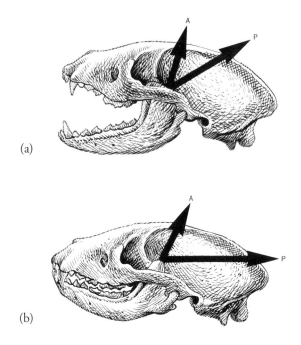

(a)

(b)

FIG 2.13   *Skull (a) with mouth wide open, (b) with mouth nearly shut to show direction of main fibres of the temporalis muscle, which gives great leverage to the jaw. A = anterior fibres, P = posterior fibres. For further details see main text.*

The juvenile skull has no sagittal crest. This appears at about 10 months when the temporal ridges coalesce in the mid line. These temporal ridges appear in the young cub as lines on the skull surface marking the upper limit of the temporalis muscles on the side of the brain case of the skull (Fig. 2.14). As the skull grows and the muscles increase in size, these temporal lines gradually migrate nearer to the mid line forming slight ridges which eventually meet to form the sagittal crest. The gap between the temporal lines or ridges in young skulls is therefore a useful guide to the age of the skull (Fig. 2.14).

After establishment of the median ridge, growth in depth of the crest is rapid for the next 2–3 years, but after that, growth gradually slows down. The maximum depth recorded is 15 mm. However, actual size is an unreliable indicator of age as there is much individual variation. Skulls of 1–2 years can usually be recognised by the persistence of rough porous bone along the apical line of the crest which is indicative of continuing rapid growth. This subsequently becomes covered with smooth, hard bone. Also, the sides of the crest in younger animals are smooth but become progressively roughened by bone accretion in older animals. In much older skulls there is a lateral thickening of the crest posteriorly and the crest comes to overhang the back of the skull.

Further factors for estimating the age of a badger include the degree of closure of skull

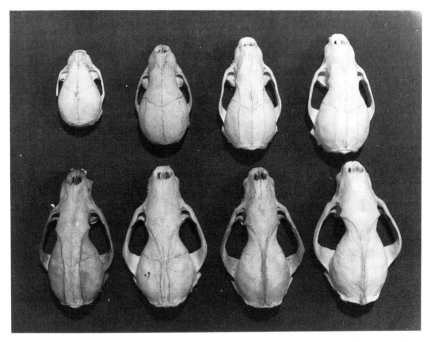

FIG 2.14   *Development of the skull up to one year, showing formation of the sagittal crest. Top: 6 weeks, 8 weeks, 12 weeks, 16 weeks; bottom: 7 months, 9 months, 10 months and 1 year.*

sutures, the degree of ossification of the epiphyses (end of the long bones), the size of the baculum, tooth wear and dentine rings. These are summarised and their usefulness assessed in Appendix 2.

Determining the sex from skull features is not easy especially in older animals. However, in younger females the nasal bones are shorter and broader, having more rounded posterior regions; in males they are longer and narrower (Ognev 1935, Hancox 1973).

DENTITION

Although the badger is a member of the Carnivora, it is omnivorous in its diet; this is reflected in its dentition. Thus the incisors, canines and front premolars are typical of a carnivore, but the last premolars and the molars are greatly modified for crushing and grinding, being broad, flat and multicuspid, more typical of a herbivore. The dental formula for the permanent dentition is:

$$\text{Incisors } \frac{3}{3} \quad \text{Canines } \frac{1}{1} \quad \text{Premolars } \frac{4}{4} \quad \text{Molars } \frac{1}{2} = 38$$

However, the first premolar is either vestigial or absent. Of 212 British skulls examined by Hancox (1988c), 16% had all four vestigial premolars present, 14% had three, 61%, two (57% of these in the lower jaw), 3% had one and 6%, none. In Switzerland, Lups (1990) found that in 315 skulls of known sex there were no significant differences in this respect between males and females, or between the left and right sides of the skull, neither was there any correlation between premolar absence and skull length.

In eastern races (Russia and Siberia), there is usually a complete absence of the first premolar. In this they resemble the mink, polecat, stoat and weasel. The otter is intermediate, normally having four premolars in the upper jaw and three in the lower, all of them functional.

An unusual variation of the dentition was described by Fullager *et al.* (1960) in which the large upper molar was replaced by two separate and smaller teeth, each having three roots. As four vestigial premolars were present in addition, this brought the full number up to 40. Also, Hancox (1988c) describes a skull with supernumerary upper second premolars.

The milk dentition is expressed by the dental formula:

$$\text{Incisors } \frac{3}{3} \quad \text{Canines } \frac{1}{1} \quad \text{Premolars } \frac{4}{4} = 32$$

But again, the first premolar is not always present and if it does occur, is often shed very early or does not penetrate the gums. Similarly, the milk incisors, although present, may not all penetrate; this is often the case for incisors 1 and 2. Their absence may well be looked upon as an adaptation for suckling which exceeds 3 months.

The time of eruption of the milk teeth appears to be variable, but E. Overend (pers. comm.) gives the following sequence for a cub she reared:

4 weeks Milk canines erupted in both jaws.

4½ weeks First signs of upper premolars.

5 weeks First signs of lower premolars. Upper incisors 2 and 3 through, 1 did not penetrate. Lower incisors all absent or did not show.

6 weeks All premolars through in both jaws.

The first permanent teeth, the upper incisors, erupted at 10 weeks and the lower incisors came through a week later.

The skulls of known age examined by Ernest (Neal 1977) confirm that the first permanent incisors appear at about 10 weeks in the upper jaw and the full transition to a permanent dentition takes place during the following 6 weeks. The sequence follows closely the order of the teeth from the front backwards, those of the lower jaw lagging behind the upper by about a week in most cases. However, the large carnassial (PM^4) is exceptional in erupting before PM^3. This allows the former to become functional at an earlier age in relation to the large first molar into which it fits when grinding. The detailed sequence is as follows:

Upper jaw	I^1	I^2	I^3	C^1	(M^1)	PM^1	PM^2	PM^4	PM^3	
Lower jaw	I^1	I^2	I^3	(M^1)	C^1	PM^1	PM^2	(M^2)	PM^3	PM^4

It is interesting that during the last phase of the transition from milk to permanent dentition around the 15–16th week after birth, some of the milk teeth may still be present and functional in addition to the permanent teeth which have already come through. This is possible because some permanent teeth do not emerge from the same socket as their milk precursors, but to one side. In a skull shown in Fig. 2.15 there are two functional canines in each upper jaw and a double set of PM^3 in the upper jaw and of PM^4 in the lower.

BODY TEMPERATURE

The body temperatures of three badgers living under semi-natural conditions at 57°N in Scotland were determined (Fowler & Racey 1988). From spring to autumn the badgers were typically homoeothermic with an average daily temperature around 37°C. The body temperature started to fall in October, reaching the lowest level in December and started to rise again in January to reach homoeothermic levels by April. The fall in temperature during the winter varied between the three animals, the largest fall, to 28°C, occurring in a sow just before ovo-implantation (p. 178). The differences between mean daily maximum and minimum varied from 1.6 to 8.9°C and were associated with degree of activity outside the sett in mid-winter. Body temperature did not follow a circadian rhythm.

The winter drop in body temperature is associated with certain physiological changes such as depression of thyroxin levels (a growth hormone secreted by the thyroid gland) and utilisation of stored fat, comparable to those found in deep hibernators (Ringberg & Oen 1978, Maurel & Boissin 1979, Maurel 1981). In the badger the condition is best described as semi-dormancy. More data are needed to establish to what extent these changes occur throughout the badger's range.

THE SPECIAL SENSES

The size of the brain and the relative proportions of its parts usually reflect the degree of intelligence of its possessor and the relative importance of the various sense organs of the animal concerned. A badger's brain, like that of most carnivores, is very well developed. This applies particularly to the two cerebral hemispheres which cover most of the dorsal

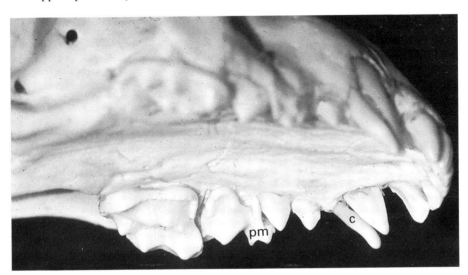

FIG 2.15   *Dentition of cub aged 15 weeks, showing permanent teeth all present, with extra canine (c) and premolar (pm) of the milk dentition still not shed.*

region. Their surfaces are considerably convoluted, thus increasing the surface area of the cerebral cortex which is the main co-ordinating centre of the brain and the part associated with the degree of intelligence.

The other parts which are particularly well developed are the olfactory lobes and cerebellum. These are concerned with information sent by the nose and ears respectively. By contrast, the corpora quadrigemmina, which are completely hidden by the cerebral hemispheres, are small. These are the structures which receive information from the eyes. So the gross structure of the brain suggests that the badger, like most members of the order Carnivora, is intelligent and that the senses of smell and hearing are well developed, but eyesight is less important. This is confirmed by behavioural observations and experiments.

Eyesight

The eyes of most mammals which are adapted for good night vision have three main characteristics. First, the eyes are large and the pupil capable of much dilation so that as much light as possible can reach the retina. Second, the retina is very sensitive to low light intensities, which means that it has a high proportion of cells called rods compared with other cells, the cones, which are adapted for strong light conditions and may also be used for colour vision. Third, there is present behind the retina a special structure, the tapetum, which reflects back through the retina any light not absorbed on entry; in this way the retinal cells are given a second chance to be stimulated and the sensitivity of the eye is greatly increased. It is the tapetum that gives the characteristic eye reflection, often coloured, when a light is shone into the eyes of a nocturnal mammal.

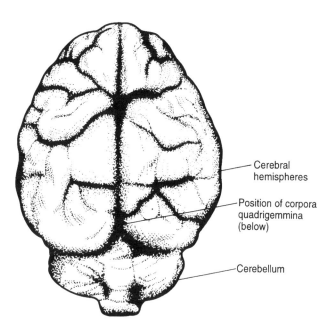

FIG 2.16   *Brain of badger: dorsal view.*

If a badger's eyes fulfilled all these conditions one would say that night sight was important to the animal. This is only partially true. A tapetum is present as badger photographers know to their cost when they see on their photographs the blank, staring look caused by the reflection of their flash from this structure. It is also true that the retina consists largely of rods. This is borne out by the badgers' behaviour; they have an aversion to strong sunlight and tame animals will retreat to the darkest corner or cover their eyes with their paws under bright conditions. However, a badger's eyes are unusually small for a nocturnal animal, so it would appear that night sight is probably quite good but of less importance than the other main senses.

This conclusion is not surprising when one considers the very significant fact that badger cubs spend approximately the first 8 weeks of their lives underground in almost complete darkness and during this period have no opportunity of associating any event with sight stimuli. Even after they come above ground their learning processes are mainly associated with smells and sounds.

There are therefore two main questions to ask: how well can they see and how important is sight to them? These are best answered by giving some illustrations.

Ernest was watching a sett in June: there had been a severe drought, food was scarce and the badgers were coming out unusually early. He was standing 5 m from the sett with the wind blowing steadily in his face. An adult sow emerged a full hour before sunset. Ernest was wearing dull-coloured clothes and kept quite still. The sow scented carefully, moved her head in most directions including that of the observer but was completely oblivious of his presence. Two large cubs joined her and they played together, obviously not knowing that Ernest was there, although to human eyes he was plainly visible. The factors in favour of not being seen were: the light was very strong in contrast to the darkness below ground; the badgers were unsuspicious as they detected no human scent or sound; Ernest made no movement and was not standing against a clear background.

John O'Connor (pers. comm.) described a rather different reaction to his presence:

> I reached the sett long before dark, and assuming that no badgers would be out for some time, made no attempt to hide myself. I was standing at the edge of the sett when an adult badger backed into view with a load of earth. It stared at me in obvious surprise (I was about 3 m away), but when I made no sound or movement it returned to its digging. Within a few minutes it had re-appeared three times with earth and stones and each time was obviously more curious. It would look at me several times and advance a few steps to scent me. Only after its fourth load did it become sufficiently curious to walk right up to me and get my scent. It then slowly retreated to the sett and did not re-emerge.

In this case the observer was seen at once and apparently recognised as something different from the usual surroundings of the sett. This caused the badger to show curiosity but not fear as the senses of smell and hearing gave no alarm stimuli.

Paget & Middleton (1974b) described an occasion where the sett was in an open field and the observers about 50 m from it — a very long way! When a badger emerged, it looked straight at the watchers who were silhouetted above a low hedge, and retreated hastily below. The wind was blowing strongly into the observers' faces and they had made no noise. There are many other instances recorded of where badgers have reacted at once to the sight of a strange silhouette in the neighbourhood of the sett, but in an open situation such as the one Paget & Middleton described, one suspects that badgers would show more caution when emerging and that vision might play a more important part than when setts have greater cover nearby.

These examples strongly suggest that a badger's eyesight is more concerned with shapes than details; it is very probable that a badger soon learns the outlines of the main objects in the vicinity of the sett and that any additional feature that is noted on emergence is treated with curiosity or suspicion until it has been investigated.

The reaction tends to vary according to what information the badger has previously received from its other important sense organs. If it is already slightly suspicious through smell or sound, the sight of a strange object will cause an alarm reaction, but if it is unsuspicious, curiosity is more likely to be shown. The same applies to movement. There is no doubt that badgers can detect movement quite easily even when it is unaccompanied by sound, but their reaction to it varies according to whether it is familiar or not.

What happens when the light has nearly gone? There is plenty of evidence that a silhouette against the night sky will cause alarm in just the same way as in better light. In addition, anything that reflects any remaining light such as the shiny surface of a photographic flashgun, the moving hands of an observer or a white handkerchief or article of clothing, is often noticed at once on emergence and treated in the same way as any other unfamiliar object when seen in better light. It appears that the eyesight of badgers is good in low intensity light and certainly good enough to recognise the face-mask of their own kind very quickly.

To sum up: because a badger's retina consists mainly of rods it tends to be blinded by strong light — especially so on first emerging from the darkness of its tunnel; also it does not have the visual acuity to enable it to see details from any distance, but shapes, silhouettes and movement can easily be detected even under extremely poor light conditions. One can conclude that the importance of sight to a badger is to alert it in a general way to possible danger so that its other sense organs may analyse the situation in more detail or confirm a suspicion that has already been aroused.

Badgers have often been described as shortsighted but this would appear to apply much more to cubs than adults. Paget & Middleton's evidence previously described suggests that an adult can see a silhouette at 50 m. However, cubs are very different. Cubs first open their eyes at around 5 weeks, but it is unlikely that they can focus them properly until about 7 weeks at the earliest. By 8–9 weeks a tame cub will follow an object with its eyes if it moves within 300 mm of its head. As it gets older the range of focus increases. Most watchers have had experiences of young cubs coming right up to them if the wind is favourable, apparently without seeing them. It is when the watcher is scented that alarm is shown. It is almost impossible to determine whether this initial lack of fear is due to the inability to see or to lack of experience, but in cubs of 10–11 weeks the former would seem to be one reason.

Hearing

We are not aware of any critical experiments done on the range of sounds detected by badgers. For those carnivores which have been investigated, the upper limit is well above that of humans. Observations on badgers suggest they too have a good sensitivity to high frequencies. For example, B. Vesey-Fitzgerald (pers. comm.) had demonstrated that badgers could hear a Galton whistle; they can also hear the high-pitched whine of a re-charging electronic flash as Ernest know to his cost.

Many carnivores which feed on small prey can hear the high-pitched squeaks (some of which are ultrasonic) of small rodents. It is likely that badgers can do this too, but it is difficult to tell from their behaviour whether the prey is detected by sound or scent. Earthworms can be detected when still below ground; can they hear the scraping of the chaetae or can they smell them? Perhaps its a combination of both.

Badgers make a great variety of sounds which are of value for communication (p. 136). These cover a wide range of frequencies from the low murmuring of a sow, when with cubs, to the high-pitched whickering of the cubs and the staccato warning notes of the sow. Within this range a badger's hearing seems to be quite as good as ours within our range and better in the higher frequencies.

Low-frequency vibrations may be felt directly through the ground. Badgers, when crossing roads, can detect oncoming traffic in this way. Unfortunately for them, their response to this is similar to a hedgehog's, which is to stop still. In consequence, large numbers are killed on the roads (p. 194).

When filming badgers at night, Ernest and Professor H.R. Hewer (Hewer & Neal 1954) found the sound of the camera was a great problem. Although the camera was cased in a box with a plate glass front and heavily blimped (lined with foam rubber to reduce noise) the badgers heard the motor without difficulty. The photographers' first success came when it was raining heavily, so they assumed that the noise of the rain had effectively drowned that of the camera. They fixed up a device which kept up a continuous low-frequency vibration which they hoped would have the same effect, but this was a failure as the badgers appeared to distinguish both noises at the same time. They finally habituated the badgers to the noise by giving them food over several weeks and running the camera every time they ate it. Thus they associated something pleasant with the noise.

Badgers quickly become habituated to noises if repeated often enough. In built-up areas they soon become accustomed to the noise of traffic, gates banging and dogs barking. Badgers which made their sett in a railway embankment on the main London–Hastings line seemed to take no notice of the vibrations and noise whenever a train passed. Low-flying aircraft had no effect on badgers' activity at a sett below a flight path to London's Heathrow airport, though men with a tractor 200 m away made them pause to listen (A.D. Mennear, pers. comm.). John Whall made use of this tolerance to sound, once they were accustomed to it, by taking a radio with him when watching. They took little notice of either talking or music. Because of this, he and Ernest were able to speak into a microphone and do a live radio commentary from 5 m of a group of badgers.

The response of badgers to sudden sound is often immediate and striking. It is the unexpected nature of the sound that mainly causes alarm. This is particularly obvious around the time of emergence when the badgers are specially alert. The sudden crackle of leaves, the noise of a camera shutter or the rustle of clothing may result in a dash for home. The fear reaction to a sudden noise seems to be inherited. Up to the age of about 12 weeks badgers may be startled by the thumping of a rabbit nearby or a bird flying to its roost, even some dry leaves blown by a gust of wind, but gradually they learn to discriminate and take little or no notice of those sounds learned to be harmless.

FIG 2.17   *Badger listening with paw raised.*

Distant sounds seldom disturb badgers. You may see a badger pause at the entrance to a sett at the sound of a dog's bark or distant human voices but it seldom retreats unless the sound gets nearer. Professor Hewer and Ernest were able to film badgers quite successfully at Camberley on Coronation night in 1953 when fireworks were being let off although none was nearer than 100 m. Brigadier R.E. Fryer (pers. comm.) gave an even more extreme example. He regularly watched at a sett on War Department land and on one occasion when troops were carrying out night exercises, even the rifle fire (blanks) and thunder flashes didn't seem to worry the badgers for long. They stopped and listened but did not always bother to seek refuge in their holes. In contrast, even a slight sudden noise near the sett would alarm them.

Once badgers are out and foraging certain shuffling sounds may make them curious. John Brodribb (pers. comm.) described how, when watching had become uninteresting, he had moved about quite noisily and badgers had come to investigate the sounds he made. One night he was trying to move quietly, imitating the noise made by a foraging badger, when he slipped and landed with a terrific crash. At once, two badgers from different directions rushed towards him, one coming within 3 m of where he lay!

Smell

The sense of smell in badgers is extremely well developed and is undoubtedly their most important sense. This is not surprising if you examine the scroll bones in the nasal chambers of the skull. These provide an extremely large surface area for the sensory epithelium that covers them. Some of this area is concerned with temperature and humidity regulation of the inhaled air; nevertheless, the olfactory portion is extensive and is provided with a generous supply of nerve endings. It is probable that by increasing the humidity of the inhaled air as it passes through the first part of the nasal chambers, the sensitivity of the olfactory region further back is increased.

A badger's world is a world of smells. For us, with sight and hearing dominant and our olfactory sense so poorly developed, it is difficult to imagine what it is like to live in a world dominated by smells. However, for badgers, scent plays a leading role in recognising individuals, their sexual state, for finding food, detecting danger and finding their way about.

When a badger emerges from its sett in the dusk, a very sensitive snout is enquiringly raised to investigate the evening's news; first in one direction, then another, testing the air. In this way it detects the slightest sign of danger. If it catches the strong scent of the watcher, it will withdraw immediately; if not quite sure and only slightly suspicious, it may move its head up and down testing the air at different levels and sniffing all the time as it does so. If no scent of humans is detected it will come out and soon relax.

On one occasion a sow had emerged quite unsuspicious of Ernest's presence, and her cubs, which were quite small, soon followed and started to fiddle with a piece of stick at the sett entrance. However, the wind was variable and the sow suddenly got Ernest's scent. There was a gruff, suppressed, but urgent bark of warning and she bundled the cubs down the hole in front of her. Experiences such as this cause cubs to associate human scent with danger.

When badgers are foraging, they keep their noses near the ground and as they search amongst the vegetation they constantly make loud snuffling noises. These are made in two ways and serve different purposes. The first is caused by a rapid intake of breath through the nose, this helps concentrate faint scents and enables the badgers to locate prey more easily. It occurs in a dramatic fashion when a badger is suddenly frightened, the snort of fear probably helping the animal to obtain more olfactory information about the cause of the alarm. Other snuffling noises are made when air is blown out through the nostrils to clear away particles when foraging under dusty conditions.

Badgers can be very preoccupied when foraging, but periodically they will raise their snouts and scent the air carefully. When the snout is near the ground, other smells tend to overcome direct wind-borne scents. This explains why a badger when travelling, snout down while following a scent trail, may come quite near before detecting your presence if you stand still, even if the wind is wrong. However, usually when travelling, it will periodically stop and sniff the air.

The acuteness of a badger's sense of smell is illustrated by experiments done by Howard Lancum (1954). At 11.00 a.m. in late May, he placed the palm of his hand on a badger path for 1 minute. That evening, two adults emerged at 22.00 followed by three cubs. When the boar reached the spot, it stopped, sniffed and made a slight detour before continuing, but the sow would not pass and returned with her cubs to the sett. Two days later at a different sett he repeated the experiment, this time at 15.30. At 22.15 that evening an adult emerged and on reaching the spot, 'shied like a frightened horse and bolted underground'. Two hours later it had not re-appeared. Eric Ashby some years later repeated the experiment in the New Forest using gum boots instead of the palm of the hand. He successfully filmed the startled reaction of the badger when it reached the exact place.

Their power of detecting their own scent trails is even more remarkable. Ernest knew a well-marked trail across a grassy field from a wood in which there was a sett. The field was ploughed up and put down as corn, but the badgers continued to use exactly the same route, presumably because the scent still lingered even though all visual signs of the path had gone.

It is common experience when watching badgers that on some evenings they react to your scent more obviously than on others, irrespective of the direction of the wind. This seems to be due to an increase in the humidity of the atmosphere — just as everything to us seems to smell more after rain. It is possible, therefore, as F. Frazer Darling (Darling 1937) found for red deer, that on these occasions a badger may react in panic to your scent even if you are some way off because you are scented with the same intensity as when you are nearer on a drier night. For the same reason Ernest has found that watching badgers in a damp wood in Somerset is much more difficult than in drier chalk or limestone habitats.

Temperature also seems to be an important factor in scent detection. Budgett (1933), working on dogs, showed that the optimal condition for tracking was when the ground temperature was a little higher than air temperature. Because air temperature falls faster than ground temperature in the evening, this is usually the best time for tracking. This might be one factor in determining when badgers start foraging.

In the breeding season sows appear to be more sensitive to human scent than boars, a point corroborated by Howard Lancum's experiment quoted earlier. It seems that the level of scent stimuli to which a sow will react is lowered. However, it should be borne in mind that as with us, individuals may differ in their powers of sensory perception.

The acuteness of a badger's sense of smell is very great but it is probably its ability to discriminate between scents that makes it so outstanding. Badgers can easily detect differences between humans, a fact well demonstrated by tame badgers when a stranger comes into the room. Also, in the wild they soon become accustomed to the scent of one watcher; however, if a stranger is also present, they are much more shy. Badgers can also recognise other badgers by their individual scents, whether members of their own social group or of neighbouring ones (p. 140).

This power to discriminate between a wide variety of scents obviously has a bearing on a badger's ability to find many kinds of food; it also helps it to find its way about. One can imagine how a badger gradually learns to orientate itself when on its travels by the scent pictures it has previously experienced and memorised of specific parts of its home range. This is clearly reflected in the exploratory behaviour of cubs. At first, they keep to their underground system, then to the area just around the entrance and later, they explore the whole region around the sett. However, it is some time before they have built up sufficient experience of the terrain by smell that they venture far from home. It is then often necessary to provide their own scent trails for finding their way back.

CHAPTER 3

The Badger's Home and Environs

SETTS

THE burrow system of badgers is known as a sett, a name probably derived from the ancient word 'cete' which was the collective noun for a group of badgers. Today it refers only to its home.

Setts provide shelter during the day and are used for breeding, while their immediate surroundings are used for socialising. They vary greatly in size, the extent of the tunnels and the number of entrances. If there were such a thing as a typical sett it would have 3–10 large entrances leading to an intricate system of interconnected tunnels and chambers. Outside each entrance would be a large mound of excavated soil.

A badger sett may be distinguished from a fox earth by the much larger heaps of soil outside the entrances and the remnants of vegetation always present in the excavated soil. Occasionally some rabbit holes, if dug in loose soil, may be large enough to cause doubt, but on closer inspection, within a short distance of the entrance they narrow considerably to no more than 150 mm.

The entrances of a badger sett are not less than 250 mm in diameter, typically 300–350 mm and occasionally in old, well-used ones, up to 600 mm. Newly excavated holes have rough edges, those of well-used ones appear smooth and polished from the constant rubbing of the badgers' bodies.

The spoil heap

The mound of earth, or spoil heap, outside each entrance is sometimes very large and contains as much as 30–40 m^3 of soil weighing several tonnes. This may have been excavated by generations of badgers, although it is surprising how much can be dug out in a single night. In a large sett, the whole configuration of the ground may be altered by these immense digging operations (Neal & Roper 1991). If the stratum in which the badgers have been digging is chalk, recent diggings may be seen from a great distance as white patches spilling down the otherwise green hillside. Incorporated with the soil is always some old bedding in the form of hay, bracken, leaves, etc (p. 46), and by breaking up some of the lumps of soil you often find badger hairs. In May, if the spoil heap is flattened and hardened, it is a good sign that cubs are present. A broad furrow leading from the entrance across the spoil heap is a sign of recent digging, the furrow having been made by the occupants when removing the soil.

FIG 3.1   *Badger sett in elder thicket showing spoil heap and digging furrow.*

The underground labyrinth

Local conditions differ so greatly that no two setts are alike; even when dug in similar soil and comparable situations the pattern of tunnels can be quite different. Each badger seems to be its own architect.

The simplest form of sett is one dug as a temporary shelter. It consists of a simple tunnel which usually bends a metre or so from the entrance and ends in an enlarged chamber. A badger would not use such a sett for long without enlarging it considerably by making new tunnels and alternative entrances. The latter usually arise from side tunnels which run at a depth of about a metre and parallel to the ground surface, often following the same contour if the sett is on a slope, reaching the surface again 3–4 m from the first entrance. Other tunnels are constructed which follow any kind of pattern according to the type of soil, position of rocks or tree roots and perhaps the inclinations of the diggers! More chambers are added periodically.

In sandy soil, the tunnels may penetrate deeply into the hillside, and even when the site is flat, may reach a considerable depth. An abortive badger dig by Sir Alfred Pease (1898) makes the point very well. The sett, which was in a flat field, had only three entrances, but the badgers had been there for generations. A trench was dug about 2 m in depth, but the sound of the dogs they had sent into the sett were heard to come from below, so they dug a further shaft from the floor of this trench to a depth of another metre. By this time they had cut through badger tunnels at three different levels. On hearing the dogs still below them they gave up in despair. So in this sett there were definitely four storeys of tunnels going down a minimum of 4 m. Ernest also examined a recently dug sett in the greensand of the Blackdown Hills in Somerset where tunnels were at three levels.

More typically, and where the soil is more difficult to penetrate because of the underlying rock, the labyrinth is roughly at one level and may not penetrate much more than a metre. This is a common feature in the Cotswolds where the underlying limestone is very hard and the soil shallow; here badgers utilise the subsoil for their tunnels. Under these circumstances some tunnels may come too near the surface and the roof falls in. New entrances are often formed in this way.

Shallow setts also occur in the shales of the Quantock Hills, Somerset and in many chalky districts such as the Wiltshire and South Downs. A characteristic pattern here is for the main tunnel to go down less than a metre before turning in one or more directions and running roughly horizontally along the contour.

Tunnels in section are wider than they are high with a domed roof and a more flattened floor. The average width for six setts excavated in Sussex was 310 mm (range 250–350 mm), and the average height, 200 mm (range 170–250 mm) (Roper 1992). This is just right for a large adult to pass without touching roof or sides. However, newly dug tunnels, 210 mm in diameter, excavated under a road in Yorkshire, were circular (P. Johnson, pers. comm.) This suggests that the more flattened base of a typical tunnel is caused by repeated removal of earth along it during digging operations and that some earth is inevitably lost *en route* and trampled flat, thus raising the floor. From time to time the tunnels widen to act as passing places and can be much larger near entrances. In one very ancient sett dug in red sandstone, it was possible to measure the dimensions of one of the main tunnels as badger diggers had made an abortive onslaught on it a few days previously. Four metres from the original entrance the tunnel was still 600 mm in height and a man (if he so wished!) could easily have crawled down it for some distance further. The floors of the main tunnels are often compacted like concrete owing to the constant traffic. From above ground, it is sometimes possible to hear the pounding of feet on the hard ground when a badger has been frightened and rushed down its sett. As you hear this pounding getting fainter and fainter it makes you realise how extensive some tunnels are. One in solid sandstone went in over 40 m (Wijngaarden & Peppel 1964) and in soft sand they may go in much further.

All but the smallest setts contain several or many chambers which are hemi-ellipsoidal or hemi-spherical. The average dimensions of chambers in 10 setts were $600 \times 540 \times 420$ mm (length $\times$ width $\times$ height), the largest being $860 \times 700 \times 330$ mm (Roper 1992). Some contain bedding, probably indicating present or recent use for sleeping or breeding; others may contain none. The bigger ones are large enough for two adults, or a sow and her small cubs to occupy. Judging from badgers kept in captivity, it is likely that two adults often sleep together lying side by side and head to tail.

The position of the chambers varies considerably, some being near an entrance, others deep within the sett, some at intersections, others at the end of side tunnels. There was a sett in Gloucestershire where a large hollow tree stump appeared to be a major junction of underground tunnels, 11 radiating from it at three levels (Humphries 1958).

Breeding chambers in well-established setts seem to be 'well chosen'. Some are situated below large boulders or slabs of rock, others under tree roots. Often the tunnel slopes upwards towards such chambers; this helps drainage — a very important feature if young are to be reared successfully. Sometimes this incline takes the form of a kind of step which gives a badger considerable positional advantage if attacked by a dog since it lies above the step in an almost impregnable position.

Although badgers usually defecate above ground, it is not unusual to find dung in excavated setts, occasionally in large amounts. It is likely that in many cases this relates to winter activity, including breeding (p. 60).

Size of setts

Setts vary greatly in size. A number have now been excavated and meticulously surveyed and their structure compared (Roper 1992). The architecture of some of these is shown in Fig. 3.2, and data concerning four main setts are shown in Table 3.1.

The enormity of the effort put into digging a large sett can be gauged by the fact that in sett no. 2 in Table 3.1, it was calculated that 25 tonnes of soil had been excavated over the years.

The size of sett is not related to the number of entrances; this is affected by local conditions such as the diggability of the soil and its age. Human interference is another factor as holes are commonly stopped before a hunt and some may remain blocked for months and even years. Also, sett size has no bearing on the number of badgers living in it, the latter being determined by the size of the social group which in turn is controlled amongst other factors by food availability within the territory (Chapter 7).

The largest setts are those which have been long established and where the soil is ideal for digging. Some of these can almost be described as badger cities. One such sett, visited in the Brendons, Somerset one April, covered an area of 1575 m² (45×35 m). This is more than double the size of the largest sett excavated so far (Table 3.1). Over 76 entrances were concentrated in this favourable situation of which 48 had recently been cleaned out. It had been undisturbed for years (Fig. 3.3).

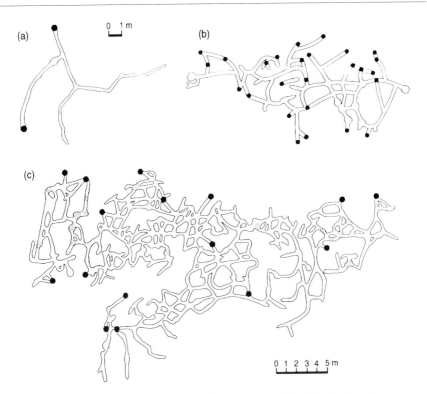

FIG 3.2   *Excavations of three setts (a) outlier (Cowlin 1967), (b) subsidiary (Roper et al. 1991b), (c) main (reproduced by permission of MAFF/ADAS; Crown Copyright 1990). Filled circles show entrances; stippled areas show bedding material. Source: modified from Roper et al. (1992).*

TABLE 3.1.   *Dimensions of four excavated main setts (after Roper 1991).*

Sett (no.)	Area (m²)	Volume (m³)	Tunnel length (m)	Mean depth (cm)	Entrances	Chambers total number	Chambers with bedding	Chambers with dung
1	304	4.6	102	124	2	8	8	1
2	525	15.3	310	76	15	39	26	8
3	740	25.2	360	62	38	78	15	7
4	704	14.7	354	84	80	20	11	4

Sources: sett no. 1 Frewin (1976), nos 2 and 3 Leeson & Mills (1977), no. 4 Roper *et al.* (1991); after Roper (1992).

Badgers have an instinctive urge to dig even if the sett is far too large for their needs, so some parts become derelict while new tunnels and chambers are dug elsewhere. The distribution of chambers containing bedding, for example in Fig. 3.2 sett c, illustrates what parts had been recently used. Fig. 3.2 also shows centres of activity, past and present. Sometimes the badgers will clear out old entrances not used for a year or so and renovate previous

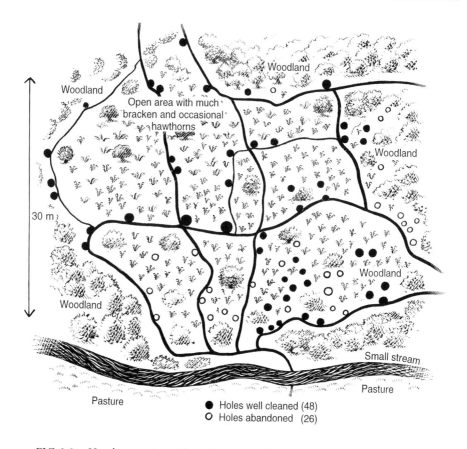

FIG 3.3   *Very large main sett in a clearing in deciduous woodland, Brendon Hills, Somerset. Activity shown by fresh digging (48 entrances, filled circles), unused (28 entrances, open circles. April 1985).*

breeding and sleeping chambers. So a large sett may alter its centres of activity from season to season.

Setts can 'move' considerably during the course of 20–30 years. One on a hillside in Somerset started as a small sett with three or four entrances at one level (their position can still be made out by old mounds although the holes have become filled in over the years). Later, other entrances were excavated below them and more recently still others below them, so the active position of the sett has changed location by 20–25 m (E. Neal, pers. obs). In a similar manner, setts may 'move' along a hillside following an ideal soil stratum.

Internal environment of the sett

Setts need to be well aerated, but how this is achieved is not fully understood; several factors appear to play a part. One, applying particularly to setts on steep slopes, is that by having entrances at different levels a flow of air is created. This can be demonstrated by placing smouldering material at different entrances, the smoke being sucked into some and forced out at others. Also, on frosty mornings some entrances 'steam' when the moisture in the air, warmed by the badgers' bodies, condenses on reaching the colder atmosphere. However, preliminary findings from current unpublished research by Jude Moore and Tim Roper have shown that although under windy conditions slight air movements were detected, even in gale force winds the air was completely still in deep parts of the sett. An interesting finding was that badgers when moving about in a sett cause air movement. This 'piston effect' is the same as when an underground train pushes air in front of it and sucks air in behind, thus causing an air flow. During the same research, although oxygen concentration in occupied chambers was found to drop only slightly, carbon dioxide accumulated markedly — the highest levels found being 6000 ppm compared with the usual atmospheric figure of 325 ppm. What is more, return to normal took a very long time (a week or more) even though the chamber was no longer occupied. Moore and Roper suggest that this may be a reason why badgers often move around from one chamber to another. A further factor must be the diffusion of gases between the air in the sett and the soil, the rate varying with the soil type. This is probably another reason why there is a preference to dig setts in sandy soils rather than clay.

Ventilation holes also exist in some setts. Whether they are formed deliberately or accidentally is difficult to determine, but the latter appears more likely. They are usually 30–40 mm across and lead from the ground surface to a tunnel below. It is important when watching badgers not to choose a position close to one of these holes as a badger may scent you before emerging. It is disconcerting to hear a sudden snort from below as a badger takes fright.

The practice of blocking setts ('earth stopping') has long been carried out by fox hunts to deny foxes a bolt hole during the course of a hunt. Although behavioural changes have been noted after sett stopping (later and more wary emergence), Lindsay & Macdonald (1985) concluded that this practice had no deleterious effect on badgers provided that it was carried out strictly according to the procedure laid down by legislation (Appendix 1). However, we have no evidence of the physiological effects of sett blocking on badgers. Of course these are likely to vary according to local conditions; this is a subject ripe for study.

The temperature of a sett is much more constant than on the surface. Within a few metres of an entrance it varies vary little over 24 h, but over a full year Moore and Roper found that it ranged from 6 to 19°C compared with outside figures of -4 to 33°C. Interestingly, they found that the main factor influencing the maximum and minimum temperatures within different setts was the cover surrounding the entrances, those with woody cover showing less extremes of hot and cold. That some chambers near the surface dissipate heat from the occupying badgers was very evident at a sett watched in the Cotswolds. When there was a light covering of snow, a patch just above was always the first to melt (Neal 1948). The humidity in all setts investigated was a constant 100% (Bock 1988, J. Moore & T.J. Roper, unpubl. data).

Categories of setts

Various attempts have been made to classify setts according to size and function (Neal 1948, Likhachev 1956, Kruuk 1978, Thornton 1988). The territory occupied by a social group may include several categories of sett, although it is not always easy to distinguish between them in some areas as there is so much variation. However, the most important sett on the territory is termed *the main sett* which is usually large, typically has five or more entrances, is used throughout the year and acts as the main breeding sett. Each social group has just one main sett within its territory. This is useful in surveys where the number of main setts gives an estimate of the number of social groups, and thus the number of badgers in the area.

In contrast there are small setts with only one or two holes and a simple, often unbranched tunnel system; they are used only occasionally as a temporary refuge, often by a single badger; these are called *outliers*. There may be several of these within a territory.

Between these two extremes, setts of intermediate size may occur which are occupied for prolonged periods. They may be used as alternative breeding dens when more than one sow within a social group is breeding, or by immatures or sub-dominant animals at certain seasons. In some territories a sett such as this may be quite close to a main sett and be connected to it by obvious paths. This type has been classified by Kruuk (1978) and Thornton (1988) as an *annexe* sett. There are other setts in some territories which are some way away from the main sett which Thornton has called *subsidiary* setts. She separates them from annexe setts, not only because of their position, but also because they are not connected by paths to the main sett.

These four categories are useful for field surveys, but badgers, like humans, delight in nonconformity. We are least happy about the distinction between annexe and subsidiary setts because as far as we are aware there is no difference in function between them — they both serve as alternative accommodation when occasion demands, including the opportunity for other sows in the social group to rear cubs (Chapter 8). Also, the distinction of having or not having interconnecting paths is often misleading as at some seasons, for example, spring, paths can usually be seen connecting both categories. Obviously the conspicuousness of the paths is related to the degree of usage and the state of the vegetation. It seems probable that the different position of annexe and subsidiary setts relative to the main sett is due to the distribution of suitable sites or the lack of them within the territory. For example, when there is a stratum of soil along the contour of a hill which is favourable for digging, the main sett will be located there, and if there are no other sites on the territory which are as suitable as an alternative, an annexe sett is likely to occur. However, in territories where suitable sites for setts are more spaced out, subsidiary setts may be found.

Of course, whatever scheme is devised there are bound to be exceptions; a few will be mentioned. Main setts are *not* always used throughout the year; they may be abandoned for short or long periods, perhaps due to a catastrophe such as when trees are felled in the vicinity. Then the badgers may use an alternative sett for many months and not return until vegetation has grown up. Also, if cattle trample the ground and dung around the sett they may leave for a few weeks, and the same applies to human interference. These exceptions are more likely to occur when good alternative accommodation is available.

Main setts may be difficult to distinguish by size alone. Typical ones with 5–15 entrances are easy, others may have holes stretching along a hillside for a kilometre in a favourable stratum, as in the Blackdown Hills, Somerset. Such setts are probably an amalgamation of main and annexe setts, but in time have become two main setts. In contrast, one in the Cotswolds (Neal 1948) had only one entrance out of which 12 badgers were seen to emerge in quick succession.

To complicate the matter still further, Kruuk (1989) showed that where badgers are scarce and territories very large, as in western Scotland, badgers may be vagrants, moving from sett to sett according to foraging strategy with no one sett occupied all the time. This is also true in parts of Sweden where Skoog (pers. comm.) found setts only used seasonally, some as a winter refuge and for breeding and then abandoned for setts near good food supplies.

Setts also change status; outliers may prove suitable for more sustained occupation, be enlarged and become subsidiaries; subsidiaries and annexe setts may become main setts and vice versa. Setts visited regularly by Ernest for 16 years occurred in a narrow copse 300 m in length. Two social groups used them, each having three discrete setts and many outliers. One groups used setts A, B and C, and A was the main sett for 12 years, cubs being produced there most years; for the next 4 years, B was the main sett, breeding taking place there. The other group used setts D, E and F, and had D as the main sett for 10 years; towards the end of this period, sett F was dug and enlarged rapidly; 3 years later it became the main breeding sett and remained so. In both cases the main setts reverted to annexe setts.

These exceptions illustrate the difficulty of devising definitions — very little in nature can be easily categorised — but it is nevertheless advisable to discipline ourselves and try to keep to some convention, otherwise people develop different schemes and a state of general confusion arises.

Ancient setts

Badgers are very conservative regarding their homes. If generations of badgers have found a sett suitable, it will continue to be used unless new factors make this impossible. Setts in Gloucestershire, where badgers were subjected at one time or another to digging, snaring and repeated gassing, are still occupied today. Having talked to certain countrymen whose memories have gone back 60 or more years and asked them about the location of setts they knew as boys, it was remarkable to find that the majority were still there.

One sett at Ashlyns in Hertfordshire is famous for both its antiquity and size. It was certainly extant towards the end of the 18th century and is probably much older than that. It is situated in a wide pit in the chalk with beech trees growing in and around it. In 1890, a great effort was made to eliminate the sett in order to get rid of mange in foxes which lived there too. This was a time of great unemployment, so eight men were given the job. They dug steadily for 10 days without coming up with the badgers (Roberts 1893). Michael Clark (pers. comm.) reports that the sett is still used by badgers today.

The Mendip Hills are honeycombed with caves in the limestone and badgers are plentiful. One ancient cave known as Badgers' Hole was being investigated for archaeological remains by W. Balch (pers. comm.). When digging out an area where the roof had fallen in many centuries before, he found a number of badger bones along with those of elk (*Alces sp.*) and cave bear (*Ursus spelaeus*) estimated around 60 000 years old. Badgers still live in part of that cave today! In fact Balch met one face to face in one of the tunnels. He also discovered an ancient runway he believed had been made by badgers.

Why such large setts?

At first sight it seems strange that in some districts very large setts are dug when in others, small ones suffice for successful breeding and as a refuge. Apart from age and diggability of the soil which are obvious explanations of size, are there benefits arising from them? One possibility is that a large sett enables more than one sow to breed without hindrance. This would be comparable to a subordinate sow using an annexe sett to have her cubs. Large setts also give scope for change in living quarters as bedding soon becomes infested with ectoparasites (Hancox 1980). However, this is probably one reason why badgers replace their bedding at intervals. Bock (1988) suggested that in complex setts the occupants could take advantage of different microclimates according to season. The ventilation required and the 'fortress' properties of setts may be other reasons why large setts are an advantage. Or perhaps the instinct to dig is uncontrollable given good opportunities!

Origin of setts

When new setts are formed they are usually dug on existing territories as outliers of the main sett. If one of these is found to be suitable it may be enlarged and eventually become a breeding sett (Neal 1948).

Some setts are excavated where no previous digging has taken place, but it is more usual for badgers to enlarge rabbit burrows. The latter are often dug in soils and situations equally suitable for badgers, so they make a useful starting point. They may also enlarge marmot burrows (Novikov 1956).

DIGGING

There is something very appealing in Nicholas Cox's description of how badgers dig their sett. In 1721 he described the process as follows:

> One badger falleth on his back, another layeth earth on his belly, so taking the hinder feet in his mouth draweth the belly-laden badger out of the hole and having disburthened himself re-enters and doth the like until all be finished.

The badgers must have changed their habits during the 274 years since those words were written! However, it is not easy to see exactly what happens except for the final stage when the badger emerges backwards from the entrance.

When digging, a badger appears to be very preoccupied with the process. On several occasions Ernest has been able to stand close by an entrance and been showered with earth as a badger has backed out and kicked away the loose soil with its hind limbs.

When enlarging a tunnel, a badger makes rapid movements with its fore limbs and claws to loosen the earth, then when sufficient has accumulated, it arches its back and brings its hind limbs forward to push the earth backwards, causing a heap of loose soil to form behind it. It then moves backwards, partly using its hind quarters as a ramrod and partly hugging the earth below its belly with the help of its fore limbs and chin, moving in a series of jerks until clear of the entrance. When the spoil heap is large it will continue to drag the soil to the edge and kick it away with its hind legs. Consequently, in loose soil, a furrow is formed between the entrance and the edge of the heap. Before returning for another load the badger may shake itself to get rid of the loose soil from its fur.

When digging in very stony soil, chalk or limestone, large stones are removed along with the earth. Much effort is involved in winkling out these rocks when firmly embedded, and in chalk especially, you can often see the evidence of this in the deep furrows made by the front claws in the surface of excavated pieces. Stones of up to 4 kg have been recorded. If very large, they may be pushed out by the snout or dragged out backwards with the fore legs, or occasionally, even carried by mouth.

On one occasion a badger was seen dragging boulders of some 150 mm in diameter from its sett high upon a hillside: 'each time the animal sent one rattling down the steep slope to the stream below, it stopped and looked down the slope until the noise abated before continuing!' (Paget & Middleton 1974a).

On some nights digging may continue for 2 h or more and huge quantities of sand removed. Usually one badger does the digging, but occasionally others join in. In Essex, a badger was seen to emerge in good daylight in May and start digging (D. Bradnam, pers. comm.). It was soon joined by another — this one already covered in sand. Shortly after, a third came along and helped in the digging and one after the other brought out sand from the hole. A load was removed at exactly half-minute intervals by these three badgers. All badgers, apart from young cubs, dig, regardless of sex and age.

In several consecutive years some clay balls — rounded structures ranging from golf to tennis ball size — were found outside a sett dug in shale (Neal 1977). When sectioned they showed concentric rings, indicating that they had been formed by some rolling action; numerous badger hairs were incorporated. They have since been found at many setts, but always where the clay was thick and sticky. It is not certain how they are formed. Michael Clark actually photographed a badger rolling one between its front feet as it backed out of the entrance. He thought they might be made when a badger's claws became coated with sticky clay and it tried to clean itself below ground. However, G. Göransson sent Ernest a transparency of a Swedish badger showing a number of clay balls sticking to its fur. He believes that when clay in the tunnel is just the right stickiness it adheres to the fur in patches and as the badger moves along the tunnel, the patches enlarge with further accretions and rotate on the fur whenever contact is made with the clay of the tunnel thus forming concentric rings with hairs incorporated.

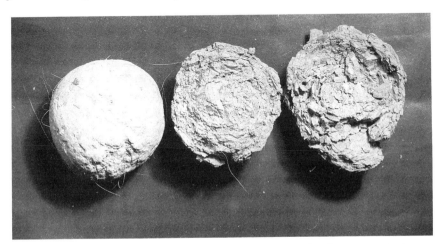

FIG 3.4   *Clay balls collected from the spoil heap. When cut they show concentric rings due to rolling and hairs which have become incorporated.*

BEDDING

Bedding collection is one of the badger's most characteristic activities. The bedding is gathered in bundles and brought back for storage in sleeping and breeding chambers. The material used varies according to availability, the badgers of each sett tending to use the same type of bedding each year according to season, although they are not averse to a change if unusual opportunities occur.

In one sett in hill country near Taunton where there are no arable fields, in summer and autumn the badgers use grass, but after the bracken has died and becomes dry they use this until April. In May they switch to bluebell leaves which are brought in green.

Hay or coarse grass, whenever this is available, seems the badger's first choice all over the country even when good alternatives exist. For example, the badgers from one sett in a copse on a steep slope separating two arable fields had a choice between hay from the lower field and straw from the upper. They invariably chose the hay although it was further away and much more difficult to bring back up the slope. If no long grass is available, straw is a good substitute. Some badgers in the Mendip area of Somerset brought back a complete bale of straw. Unfortunately, this unusually large bundle got stuck in a fence just short of the sett, but undeterred, they pulled it to pieces and eventually brought it all in (G. Walton, pers. comm.). Straw seems to be particularly welcome in the winter in places where bracken is unavailable. Some was collected from a field where it was put out for cattle in hard weather and laboriously brought back more than 80 m through difficult terrain to the badgers' woodland sett.

With setts deep in woodland, badgers may use dry leaves; oak (*Quercus sp.*) and sweet chestnut (*Castanea sativa*) are favoured. Other plants used in winter include the fronds of male fern (*Dryopteris filix mas*), dry trailing branches of wild clematis (*Clematis vitalba*), rock rose (*Helianthemum chamaecistus*) and even gorse (*Ulex sp.*) and thistles (*Carduus sp.*).

Green bedding collected in May, apart from bluebell leaves (*Scilla nonscripta*), may include dog's mercury (*Mercurialia perennis*), daffodil (*Narcissus sp.*) leaves (S. Patten, pers. comm.) and the fronds of hart's-tongue ferns (*Scolopendrium*). Badgers often use wild garlic (*Allium ursinum*) in the Cotswolds. When a storm brought down branches of sycamore (*Acer pseudoplatinus*) in May near a sett, the badgers stripped off the green leaves and took them below (P. Tolputt, pers. comm.).

The method of collection varies according to the material. Grass is scratched up with the front claws which act as hay rakes, but when it is tough, badgers get a grip with their teeth, arch their neck and shoulders and pull with great strength, sometimes uprooting the whole plant. They make much noise while doing so.

Tough materials like bracken and male fern fronds are usually bitten before bundling, but sometimes the latter are pulled up by the roots, the whole plant being carried back to the sett when the fronds are bitten off and the rhizomes left scattered about (Neal 1977). Leaves are scraped together with the fore feet into small heaps before transportation.

Eunice Overend used to give newspaper as substitute bedding to a cub she was rearing. It would never bring it back whole, but would shred it first, then bundle the pieces together and drag them backwards to its day nest in the bend of the stairs. 'It left a trail behind which looked like a paper chase!' (pers. comm.).

Whatever the material, it is normally brought back to the sett after bundling, hugged to the chest, the chin and forelegs keeping it in place. The badger shuffles backwards with a series of jerky movements of the hind limbs, more or less sliding on its front ones. This backward movement is surprisingly fast, but periodically, the badger stops to listen or to retrieve any bedding that has become loose. Its direction is seldom at fault although it is not looking where it is going. When nearing the sett it follows a well-used path the scent of which almost certainly guides it. It enters the sett still going backwards.

Occasionally unorthodox methods are adopted. In Cumbria, a badger was watched bringing bedding back in the usual way, but because the slope was very steep, it picked up the bundle in its mouth for the last part of the journey (J. Webster, pers. comm.) Also, a sow in Hertfordshire, on emerging from a sett, found a bundle of bedding outside, took it up in her mouth and walked with it towards the sett, but after a few paces turned round and brought it in backwards in the usual manner (Soper 1957).

Bedding is collected quite systematically. One October a sow collected beech leaves from about 3 m from where Ernest was standing on a low fork of a tree; on its next trip it came still nearer, not suspecting his presence. When it came once more Ernest anticipated it would come right up to him, and sure enough, it collected more leaves from within a few centimetres of where he was standing! In some places where setts are surrounded by bracken, the whole area is progressively denuded of dry fronds as the winter proceeds.

The route used when bringing back bedding is often difficult to negotiate. At one sett at the base of a quarry, hay was brought from a field above, over a bank, across a road, over another bank and then down the quarry face with an incline of 1 in 1; a distance of about 50 m. Much greater distances have been recorded including one of 230 m (D. Bradnam, pers. comm.).

FIG 3.5   *Bringing back bedding to the sett.*

The amount of bedding carried each trip can be quite large. Some bundles of wet grass were found to weigh 0.5 kg (J. O'Connor, pers. comm.). Some nights, a badger may take in a few bundles and then go off to forage, but occasionally there are gala nights when a single animal may bring in 20–30. This activity may stimulate others to do likewise. One April Ernest saw three adults at it at the same time, a boar and a sow bringing bedding back to one entrance and another sow to a different one.

The bringing in of bedding seems to be an inherited action as it took place in cubs brought up in captivity from the time they were only 2–3 weeks old (Brian Nettleton, pers. comm.). At 8–9 weeks they collected small piles of grass or leaves, started to move them, but then appeared to forget and do something quite different; however by 12 weeks they carried out the operation in a much more effective manner.

FACTORS AFFECTING DIGGING AND BEDDING COLLECTION

Digging and bedding collection are often associated. The usual pattern is for part of the sett to be cleaned out first and then bedding is brought back; so these activities will be discussed together and from a seasonal standpoint.

Digging and bedding collection can take place during any month of the year although there are peaks of activity correlated with important events in the lives of the badgers. The most unpredictable diggings occur when an entrance, not used for some time, is cleared and subsequently used by one or more of the sett's occupants; this can occur during any month.

Keith Neal and Roger Avery (1956 pers. comm.). carried out observations on a single, large main sett near Taunton, Somerset over 4 years involving 800 visits, more than half being night watches. Digging and bedding collecting were noted and from these data Ernest has correlated their frequency in relation to the birth of cubs, number of litters and fluctuations of badger numbers. Bouts of digging were far less frequent than bedding collection but both activities showed peaks which varied only slightly over the 4 years (see Figs 3.6–3.8).

It is convenient to start with the period June–July as this is the quietest period for digging and bedding collection in south-west England; at this time the cubs are becoming independent and the whole social group is most concerned with feeding. Nevertheless, Ernest has found in some other localities when a family has moved to an alternative sett in July, much digging activity has occurred at both setts involved.

Sometime during the August–October period a lot of digging took place each year but peak times were variable. Two factors appeared to influence the timing. The first was the weather; for example there was far less digging during very dry conditions. This could have been due to the hardness of the earth, but one possibly important reason was the longer time needed to find food, thus leaving less time and energy for digging. The second factor appeared to be population numbers. For instance, few badgers were present in August 1955 compared with other years, but when more badgers arrived at the end of September, presumably from a subsidiary sett, a great deal of digging took place the following week. Digging during the August–October period was followed by the taking in of much bedding and presumably both activities were connected with preparations for the winter. Huge amounts of earth were excavated at this time and it is logical to assume that this is the main period when new tunnels and chambers are dug.

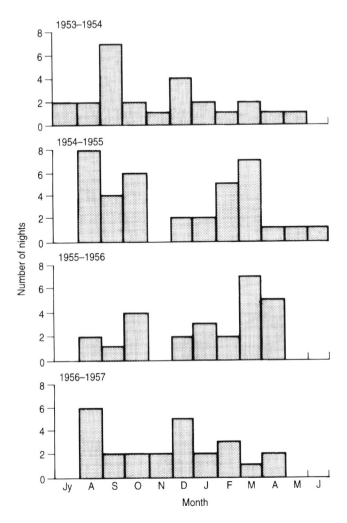

FIG 3.6 *Number of nights per month when some digging was known to have taken place at one permanently occupied main sett near Taunton, Somerset. Data from 260 observations over 4 years. Source: K.R.C. Neal and R.A. Avery (unpubl. data).*

Very little digging took place in November and the first half of December, which is the quietest period in a badger's life, although small amounts of bedding were taken in during early November.

During the second half of December and in January, small-scale digging was resumed and during the latter month significant amounts of bedding were collected. It is highly probable that this is connected with preparations for the birth of cubs since it takes place whenever the weather is suitable within a few weeks of cubbing. In 1954, bedding was brought in on 2 January (the first collected since October), more on the 4th and 6th; the

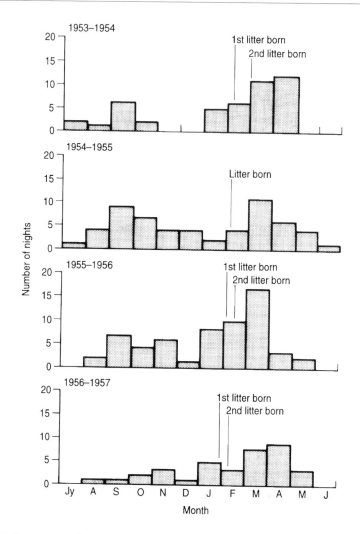

FIG 3.7   *Number of nights per month when bedding collecting was known to have taken place as for Fig. 3.6.*

entrance was cleared on the 11th, and after three successive dry nights, further bedding was brought in. A wet week followed, but on the 25th, after another spell of dry nights, more was collected. The first litter was born at the beginning of February. As can be seen in Fig. 3.7, a rather similar pattern occurred in succeeding years. So collection of bedding at this season provides excellent evidence that there will be cubs subsequently. What is more, the entrances into which it is taken appear to be the ones nearest the breeding chamber and the ones the cubs will use during their early appearances above ground. Ernest was able to use this correlation very usefully when planning to film a badger family with Professor Hewer. Lights had to be installed above the entrances well in advance of the time when the cubs

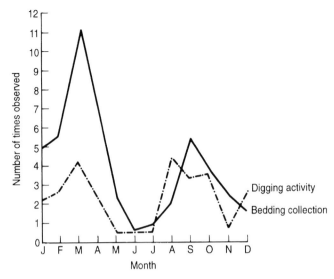

FIG 3.8   *The relationship between bedding collecting and digging activity based on the average frequencies for each month, incorporating the same data as for Figures 3.6 and 3.7.*

would come above ground to habituate the adults to the illumination. There were many possibilities, but by choosing the entrances into which bedding had been dragged in January they fortunately hit on the ones the family subsequently used.

In northern districts of England where litters tend to be later, this bout of bedding collecting is often several weeks later than in the mild south-west.

It was found that much more digging and bedding collecting occurred during the February–April period when the cubs were confined below ground. Then, much of the digging was associated with the removal of old bedding, fouled by the cubs. This was particularly evident in years when there were two litters. Fresh digging also occurred at other entrances, particularly in February (Neal & Avery 1956). At this time boar badgers are usually banished from the breeding area of the sett, so this may be one factor. However, a general spring clean seems to take place at most setts whether or not breeding takes place.

In May little new digging took place but in most years a lot of bluebell leaves were brought in when green.

THE SIGNIFICANCE OF THE BEDDING

The major function of bedding is to prevent heat loss. This applies to adults when sleeping during the daytime, but to a far greater extent to the cubs during the first few weeks of life. When cubs snuggle right inside this mass of dry bedding, the heat generated by their bodies and that from the sow when she is with them is retained in the nest owing to the excellent insulating properties of the bedding. There is no doubt that a high nest temperature is maintained in this way (p. 161). The dryness of the bedding and its presence in large quantities are important factors for survival. This is illustrated by the lengths to which some sows will go to provide dry bedding when conditions are difficult. For example, in one locality good use was made of the fibrous bark of sequoia trees — the only dry material available. This was clawed off and brought back a considerable distance. More circumstantial evidence of the essential nature of bedding may be deduced from hand-rearing young cubs, which need to be kept at a warm temperature if they are to survive.

Norah Burke (pers. comm.) considered that badgers sometimes draw sticks and sometimes pine cones into the sett to act as a mattress between the damp earth and the bedding. She found in a chamber she had excavated that the sticks below the bedding showed signs of having been chopped up into suitable lengths. There is no doubt that sticks, especially dead elders, are brought back by badgers and it is not unusual to find one stuck in the entrance. Michael Clark (pers. comm.) found a long stick projecting from a sett in a fir wood; it looked as if someone had stuck it in when passing. He relates:

> I was about to pull it out, when I realised it was waving slightly in the air. It was then given a sharp pull and I saw it move further below ground. This continued but it did not sink in much further because of the turn of the tunnel. Eventually, I took hold of

FIG 3.9   *Bedding being aired on a sunny morning in winter.*

the waving end and gave a pull. There was immediate resistance, but after a few moments the tug-of-war with the badger was over and out came the stick. The far end showed badger hairs and tooth marks!

Although most bedding is brought in dry, there are exceptions which many badger watchers confirm. Enid Smith (pers. comm.) gave two instances of it being brought in after light snowfall, on nights when dew had been heavy and several times after rainfall. It is probable that slightly damp bedding will ferment and raise the temperature of the nest, just as a heap of compost generates heat. Rotting bedding has been found in excavated setts. The use of green bedding in spring probably has a similar function, providing extra heat for the cubs when their coats provide less effective insulation.

On several occasions it has been noticed in exposed setts that badgers have blocked up entrances with bedding during cold windy weather. This could be more than a coincidence as an injured one kept in captivity also blocked up its only entrance under similar circumstances (G. Pearce, pers. comm.).

Badgers occasionally 'air' their bedding. This activity should not be confused with the odd bundle of dropped bedding near a sett entrance. It occurs most often on dry sunny mornings in winter. Great quantities of bedding — usually hay — are dragged out and fluffed up into loose piles scattered around the entrances (Fig. 3.9). After a few hours in the sun the badgers drag it back again.

NESTS AND COUCHES ABOVE GROUND

It is not unusual for some badgers from a social group to leave their setts for varying periods of time and live above ground during the day in nests or couches. This is one reason why numbers seen at a main sett may fluctuate, especially in summer and autumn. Three kinds of day nests may be distinguished: those used for breeding; summer nests some distance from a main sett; and nests in close proximity to a sett. In addition there are couches which are usually used at night.

Breeding nests above ground are unusual but may be found where the water table is too high for digging or where for some reason a sow has been displaced from a more normal situation. These will be described in Chapter 8.

Summer nests often occur when badgers move to other parts of a territory where there is a more abundant supply of food at that season. Special places are chosen such as a hollowed-out bramble bush, dense bracken or the centre of a cereal field. Conspicuous paths lead to them and they contain much bedding which may sometimes be collected from a distance. Latrines are often found nearby.

A most extraordinary summer nest was shown to Ernest by Perarvid Skoog (Neal 1977). It was in a hollow tree on an island in the Baltic and regularly used when the whortleberries were ripe in that part of the island. Not only was it full of bedding but it overflowed in a great heap outside (Plate 18). A second hollow tree in the same area was also used but it did not contain such a spectacular amount of bedding.

Badgers have been disturbed from summer nests on several occasions. Blakeborough & Pease (1914) described how hounds came across a badger asleep in some deep bracken. The lair contained 'quite a cartload of bracken, well pressed down and so arranged as to shelter the sleeping animal'. They also mention another occasion when they were able to creep up to a day nest and to their delight see two adults lying there fast asleep. Chris' pointer dog has found badgers in such situations on a number of occasions in the Cotswolds where he lives. Having called away the barking dog it has sometimes been possible to peer in and see a disgruntled badger peering back out. Also, badgers may sometimes lie out during the day in old farm buildings, especially if they are remote and contain some hay or straw, use artificial drains put down for foxes, or hide in natural fissures in rocky areas.

Other nests are near sett entrances. Ernest has watched badgers using such a nest (Neal 1982). When making a routine visit to a favourite sett in Somerset on 19 June, he found a heavy crop of hay had recently been cut and the badgers in the nearby copse had made the most of this superabundance of potential bedding. Outside one of the entrances was a huge mass of green hay about a third of a metre deep covering an area of 2×1.4 m. Two hollowed-out regions showed where badgers had compressed the hay by lying on it.

A few days later when Ernest arrived at 19.30 with the sun still high, the nest was unoccupied, but shortly after, a boar emerged, went straight to the nest and thoroughly groomed himself in one of the hollows before leaving. A sow then emerged, used the nest for grooming for a few minutes and then retired below. Later, yearlings emerged but left the sett without taking any notice of the hay. Soon the sow re-emerged, this time with a well-grown cub, and at the same time the boar returned. All three made a bee-line for the nest; the sow and cub used one hollow, the boar the other. After a long session of grooming, the sow took some hay from the edge of the pile and shuffled backwards with it below. Later she went off with the cub leaving the boar in full possession of the nest. It was some time before he ambled off. Badgers had been in view for over 2 h and most of the time their activities had been centred on that remarkable nest.

Several evenings later Ernest went again. This time the sow went off at once, but the boar made straight for the nest — no grooming this time. Instead, he pivoted round and round, put his head between his paws and prepared to go to sleep. With his muzzle deep in the hay he sneezed several times and then went into a deep sleep. His respirations were slow — 10–11 breaths per min. Ernest took several flash pictures but he just went on sleeping. After more than an hour, Ernest moved the camera and tripod to within 2.5 m for better pictures: still no response. Losing patience, he retreated to 5 m and tried to wake him by throwing a twig. It landed on his back; he gave a twitch and went on sleeping! Eventually Ernest woke him up by clicking his tongue. The badger shot bolt upright and stared straight at Ernest as if he couldn't believe his eyes. Even after another photograph he continued to stare; then without hurry or even a backward glance he slipped away into the bushes. Ernest was sorry to have disturbed the badger's dreams but felt very privileged to have been present on such an occasion.

Shallow hollows are also seen near sett entrances and sometimes they may contain bedding. Badgers use them when grooming soon after emergence; occasionally, two animals will use the same hollow.

Couches are found in various parts of a territory. They are used as temporary nests where a badger may lie up for a few hours during the night rather than go back to the sett. After a period of worming, one may sleep there for a time and digest its meal before embarking on another feeding session. Couches are usually in sheltered positions under a bush or some overhang and contain bedding.

PATHS

Occupied setts have a well-marked system of paths, relatively few in number, which lead from one entrance to another and away to places of importance within the territory of the social group such as alternative setts, main feeding grounds and latrines. They are often very distinct and denuded of vegetation owing to the constant trampling. Main paths may be followed in woodland for 300–400 m and people often use them without realising their origins until they pass under bushes or the lower branches of trees. It is tempting to believe that some of the ancient human trackways had their origins in animal paths such as these.

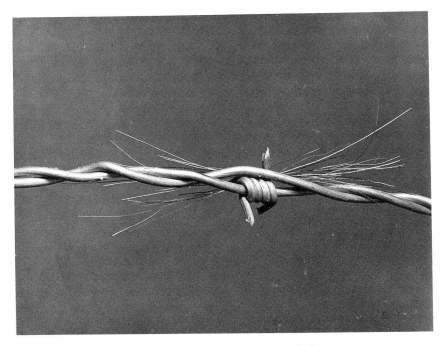

FIG 3.10 *Badger hairs caught in barbed wire.*

Where the undergrowth is thick, they take the form of tunnels, just as they do when penetrating a hedgerow. Where a badger path leaves a wood, badger hairs may often be found caught in the lowest strand of barbed wire. Occasionally, instead of finding the characteristic straight, wiry guard hairs, you find much finer black ones. This happens when the badger passes over the wire rather than below it, so the ventral hairs get caught.

Paths in woods often meander according to the lie of the land and the position of trees and other barriers to a badger's progress; they usually represent the easiest route to travel. Badgers follow these paths largely by scent, the snout being held just above ground level to recognise the scenting places marked by badgers using the path on previous occasions (p. 140). Humphries (1958) suggested that a badger's knowledge of a path system is related to maze learning in other animals. This seems very probable as a badger, if frightened near its sett, rushes for home along one of these paths rather than by a shorter route 'cross country'.

The path system near main and annexe setts changes very little over the years. In one wood in the Quantocks well documented for over 30 years (Fig. 3.11) the few changes in the main paths were due to the falling into disuse of one of the setts and the excavation of new holes.

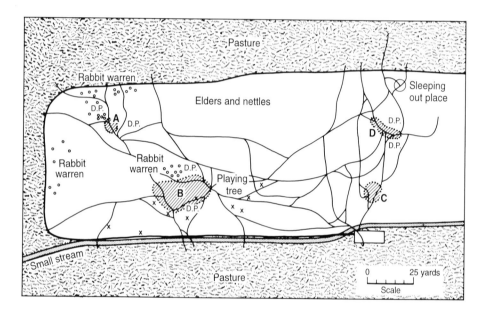

FIG 3.11   *A deciduous wood in the Quantock Hills, Somerset, containing four setts belonging to the same social group. C was the main sett, but cubs were also born at A and D in some years.*

Some paths, especially in early spring before much grass has grown, can easily be seen crossing pasture (Fig. 3.12). They may mark the perimeter of a territory. Their conspicuousness is partly due to regular patrolling by boars, during the early months of the year (Chapter 7).

Long-established paths often pass across man-made barriers such as lanes, main roads or railways. In the sunken lanes of south-west England you can often find their 'up-and-overs'. These are bare slides down the steep banks which badgers use when crossing. If you find one on one side of the lane there is usually another not quite opposite on the other. Similarly, if there are dry stone walls as in the Cotswolds or Cornwall, you can sometimes see where a

FIG 3.12   *Badger path from wood to pasture. This well-worn track marks the boundary between two territories. Photo K. Neal.*

few stones have been dislodged where badgers have climbed over. The moss or lichens are often worn away at such places (Fig. 3.13).

Where the territory is very large, badger paths may be traced over very long distances. In Sweden, P. Skoog showed Ernest a path which led from a sett across a bare rocky area where food was scarce to a place 1 km away where it was seasonally plentiful. Where the path crossed the rocky area for several hundred metres, it could be traced easily as the lichen, *Cladonia*, which covered the rock was worn away by badger traffic.

Badgers in Cornwall are known to use paths which traverse the seashore as a short cut between feeding grounds.

When roads are enlarged or new ones constructed, badgers are often killed while trying to cross. Many years ago Ernest had an extraordinary instance of this. A taximan called at his house in Somerset early one February morning; he said he had a dead badger in the taxi and would Ernest like it? He said he was taking a client to catch an early morning train while it was still dark. Just outside Taunton, he rounded a sharp bend, went straight into the badger and killed it. It was a sow. The incredible thing was that a few days later he turned up again with another badger which he had killed at the same place when taking the same

FIG 3.13   *When badgers clamber over stone walls, they regularly use the same place, wearing away lichens in the process. Cornwall. Photo G.A. Pawsey.*

FIG 3.14 *Badgers often climb over a dead tree trunk if it straddles a path and may also use it as a marker by deliberately scratching it with their front paws. Photo M. Chesworth.*

man to catch the corresponding train! This time it was a boar. The coincidence seemed remarkable, but the explanation must have been that both animals had lived in the same sett and used to cross the road at the same place just before dawn on their way home. It was unfortunate for the badgers that the taximan was also keeping to time.

LATRINES

Some latrines are found quite near a main sett, others occur at strategic places in other parts of social group territories. In Kent, Newcombe (1982) found that for 55 latrine sites near setts, 56% were within 10 m and 43% within 5 m. These pits are usually dug where the soil is soft, often under a bush, a fallen trunk or an overhanging rock. The pits are funnel-shaped, about 150 mm deep and roughly the same diameter at the top. When a pit becomes full of dung, it is left uncovered and another dug nearby. You often find five or six covering an area of 2–4 m². The focus of activity of a latrine may change with the passage of time

FIG 3.15   *Latrine pit containing soft, muddy faeces indicating that the badger had fed on earthworms.*

with new pits being dug and old ones abandoned, but generally speaking, the latrine area remains associated with the same location.

Occasionally dung is deposited in a disused sett entrance or on the spoil heap, outside a used entrance. This has been noted after cattle had trampled all over the sett area. Perhaps the invasion prevented the badgers from using their normal latrines.

Latrines near the sett are used most often in late winter and spring and it seems probable that at this season they are mainly used by sows and cubs. On one occasion in the Doncaster area of Yorkshire a sow was seen to go to the latrine area followed by her small cub and defecate in a pit; she then turned to the cub and licked its anal region. Despite the cub's playful movements and numerous attempts to rejoin the other cubs she continued to lick its anal region for about 8 minutes until it finally squatted on the ground and defecated in the latrine area; they then rejoined the others (Johnson 1989).

Some excavated setts have revealed latrines in empty chambers and side tunnels (Leeson & Mills 1977, Roper 1992). Defecation underground probably occurs more often in winter; however, with some setts, even large ones, you can find no trace of latrines above ground nearby at any season, some having this characteristic year after year. This does not appear to be associated with the presence or absence of cubs, so presumably in these cases the underground habit persists throughout the year.

Latrines are also found a considerable distance from the sett; many of there have territorial significance and are usually larger than those near a sett. Some are close to main paths, especially where they reach some obvious landmark such as a hedgerow, lane or wood edge and in particular, near 'up-and-overs'. Others mark the perimeter of the territory and may occur in large numbers. As many as 50 pits were concentrated within a relatively small area on Bredon Hill, Worcestershire (Pickvance and Babb 1960). In Wytham Wood, near Oxford, Hans Kruuk (1989) found that 70% of all latrines were near territorial borders. The importance of these communal latrines can be gauged by the prominence of the paths leading to them. An aerial photograph of the Iron Age fort at Cadbury Castle, Somerset, clearly indicated such a path leading from the main sett on the western slope of the hill, 400 m across a cornfield on the flattened top to a communal latrine area on the other side (M. Harfield, pers. comm.).

Occasionally, instead of a latrine with many pits, a single considerably larger one may be found containing much dung. These are usually located just by a path delineating the territorial boundary.

Other latrines are found scattered sparsely within the main territory, particularly near areas where there is a special abundance of food. For example, at Hodd Hill, Dorset, in a region where there were many yews (*Taxus bacata*), badgers were found to have gorged themselves for a few weeks on the fallen berries and the dung in the latrines nearby contained the undigested 'stones'. Latrines are also commonly dug in fields of cereal around harvest time and near groups of bramble bushes when the fruits are ripe. It is probable that they serve as a claim to ownership of the harvest. Sometimes the dung is deposited on the surface, not in pits (see Fig. 7.6).

Some pits are used for urination (Paget & Middleton 1974a). Eric Ashby, watching a sett in the New Forest, described how a badger emerged, went about 20 m to some empty latrines and urinated, then, taking a step forward, wiped its feet with brisk scrapes like a dog; it then walked another 20 m or so to some latrines containing droppings which it used for defecation. (The social significance of latrines will be discussed further in Chapter 7.)

SCRATCHING TREES

Near the entrance of a main sett, it is usual to find an elder (*Sambucus nigra*), or other tree with rough bark, showing obvious signs of claw marks and mud to a height of about a metre. When a badger uses such a tree, it gets up on its hind legs, reaches as high as it can and then brings them down, scraping them against the bark as it does so. The bark may eventually become worn away by this action and if the soil is coloured, the mud clinging to the trunk is very conspicuous (Plate 17).

This behaviour has been described as 'claw sharpening', but that is clearly incorrect since no such action would sharpen the claws, rather the contrary. It is not certain why badgers do this. One suggestion is that the stretching helps to tone up the muscles after sleeping; many mammals do this. However, it takes place at times other than just after emergence; sometimes on returning in the early morning. Alternatively, the action may help to remove mud after a night's foraging or after digging. It seems to take place more frequently when the ground is wet and muddy but not exclusively so. However, the most likely explanation is that it serves as a territorial marker. It is known that the wolverine (*Gulo gulo*), which is a near relative, marks trees near its den so that they become conspicuous visual signals of occupation. Badgers are mainly nocturnal, so a scratching tree is unlikely to act in the same way, but it might be a scent marker, the badger using inter-digital glands between the foot pads. Furthermore, where suitable trees are not available near a sett, you sometimes see mud

FIG 3.16 *Scratching an elder tree by the sett. Note the shredded bark. Photo M. Chesworth.*

marks on boulders or similar structures nearby. You also find scratch marks on fallen tree trunks which indicate repeated rather than random use.

More observations are needed before the function of 'scratching trees' is fully understood. It would be helpful to know what members of the social group do this, how often and whether it is a seasonal phenomenon.

VEGETATION AROUND SETTS RELATED TO BADGER ACTIVITY

The vegetation in the vicinity of well-established setts is characterised by elders, stinging nettles (*Urtica dioica*) and to a lesser extent, blackberries (*Rubus fruticosus*). Elders are present because badgers eat elder berries and deposit the seeds in latrines near the sett. Elder leaves are bitter and are not eaten by badgers or rabbits, hence seedlings survive. On one occasion Ernest found an elder seedling 150 mm high growing from a latrine. Bramble is found near setts for the same reason and in Scandinavia wild raspberry (*Rubus idaeus*) takes the place of bramble. Nettles can withstand the disturbance caused by digging and they like the acidic nature of the soil and presence of nitrates due to urination and defecation.

When badgers collect bedding, seeds are brought back with it and may germinate on the spoil heap and nearby. Much new growth of wheat may sometimes be seen on the spoil heap of an unoccupied sett entrance following the use of wheat straw for bedding. The presence of such plants as pink campion (*Lychnis dioica*), thistles (*Carduus* sp.), dock (*Rumex* sp.), red dead nettle (*Lamium purpureum*) and hemp nettle (*Galeopsis laudanum*) may be explained in the same way. Thus over time, when badgers take up residence, their activities gradually make their home and immediate surroundings more suitable. The growth of typical flora, particularly nettles, provides extra cover and elders even add another source of food on the doorstep when big enough to fruit (Neal & Roper 1991).

SETT TENANTS

It is not surprising that with so much spacious accommodation provided by badgers, many other species make use of it including a great variety of invertebrates. Some, such as bumble bees (*Bombus* sp.) and wasps (*Vespa* sp.) attempt to make their nests near tunnel entrances. These often get destroyed by the badgers, but in unoccupied setts they may persist. Other invertebrates are associated with the bedding within the chambers including parasites (p. 191) and a large number of kinds of beetles, flies and mites. A comprehensive list of these has been compiled by Hancox (1988d).

Many kinds of mammals use badger setts in one way or another (see Table 3.2). The majority are casual visitors making use of the burrow on a temporary basis, usually when the badgers are not resident. This applies to pine martens, polecats, feral cats, wild cats and several other small carnivores. Their occasional presence is of very little significance to the badgers as there are no interactions.

Other mammals may tunnel into the spoil heaps or make side burrows from the tunnels. These include woodmice, bank voles and brown rats. It is sometimes incongruous, when expecting a sizeable badger to emerge from a large entrance, to see a tiny woodmouse appear on the threshold before darting off into the vegetation! Brown rats use badger tunnels quite frequently in some districts, especially if the latter are near rubbish dumps.

In Eastern Europe, wolves and racoon dogs use unoccupied badger setts as refuges (Novikov 1956); the latter also live commensally with both badgers and foxes in Lithuania, but use different entrances (E. Mickevicius, pers. comm.). However, the most common commensals over most of Europe are the rabbit and fox, and in Italy, the porcupine (Tinelli & Tinelli 1980).

Where rabbits are common, they are regular associates. Many setts have originated as enlarged rabbit burrows and in some, the rabbits have continued to use part of the burrow system. Typically, in small setts, rabbits take over as soon as badgers move out, and you can be certain that if you find rabbit droppings near a sett entrance, no badger will emerge from the hole that evening. In large setts rabbits can live quite happily along with badgers, but

TABLE 3.2   *Mammalian tenants of setts*

English name	Scientific name	Status	Authority
Woodmouse	*Apodemus sylvaticus*	Casual	Hainard (1961), Hancox (1963), Neal (1977)
Bank vole	*Clethryonomys glareolus*	Casual	Hainard (1961) Humphries (1958)
Brown rat	*Rattus norvegicus*	Casual	Barker (1969), Hancox (1963), Neal (1977), Soper (1955)
Rabbit	*Oryctolagus cuniculus*	Commensal	Numerous
Fox	*Vulpes vulpes*	Commensel	
Wolf	*Canis lupus*	Casual	Likhachev (1956), Novikov (1956)
Porcupine	*Hystrix cristata*	Commensal	Tinelli & Tinelli (1980)
Racoon dog	*Nyctereutes procyanoides*	Commensal	Novikov (1956), Popescu & Sin (1968), Mickevicius (unpubl.)
Pine marten	*Martes martes*	Casual	Hancox (1973), Tregarthen (1925), Wijngaarden & Peppel (1964)
Stone marten	*Martes foina*	Casual	Jensen (1959)
Polecat	*Mustela putorius*	Casual	Jensen (1959)
Polecat-ferret	*Mustela foro*	Casual	Paget & Middleton (1974b)
Weasel	*Mustela nivalis*	Casual	Wood (1958)
Feral cat	*Felis catus*	Casual	Lancum (1954), Wijngaarden & Peppel (1964)
Wild cat	*Felis sylvestris*	Casual	Crossland (1934), Ognev (1935)

usually occupy holes around the perimeter digging side tunnels of smaller diameter. In the Netherlands, no fewer than 50 rabbits were ferreted from a large sett which contained a number of badgers (Wijngaarden & Peppel 1964).

Up to the end of May, rabbits usually emerge and move off before the badgers appear, but in summer it is not unusual to see both above ground at the same time within a short distance of each other. Little notice is taken of the other although a rabbit will bound off if a badger comes too near. Badgers eat rabbit nestlings (p. 119), but we have never seen evidence of this happening in or around the sett area.

Foxes occasionally dig their own earths, often by enlarging rabbit burrows, but they are lazy diggers and much prefer to use badger setts if available. Typically they use unoccupied setts, but in large setts often share the spacious accommodation, one part being used by badgers and usually perimeter holes by foxes.

In the Netherlands, Switzerland, Germany and Denmark, it is the rule for foxes and badgers to live in the same sett, the main exception being small newly formed setts which are occupied by badgers alone. It has been suggested that in the Netherlands this is due to the relative scarcity of suitable sett sites (Wijngaarden & Peppel 1964). There are many instances of fox litters in badger setts in both Britain and on the Continent. Likhachev (1956), over a 15-year period, found that in his study area 63% of fox litters were born in badger setts.

Foxes and badgers may also live together in man-made sites such as old mine workings. Gamekeepers have regularly caused foxes to bolt from these setts in some numbers (Paget & Middleton 1974b).

In general, foxes spend much time above ground, lying up during the day in good cover. It is largely during the winter and up to June before the cubs disperse that they occupy badger setts. For the rest of the year occupation is more casual. Only when fox cubs are about do you see foxes for long near a sett; at other times they usually go straight off.

It is rare to see a fox emerge from the same hole as a badger. If this happens it is due to some emergency, such as when a fox has been hunted or frightened and takes refuge temporarily. However, at a sett in Surrey in early April, both fox and badger cubs were seen to emerge from the only exit (E. Bartlett, pers. comm.). Both sets of cubs were estimated to be about 2 months old as they kept near the entrance, nosing at each other and tumbling at the slightest prod. The sett was dug out a month later and consisted of a main tunnel leading to a large cavern-like chamber in which the badger cubs had been brought up. From this chamber two tunnels diverged; one an 'upright chimney' leading to another badger chamber, the other to a fox's lair which was foul with debris. It is surprising they tolerated each other within a relatively small sett. Typically, the rotting remains of prey, fox scent and urine are greatly disliked by badgers causing them to use different parts of a sett, or if not breeding themselves, move to another sett, leaving the vixen and cubs in possession.

Usually, badgers are dominant to foxes and can evict them at will, but this is not necessarily true in the breeding season. Hancox (1973) cites an example in a wildlife park in Avon where a mixed community of badgers and foxes resulted from burrowing between adjacent pens. In this situation foxes were only dominant when they alone possessed cubs.

One year, badgers were using the whole of a 20-entrance sett; some rabbits were present but no foxes (Willan 1963). In the late autumn the badgers moved over to a smaller sett 70 m away but returned to the main sett in February where foxes had already moved into one part. The badgers did not breed and put up with the large litter of fox cubs for some weeks, keeping to their part of the sett, but eventually moved back again to the smaller sett nearby. However, in July, once the fox cubs had dispersed, the badgers thoroughly spring-cleaned the sett and took up residence once more.

When badgers have cubs below, any intrusion by a fox usually meets with strong aggression. W. McGreggor (pers. comm.) watched a sow with a very small cub which was poking out from below its mother at the sett entrance while she kept nosing it down the hole to keep it in. After collecting some bedding from close by, she disappeared down the tunnel. Later, a fox strolled nonchalantly over the sett area and when level with the occupied entrance the sow shot out and nearly knocked it flying — chasing it off for 25 m before returning to her cub.

Most other recorded cases of this kind of aggression occurred during the period February–May and involved sows with small cubs. One such, observed by H. Wilson (pers. comm.) occurred at 09.00. Pandemonium was going on in a dell near her house in Worcestershire. She found a badger had apparently pushed a fox into a pool which was near its sett. The fox appeared to be trying to get out of the pool but was kept from doing so by the badger.

However, on seeing her, the badger dashed down the sett and the fox, very bedraggled, struggled out of the water, shook itself and ambled off across the fields.

Usually these fights end with the fox running away, but occasionally this is not possible. There was such an incident on a cliff edge in North Wales which Abel James witnessed one morning. At 07.00 he heard a scuffle on the cliffs above and saw a vixen on a ledge which he realised had a dead end. He climbed up and saw she was being followed along the ledge by a badger. Both animals were snarling at each other. The vixen, finding herself trapped, faced the badger and as a last bid for safety attempted to leap over her opponent, but the badger was too quick for her and caught her by one of her legs. For a few moments they rolled over and over on the ledge and then went over the side still locked together. When Abel James reached them they were both dead (Ian Niall, in *Country Life*, 4 June 1959).

Another instance of mutual killing was recounted by C.M. Cowland (1953). He found in an oak wood the bodies of a medium-sized fox and a large badger locked together in death. The badger's jaws were firmly buried in the fox's head. Presumably it was unable to withdraw its teeth and had died, possibly of suffocation. No other wounds were visible. Monica Edwards (1971) tells how she saw a badger take a vixen out of an outlying hole of a main sett and while it was still struggling in its jaws take it down another entrance.

Fights between badgers and foxes often attract attention because of the noise that ensues and the contestants are too engrossed to notice a person's approach. Such a fight took place on 21 January near a sanatorium on the Quantocks, Somerset. When the noise was investigated, a fox and a badger were seen on the drive in furious combat and it was possible to get quite near before they were aware of being watched and rushed away (H. Pearson, pers. comm.).

Very occasionally a fox will kill a badger. P.D. Hager (1957) describes how the contestants were fighting in a lane near Chesham, Buckinghamshire, making a great deal of noise. When a car came along, the fox made off across a field and the badger was found to be dead. This was in July and could have involved a well-grown cub. No age was mentioned in the report.

There are many instances of adult badgers killing fox cubs (Batten 1923). This can be the work of a boar but more often involves a sow with cubs. Most reports are from circumstantial evidence but occasionally the deed has been witnessed. E. Clay described in *The Countryman* how he used to watch four half-grown fox cubs playing on the hill side opposite his home in Devon. One hot evening in June, he heard screams from that direction which continued during the time he was making his way towards the place. The screams came from a dense blackberry bush and were mingled with a grunting, snuffling noise. Parting the brambles he saw one of the fox cubs lying there, one back foot bitten off, its hind quarters apparently paralysed and skin torn on its shoulders. As it turned to look at him the head and fore quarters of a huge badger appeared from a hole at the back of a bush. It gripped the cub by the throat and dragged it down the hole.

Occasionally it is the fox that is the aggressor and badger cubs the victims. Roger Burrows (1968) found large quantities of badger fur in a fox dropping and on another occasion a large piece of badger skin. Of course, the badgers could have been eaten as carrion but the circumstances did not suggest this.

From these accounts of aggression between badgers and foxes it should not be assumed that fighting is usual. In the great majority of cases they are respectfully tolerant of each other's presence and go their own ways, but trespass by either when cubs are about may lead to aggression. A wary, armed neutrality might be a better way of expressing the relationship.

However, sometimes all the rules are broken. Wijngaarden & Peppel (1964) cite a case of a sow badger adopting the cubs of a couple of foxes which had been shot, and providing them with food. There are a number of accounts of litters of badger and fox cubs playing together very amicably. However, they usually play independently.

INTERACTION WITH OTHER ANIMALS

Badgers come into close contact with other mammals during the course of their wanderings. Apart from their interaction with prey species (Chapter 6) they may come across deer and various farm animals. Usually badgers take very little notice of larger mammals but if the latter have young the reverse may be true.

On one occasion a roe doe (*Capreolus capreolus*) chased a sow and two cubs back to the sett when they approached too near. It was assumed the doe had a kid nearby (J. Rowbottom, pers. comm.). Similarly, Phil Drabble (pers. comm.) watched a boar badger wandering in the direction of where he knew a roe kid was lying. When it got within about 10 m the doe rushed at the badger and passed over it at full speed striking with her forelegs as she did so. The boar turned and immediately ran for the sett, but the doe returned to the attack twice before he got there. It was over an hour before he re-emerged!

Badgers commonly come across cattle. Sometimes the latter are very curious and sniff around sett entrances at dusk, stamping and defecating. Disturbance of this kind can cause badgers to abandon a sett. However, when badgers are out in the fields they show less fear of cattle but if they can avoid them when foraging they will do so (p. 204).

Differences in behaviour when badgers are near a sett and when foraging are very marked; a typical example of this concerns sheep. On the hill sides of Cumbria, sheep and badgers take little notice of each other, but near the sett it is quite different. John Webster (pers. comm.) described a sett in open fell side which was heavily grazed by sheep. The bare area near the sett was very popular with sheep and particularly with lambs which lay out and played on it. If this area was occupied, badger emergence was delayed for up to an hour. One occasion was of special interest and we quote from his account:

> A lamb showed curiosity in the holes, scraping and putting his head into them. It then settled down with the ewe in the entrance of the main hole thus inhibiting the emergence of the badgers which looked out from various other holes but did not emerge for some time. Suddenly, the sow, two cubs and two young adults came out one after another and went a little distance up the fell where the sow started to collect some bedding. The cubs began to play and as their games rapidly became more wild they raced together towards the sett. This so excited the lamb that it too started galloping and leaping about as if to join in. However, the badgers completely ignored it.
>
> Exactly a week later, a lamb approached the sett, this time when two cubs were already out, some 50 m away. When they became aware of the lamb they immediately ran back to the sett and one slipped in through an outlying hole. The other, approaching the main hole met the lamb directly. The lamb lowered its head and making slight butting motions caused the badger to stop and then run away on a wide detour to enter the sett by another hole. On both occasions the lamb showed interest in the badgers which in turn were very wary. When the ewe was present she was quite indifferent and apparently in no way apprehensive for the lamb's welfare.

Accounts of interactions with dogs vary considerably. Many badger cubs have been brought up with dogs and the association has been companionable and amicable. Wickham Malins (1974) relates how his bull terrier bitch, which had never had puppies, was stimulated to produce milk by the badger cub and was able to suckle it successfully.

On the other hand, hounds, various kinds of terriers and some other breeds will attack a badger at once if found above ground. Hounds will probably kill it; however, the smaller breeds of terriers if they are experienced seldom come to grips. Their normal role, in the days when badger digging was legal, was to find the badger in the sett, keep it at bay and prevent it from digging away from the men with the spades who dug towards the place where the dog was barking continuously.

The most remarkable and vivid description we have found of an encounter between dogs and a badger was written by Fred Speakman in his book *A Forest by Night* (1965). He eloquently describes how he witnessed a battle royal between an Alsatian and two small mongrel dogs on the one hand and a boar badger on the other. It occurred in a wood after dark. We cannot do better than to quote extracts from his account as it typifies both the courage of the dogs and the stubborn, powerful defence of the badger.

> They are running and fighting together. Here and there, dodging and rushing, comes the short swift thud of a badger's feet, the high excited cries of dogs in chase. What a furious medley of sound! Sharp cries of eagerness, agonised yelps of pain, high scream of badger, more yelping of a dog. The badger stands at bay. The face swings low to the ground, left and right in a move so swift no dog could avoid it. The badger is fighting this fight his own way. He crouches to ground. He advances in short, swift rushes. He retreats quickly, swings about in his own length, faces the little dog at every turn. But the other is at his rear. He rushes in, bites and flashes away, safe, as the badger wheels to meet him. So they torment the strange beast, vicious feint and counterfeint, holding the badger's attention till one or other can dash in. The Alsatian waits behind. Now she is there, full face to face, growling and barking in black anger, prancing lightly for all her weight, tail lifted high. The badger rushes forwards, the Alsatian seizes it above the neck and throws it wide. The mongrels rush in. But the badger is on all fours again. It has caught the Alsatian's lower jaw a ripping slash. It makes for the big dog again, the little dogs like fiends along its flanks. The Alsatian comes in at a charge. It flings the badger high. A little dog is underneath as it lands. She cries high and terribly. The other, undaunted, dances near . . .
>
> The badger is now low to the ground. His breadth is incredibly broad. He is low, the black belly hidden under the body. The coarse grey hairs stand stiffly out like a bottle brush. His back is steeply arched — for all the world like a vast grey pear drop . . . there seems nothing for the dogs to bite on. His defence is impenetrable, and that head of black and white is provided with jaws to whose snapping the gin trap is a toy. He swings to meet a dog. A cry rings out upon the night. The dog runs off limping, whimpering pitifully . . . the badger thuds off into the distance. The sounds grow quiet. He is gone to earth.

When Speakman found the dogs, the Alsatian had her head down, her jaw slashed and her flanks were heaving; beyond her were the two mongrels stretched out on their sides, both badly bitten. One of them subsequently died.

There have been a number of reported encounters between dogs and wild badgers which by contrast have been marked by curiosity and playfulness rather than aggression. One instance involved a 6-month-old puppy, which, when being taken out for a walk, encountered a foraging badger. The animals played together quite happily while the dog's owner watched from a distance (D. Bradnam, pers. comm.).

There seems little doubt that the great variation of behaviour shown by dogs and badgers when they meet is determined by the temperament and breed of dog and the past experience or lack of it on the part of both dog and badger.

CHAPTER 4

Distribution, Status and Habitat Requirements

DISTRIBUTION IN EUROPE AND ASIA

THERE is only one species of the Eurasian badger, *Meles meles*. Its distribution is very wide, stretching from Ireland in the west, right across Europe and Asia to Japan. It is found practically all over Europe where local conditions are still suitable except in Arctic regions of Scandinavia and Russia, high-altitude areas and some islands. In the Mediterranean it is present on the islands of Rhodes and Crete. It also occurs in the Middle East including Jordan and Israel and is not uncommon in Iran where it has been found at an altitude of 2200 m.

In Asia it is not found much north of a line from where the rivers Tabor and Ob meet to the north of Amurland, not far from the Arctic Circle. It occurs on several of the more southerly Japanese islands and in most parts of China as far south as Hong Kong with the exception of the higher parts of west China. The species' southern limit is defined by the Himalayas.

Subspecies

Considering the tremendous extent of its range in Europe and Asia, it is not surprising that many different forms have been described varying in size, colour and minor dental and skeletal characteristics. At least 23 subspecies have been named (Ellerman & Morrison-Scott 1961), but a number of these are better looked upon as geographical races. In a survey of mammals in the former USSR (Bobrinskii *et al.* 1944), 10 of these races were grouped into four subspecies: *M. m. meles*, the type species which is widely distributed over most of Europe; *M. m. canescens*, a much smaller badger from Transcaucasia; *M. m. leptorhynchus* which has a wide distribution from south-east Russia through much of Siberia; and *M. m. amurensis* from Manchuria.

Further Asiatic subspecies include *M. m. anakuma*, confined to Japan. It is a small brownish badger with chocolate-brown eye stripe which in some specimens is reduced to a ring round the eye, giving it a panda-like appearance. It is largely a forest species, found up to 1700 m. *M. m. leucurus* is another subspecies found largely in China and Tibet and *M. m. albogularis* which is also found in Tibet.

Some island forms have also been given subspecific status: *M. m. rhodius* from Rhodes and *M. m. arcalis* from Crete. These are relatively small badgers.

In Western Europe, the only subspecies for which there appears to be some justification are those from Spain and Portugal, *M. m. marianensis* and the Danish badger, *M. m. danicus*. The latter (Dahl 1954) differs from the type subspecies in having a stronger dentition and a larger skull.

STATUS OF BADGERS IN WESTERN EUROPE

Data collected recently (Griffiths & Thomas 1993) give the most reliable estimates of population densities available. They were obtained from many sources: published accounts, standard questionnaires to research workers in carnivore or game biology, animal welfare/conservation groups, hunters' associations and others. The data vary considerably in reliability, but give a useful, albeit tentative, indication of the present position in most countries.

The estimates of badger density (Fig. 4.1) are expressed in three categories of abundance: high (>1 badger km^{-2}), moderate (0.1–0.99 badger km^{-2}), or low (<0.10 badger km^{-2}). From this analysis, badgers are very sparse in Albania, the Netherlands, Estonia, Belgium and Poland and abundant in Ireland, Sweden and Britain. Moderate populations occur in most other countries although little data are available for the majority of those bordering the Mediterranean. However, in terms of habitat requirements, including available food, it seems likely that here, especially in the hotter, drier, southern areas, badgers are sparse. It should be stressed that all these assessments are for whole countries; local conditions may be very different.

Badgers have come under pressures of many kinds in Western Europe over the past 50 years or so. Hunting occurs seasonally in most countries; road traffic deaths have been on the increase and persecution by farmers and gamekeepers is still widespread. However, a major cause of population decline in central Europe over several decades was the rabies virus along with methods of controlling the disease. The red fox is the major vector of the rabies

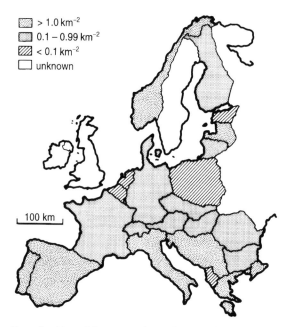

FIG 4.1   *Gross densities of the national populations of badgers in Western Europe. Source: Griffith et al (1993).*

virus while the badger is an important secondary host (Steck 1982), so the gassing of fox earths and badger setts was carried out systematically and on a large scale. However, the badger population now appears to be stable or increasing in most countries with the exception of Albania (owing to habitat destruction and subsistence hunting) and the former Yugoslavia for similar reasons associated with the war (Fig. 4.2). One important factor causing the recent increase in a number of countries may be the change in rabies control techniques from destruction of foxes and badgers to immunisation of the fox population. For further details of individual countries, legislation and conservation measures, hunting and other relevant factors, the paper by Griffiths & Thomas (1993) is recommended.

HABITAT REQUIREMENTS

Badgers inhabit a very wide range of habitats. In Britain, their setts are found in woods and copses (deciduous, coniferous and mixed), scrub, hedgerow, orchards, quarries, sea cliffs, moorland, mountainous country, open fields and downland. They also make their setts occasionally within city boundaries, on housing estates, in embankments of roads, railways and canals, in long-barrows, Iron Age forts, mines, natural caves, coal tips, rubbish dumps and even under major roads and buildings.

In Western Europe setts are found in many of the more favoured habitats as mentioned for Britain, particularly where a mosaic of suitable features are present such as deciduous

FIG 4.2   *Directional trends in the national population of badgers of Western Europe.*
Source: Griffiths & Thomas (1993).

woodland, pasture and arable. Some setts are even dug in old sand dune systems such as in the Coto Doñana in southern Spain.

In the former Soviet Union, badgers inhabit most varied habitats in all geographical zones except the tundra. In forests they prefer the south-facing slopes of ravines where snow melts early in spring; however, in the Caucasus they prefer the northern slopes where it is cooler in summer. In steppes and semi-deserts they use gullies or enlarge old marmot burrows. In Kazakhstan they dig into the banks of coastal lakes, lower parts of sand dunes or level salt marshes, but always near water. They also inhabit mountainous districts — as high as 2500–3000 m in Tian Shan (Novikov 1956).

This extraordinary adaptability has undoubtedly contributed largely to their success as a species.

Badger population densities vary considerably from place to place, so in Britain, in 1963, the Mammal Society organised a National Badger Survey, one of the aims of which was to find out the important ecological factors which had a bearing on the distribution of badgers and those local factors which influenced a badger's choice of site for a sett. To date, over 23 000 setts have been recorded and such factors noted as habitat, soil type, altitude and whether on a slope (and if so, which way it was facing) or on the flat. Many of the facts deduced from this survey (Neal 1972a, 1986, Clements *et al.* 1988) will be incorporated in the account which follows. However, the survey was based on 10 km squares which proved too large to cover adequately; thus parts of Britain were poorly represented and some not at all. Furthermore, in many instances, recorders did not distinguish between main and other types of sett; it also took place over such a long period that although many areas have been

TABLE 4.1   *Percentages of setts in various habitats in selected counties of Great Britain. From Mammal Society Survey (Clements, E.D. in Neal 1986 up-dated. Pers. comm.)*

	Deciduous and mixed woods, copses	Coniferous woods	Hedges	Scrub	Open field or downland	Quarries, pits	Sea-cliffs	Moorlands, rocky slopes	Built up areas	Any other	Setts involved
ENGLAND											
Avon	51.6	0.6	14.4	14.1	5.2	3.4	0.3	0.3	7.2	2.9	347
Bedfordshire	32.0	5.1	28.9	19.6	10.3	4.1	–	–	–	–	97
Berkshire	61.7	6.3	13.0	12.3	1.7	2.0	–	–	2.7	0.3	300
Buckinghamshire	60.3	1.0	21.0	5.5	8.5	2.8	–	–	–	0.9	529
Cambridgeshire	37.9	4.7	19.4	10.9	9.5	13.8	–	0.5	–	3.3	211
Cheshire	53.1	8.3	13.7	13.2	7.5	1.6	–	1.2	–	1.4	424
Cornwall	41.6	5.6	5.9	23.6	5.9	1.2	10.6	5.6	–	–	339
Cumbria	33.8	9.5	7.8	5.2	10.1	1.9	0.2	28.5	0.2	2.8	536
Derbyshire	44.9	7.1	7.8	17.2	12.1	3.4	–	4.3	–	3.2	1131
Devonshire	61.0	10.1	8.5	10.3	4.2	2.7	0.5	2.5	–	0.2	446
Dorset	37.2	5.9	16.7	17.8	17.9	2.2	0.9	–	0.7	0.7	681
Durham	65.1	7.2	4.6	13.7	3.2	4.2	–	0.7	1.3	–	307
Essex	53.5	1.0	14.3	13.5	3.8	5.3	–	–	3.8	4.8	624
Gloucestershire	70.9	10.0	5.5	7.3	4.5	–	–	–	–	1.8	110
Hampshire	64.8	9.0	7.9	10.4	1.3	4.1	–	1.0	0.4	1.1	797
Hereford & Worcester	59.1	9.3	9.3	6.4	11.1	3.2	–	–	–	1.6	440
Hertfordshire	57.8	2.6	16.1	7.9	2.4	12.4	–	–	0.4	0.4	533
Isle of Wight	36.7	–	17.4	32.1	9.2	–	2.8	–	–	1.8	109
Kent	66.8	2.0	10.5	9.8	5.9	3.3	0.1	–	0.1	1.5	1053
Leicestershire	43.6	2.9	16.9	12.1	12.8	5.9	–	0.7	–	5.1	273
Norfolk	31.5	13.5	2.3	20.2	6.7	20.2	–	–	–	5.6	89
Northamptonshire	36.7	5.2	23.3	11.5	13.8	5.6	–	–	1.0	2.9	305
Northumberland	55.4	20.0	3.9	12.3	3.0	2.4	0.3	1.5	–	1.2	334
Nottinghamshire	41.9	6.2	15.6	20.1	5.6	2.8	–	1.1	2.2	4.5	179
Oxfordshire	54.5	2.8	14.7	15.2	4.1	6.4	–	–	–	2.3	468
Shropshire	55.9	7.0	17.3	7.8	11.2	0.5	–	–	–	0.3	1275
Somerset	40.1	3.3	26.0	11.4	12.0	3.7	–	0.9	0.5	2.1	1542
Staffordshire	59.5	6.0	5.5	10.5	11.5	2.5	–	3.5	1.0	–	200
Suffolk	26.1	2.4	36.6	22.7	1.4	10.1	–	–	–	0.7	287
Surrey	75.5	5.9	8.0	5.2	0.9	2.8	–	0.1	1.3	0.3	1043
East Sussex (Downs)	30.5	–	5.8	43.0	17.2	0.7	–	–	1.7	1.1	465
East Sussex (Weald)	65.9	4.0	17.5	6.4	2.2	2.6	0.2	–	0.6	0.6	1055
East Sussex (Total)	55.0	2.8	14.0	17.6	6.8	2.1	0.1	–	0.9	0.7	1520
West Sussex	71.4	3.9	8.5	10.3	2.8	1.6	–	–	1.0	0.5	388
Warwickshire	53.2	–	6.0	14.4	14.4	7.0	–	–	–	5.0	201
Wiltshire	31.7	4.6	13.7	13.9	31.4	1.4	–	–	0.7	2.6	1032
North Yorkshire	50.3	19.1	2.2	9.6	8.1	3.6	0.3	5.8	0.2	0.8	642
South Yorkshire	61.2	6.0	5.5	10.9	10.9	2.2	–	2.2	–	1.1	183
All other counties	60.8	6.3	9.5	5.7	8.2	2.5	–	3.8	–	3.2	158
England %	52.1	5.7	13.3	12.2	8.9	3.5	0.3	1.6	0.7	1.7	19133

TABLE 4.1— *contd*

	Deciduous and mixed woods, copses	Coniferous woods	Hedges	Scrub	Open field or downland	Quarries, pits	Sea-cliffs	Moorlands, rocky slopes	Built up areas	Any other	Setts involved
WALES											
Clwyd	57.1	11.3	9.0	10.0	3.2	3.8	–	2.8	0.2	2.6	968
Dyfed	35.3	5.2	16.8	19.3	0.8	0.8	19.3	1.7	–	0.8	119
Glamorgan	50.6	25.3	4.8	13.3	2.4	1.2	1.2	1.2	–	–	83
Gwent	50.9	12.0	15.3	16.2	3.0	1.3	–	0.4	–	0.9	536
Gwynedd	48.7	15.6	1.9	1.9	15.6	2.6	4.6	3.6	–	5.5	308
Powys	34.6	22.1	5.9	13.1	12.7	0.6	–	10.2	–	0.8	480
Wales %	49.1	14.2	9.1	11.5	6.4	2.3	1.5	3.7	0.1	2.1	2494
SCOTLAND											
Borders	31.2	27.0	8.9	6.5	6.2	0.7	–	16.4	–	3.1	292
Dumfries & Galloway	22.1	20.3	7.1	7.5	8.0	0.9	23.0	8.0	–	3.1	226
Grampian[a]	21.7	32.6	1.0	34.5	3.4	2.1	2.9	1.8	–	–	383
Highland	32.6	11.6	1.5	8.0	3.6	–	–	42.0	–	0.7	138
Lothian	58.2	15.7	4.8	4.5	7.5	4.8	–	0.8	1.1	2.6	268
Strathclyde	65.1	4.1	5.5	5.5	4.1	1.3	2.7	11.0	–	0.7	146
Others	33.8	34.4	5.4	9.5	5.4	–	–	8.8	–	2.7	148
Scotland %	35.6	22.8	4.8	13.3	5.5	1.7	4.2	10.1	0.2	1.8	1601
Grand total %	50.7	7.8	12.3	12.2	8.4	3.2	0.7	2.4	0.6	1.7	23 228

[a]Main setts only.

rechecked, some data have become out of date. Nevertheless, since 1988, with the emphasis on main setts, the number surveyed has nearly doubled owing largely to the enthusiasm of Badger Groups and Mammal Society members and the outstanding efforts of E.D. Clements. In consequence, Table 4.1 gives an extremely good estimate of our present knowledge.

Further progress was made when Penny Thornton (1988) studied intensively a series of tetrads (4 × 4 km) in Devon and Cornwall to discover the important habitat factors which determined sett density and distribution. This confirmed statistically the findings of the Mammal Society Survey and introduced new factors of importance which will be alluded to later.

This was followed by a sett survey of England, Wales, Scotland and some islands, planned to take place over a 2-year period using pre-selected 1-km squares on a grid system (Cresswell *et al.* 1990). The survey covered 1.05% of the total land area of Britain. The number of setts recorded was related to land class as determined by Bunce *et al.* (1982) and enough squares were selected and searched in each land class to achieve a standard mean density for active main setts. Statistical results for habitat preferences showed that those actively selected for main setts were hedgerows, semi-natural deciduous woodland, tall and low scrub, bracken and quarries. Features actively avoided were improved grassland and arable. 'When all the woodland categories were added together, the active selection for woodland was even more pronounced'. Both this survey and the one carried out by the Mammal Society are in many ways complementary as the former provides a base-line for future surveys (the first of which is currently being carried out) and gives a much more

TABLE 4.2   *Estimated number of setts in Britain according to Land Class.*

Land class	Description	Main setts used	Main setts discused
1.	Hedgerow	8123	1403
2.	Tree line	5470	487
3.	Semi-natural broadleaved woodland	2046	757
4.	Broadleaf plantation	1275	187
5.	Semi-natural coniferous woodland	3199	827
6.	Coniferous plantations	5928	884
7.	Semi-natural mixed woodland	1677	187
8.	Mixed plantations	225	0
9.	Young plantations, broadleaved or coniferous	1968	990
10.	Recently felled woodland	1681	934
11.	Parkland	1051	187
12.	Tall scrub (area of bushes 3–5 m high)	294	0
13.	Low scrub (areas of bushes < 3 m high)	1001	205
14.	Bracken	58	58
15.	Coastal sand dunes	1128	482
16.	Coastal sand and mudflats	402	708
17.	Coastal shingle and boulder beaches	3321	551
18.	Lowland heath (areas with > 25% low scrub)	166	497
19.	Heather moorland (uplands with > 25% low scrub)	575	97
20.	Blanket bog (areas of peat with heather dominant)	172	88
21.	Raised bog (areas of peat > ½ raised as a dome)	550	137
22.	Marginal inundation including swamps and fen	121	121
23.	Coastal marsh including saltmarsh	179	0
24.	Wet ground in association with other areas	125	125
25.	Standing natural water pools	613	123
26.	Standing man-made water	318	521
27.	Running natural water	868	324
28.	Running canalised water	516	0
29.	Upland unimproved grassland	0	0
30.	Lowland unimproved grassland	0	0
31.	Semi-improved grassland	0	0
32.	Improved grassland	0	0

The land class refers to the dominant vegetation within the 1-km square; it may contain other habitats in which the setts were actually found.

Source: Modified from Cresswell *et al.* (1990)

accurate general picture of distribution, while the latter gives more detailed information of areas, large and small, which have been studied in great detail. Both surveys will be referred to later in terms of badger density and population numbers in Chapter 9.

It is clear that with such diversity of habitats in which setts are found some of the ecological factors involved are inter-related and differ in priority from one habitat to another. It should also be noted that much more reliable conclusions can be drawn from main setts than other categories. With these points in mind some of the more important factors which influence choice of site will be discussed.

Geological factors

The ideal sett appears to be one which is easy to dig, is dry and therefore relatively warm, is safe as a refuge and for breeding and is in little danger of the roof collapsing. Geological factors are of major importance in these respects including the diggability of the soil and its depth, the underlying rock and the nature of the subsoil and its permeability to water. There is much evidence that sandy soils are usually preferred to clay although the latter is not despised in districts where there is little choice. However, very heavy clays are avoided.

Setts in sand are predictably much more extensive than those in other soils and enormous workings have been found in suitable greensand and sandstone regions. However, if the sand is very loose, as in sand dunes, there is a risk of the roof collapsing and badgers choose places where rhizomes of marram grass or other vegetation help to consolidate the material. Similarly, many sandy soils are associated with woodland since the roots of the trees serve the same purpose.

The preference of sand over clay is well illustrated by the distribution of setts in the Weald of Sussex, an area where the badger sett density is very high. In this area, layers of sand and clay alternate to give the badgers a good choice. Almost all the setts are found in the Ashdown sand and Tunbridge Wells sand, very few in the clay. Both these sandy areas are very variable in character, ranging from pure sand in places to a very clayey texture in others. Again, the badgers select the sandy spots (Clements 1974). Further details are given in Table 4.3.

Similarly, in the Greater London area only two setts were found in the London clay compared with 84 in sand and gravel and 43 in chalk (Teagle 1969). Again, Wytham Wood near Oxford covers an area of hard corraline limestone at the higher levels and heavy clay on the lower slopes, with a belt of calcareous grit sand between. All the main setts in the wood are found in the sandy belt (Southern 1964) and on neighbouring hills all the setts follow the same sandy stratum (Hancox 1973).

Chalk is also popular with badgers. This gives excellent drainage and the setts are well protected by hard rock. However, some chalk is very hard and difficult to excavate and it is evident where a choice is available that badgers choose the softer strata or where the chalk is broken up into more easily manipulated large lumps, or is mixed with flints which can be dislodged. At Boxhill, Surrey, the large main setts are dug in soft, sandy chalk and you find many flints thrown out on the spoil heaps. In the Chiltern Hills in Buckinghamshire, only one sett was found on the extensive clay plateau compared with 117 in the chalk: 94 in the upper chalk and 23 in the middle chalk (Dunwell & Killingley 1969). The stratum of upper chalk coincided with bands of woodland and this probably explained the preference.

Further evidence of preferences can be obtained by studying an area where the

TABLE 4.3   *Number of setts in various geological strata in Sussex.*

Soil type	Number of setts	Percentage
Clay with flints	4	
Upper/middle chalk	458	27
Lower chalk	85	5
Upper greensand	1	–
Gault clay	0	–
Lower greensand	4	–
Folkestone beds	14	1
Sandgate beds	10	–
Hythe beds	43	2.5
Atherfield clay	0	–
Weald clay	13	–
Sand/sandstone in Weald clay	11	–
Tunbridge Wells sand	276	16
Grinstead clay	0	–
Ardingly sandstone	69	4
Wadhurst clay	7	–
Sand in Wadhurst clay	54	3
Ashdown sand	583	34
Purbeck beds	2	–
Head	46	2.5
Alluvium	21	1
Miscellaneous	18	1
Total	1719	–

Source: Updated from Clements (1974).

population of badgers is increasing and badgers are overflowing to less suitable areas. In parts of Wiltshire, the setts are mainly in the wooded upper greensand slopes where digging is easy, but when this first-choice habitat is fully occupied, the surplus badgers do not move down to the gault clay but up to the chalk and finally to the open, unploughed downland (Gillam 1967). However, these choices are not simply those of geology as other factors such as adequate cover and seclusion must be important. These factors will be discussed later.

Limestone regions also have high sett densities. This is particularly true of the Cotswolds, Mendips, Pennines and parts of Yorkshire. Limestone gives good drainage and protection, but in some places the rock is so hard to excavate that the badgers then make use of local regions of more friable rock, natural fissures and cave systems. Speleologists have often come across huge piles of bedding on dry ledges in caves or in small side caverns.

In many limestone districts there are strata of soft material below the solid limestone and badgers exploit the juncture between them, since the hard rock forms a strong impermeable roof which keeps the sett dry and prevents the roof falling in, while the actual digging is easily done in the sand. Thus in the Mendips, the badgers excavate the sandy stratum immediately below the hard carboniferous limestone, in Yorkshire, the Permian sand just under the magnesium limestone and in the Cotswolds, the lias sands with hard oolitic limestone as a roof.

An excellent study of the distribution of setts on the Cotswold escarpment (Findlay 1973) illustrates this preference very well. Six strata were identified (Fig. 4.3). Setts were most abundant in the well-drained lias sands (3), but particularly so, near the junctures with the oolitic limestone above. It seems probable that when the badger population increased and this stratum became saturated, they exploited the clays higher up (2). Here the disadvantages of this sticky soil were to some extent offset by choosing in many instances those places where limestone scree overlaid it. The other option was to go down-hill to the lias silts (5) where, although the soil was less well drained, there was more food available, especially earthworms.

The exploitation of soft strata with hard impermeable overlays also applies to other for-mations besides limestone. In the Blackdown Hills, Somerset, there is a long line of setts on the northern escarpment which are dug into the soft greensand leaving the hard, flint-like churt as a roof; in the Brendon Hills nearby, the new red sandstone is extremely popular especially when the setts are roofed by bunter conglomerate; in Surrey, there are many setts at the juncture between the sandy Hythe beds and the hard sandstone rock of the Bargate beds (E.D. Clements, pers. comm.); in the Highlands of Scotland and Cumbria, many setts are dug in soft soil below huge boulders, and in Yorkshire, some are made under slabs of gritstone. Others utilise the shelter of the stone walls high up on the Fells, the entrances occurring on both sides of the walls.

This habit of choosing the juncture between two strata with contrasting properties may well account for the number of setts found in disused quarries where the juncture is easily discovered. In many instances the rock is quarried to the full depth of the hard stratum, so

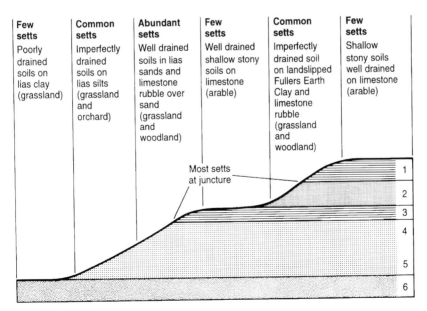

Few setts	Common setts	Abundant setts	Few setts	Common setts	Few setts
Poorly drained soils on lias clay (grassland)	Imperfectly drained soils on lias silts (grassland and orchard)	Well drained soils in lias sands and limestone rubble over sand (grassland and woodland)	Well drained shallow stony soils on limestone (arable)	Imperfectly drained soil on landslipped Fullers Earth Clay and limestone rubble (grassland and woodland)	Shallow stony soils well drained on limestone (arable)

FIG 4.3   *Distribution of setts in relation to soils and landscape (Cotswold Scarp). 1. Great oolite limestone; 2. Fuller's earth, clay; 3. inferior oolite limestone; 4. Cotswold sand; 5. Dyrham silts; 6. lower lias clay. Source: after Findlay (1973).*

FIG 4.4   *Sett in sand with churt roof, Blackdown Hills, Somerset.*

the juncture is at the bottom and the badgers dig there. However, in some quarries in the Brendons both the red sandstone and the conglomerate have been used commercially; in some of these the badgers have formed perilous paths down the quarry face to reach a ledge and have dug into the softer sand below the conglomerate. Piles of excavated sand at the base of the quarry far below bear witness to their labours. Abandoned quarries may also be popular because of the vegetation cover that soon grows up and the relative freedom from interference.

People have also provided other opportunities for badgers to exploit. A sett in south Yorkshire was dug under a much-used main road, and in spite of the vibration of traffic above and the lack of cover on emergence, the badgers appeared to thrive. However, this habit is not to be encouraged as in similar situations it has led to subsidence, and the cost of repair has been considerable. Badgers have also dug under old lime kilns and even beneath the floor of a Roman villa!

On one occasion, the rector of Curry Rivel church, Somerset, rang Ernest up to say he was worried because badgers had made a sett between the floor boards and the foundations. 'For five weeks worshippers had been distracted by badger noises from below the pews', and during a Bartok concert one Saturday afternoon, audience participation took the unusual form 'of subterranean snorts and squeaks'. Inevitably the story was reported in the national press as a 'Brock and roll concert'.

Badgers also set up house under St Mary's church at Tideswell, Derbyshire and there was much concern over the pungent odours and strange noises that emanated during evensong.

The vicar solved the problem by moving his stereo system into the appropriate part of the church and for 12 hours played classical music at full volume. The badgers departed and did not return!

In a rural churchyard near Bath, badgers had for some time occupied a sett in an adjacent graveyard. The main entrances utilised old land drains, formed by setting stone slabs horizontally on top of two vertical ones. The width of the tunnel thus formed was just about the perfect size for badgers. Local clergy and church-goers were not concerned about the presence of the badgers until some old coffin nails and small human bones were excavated with the spoil! Needless to say an exclusion exercise was carried out and the badgers persuaded to move to other setts in their territory.

A group of badgers in Avon excavated a substantial sett under a small barn. Unfortunately the entrances were inside the building and most of the spoil accumulated inside. Eventually, when one side of the barn was more than 1.5 m deep in soil, the farmer brought in a digger to remove it. Undeterred, the badgers carried on digging, and when eventually the barn was once again rendered inaccessible to domestic livestock, the barn was abandoned to the badgers.

Another problem arose when a single badger lived for several months in the hot air ducts of a corn drying plant attached to a barn. It is not known whether the animal vacated the ducts when the plant was being used! Current legislation (see Appendix 1) defines a badger sett as 'any structure or place which displays signs indicating current use by a badger', thus the occasional tendency for badgers to utilise man-made structures for refuge will obviously pose problems in some situations. (See also Chapter 11.)

Ease of digging probably accounts more than any other factor for setts being dug where people have disturbed the soil, possibly many years before, leaving it less consolidated than places nearby. If these structures rise above the level of the surrounding countryside badgers seem to find them even more attractive. It is probably for this reason that setts are dug into road, railway and canal embankments, rubbish tips and prehistoric earthworks.

This habit has been helpful to archaeologists on several occasions. In 1966, an 11th-century Roman iron-smelting site near Ticehurst in Sussex was excavated. On the site was a very large slag and rubbish bank covering 100 m of a small valley. Badgers had found this bank easy to excavate in contrast to the sticky clay elsewhere. On turning over the loose soil of the spoil heap, it was found that the badgers had unearthed some excellent shards of pottery, including a magnificent piece of Samian red-glass mortarium and some valuable pottery 'wasters', confirming the finder's theory that pottery had been manufactured on the site (H. Cleere, pers. comm.).

Long barrows provide the same sort of conditions, and some in Wiltshire are riddled with badger holes. The same applies to many ancient earthworks such as Cadbury Hill, Somerset and Wallbury Dells, Hertfordshire. Setts also occur in coal deposits in Northumberland, and in one sett in the parish of Cawthorne, Yorkshire the spoil heaps outside the entrances contained large lumps of coal mixed in with small coal and shale — the sett, in fact, being in an old pre-mechanisation mine-working known as a day-hole (Paget & Middleton 1974b). Setts are also found in some of the Cornish mines; in one of these, badgers used to emerge from a low-level mine entrance on to the beach below.

Modern coal-fired power stations produce a residue of approximately 10 million tonnes of pulverised fly ash (PFA) per annum which is deposited in various localities, sometimes in large mounds. This makes easy digging for badgers along with good security provided by industrial sites (Shaw 1994).

Soils which are periodically flooded or liable to become waterlogged are avoided, but if the land rises sufficiently to give the necessary dryness for the sett itself, the surrounding area may be exploited as a useful place for foraging. This was the case on the Somerset levels, but in recent years, with the lowering of the water table following a change in farming practice, many more setts have now been dug. Also, in the fenland district around Goole, Humberside, the only setts in this very flat region were in the banks of dykes and railways. One of these extended along the bank of a dyke for about 100 m, the whole area being covered by elders (R. Paget, pers. comm.). An unusual site for a sett, located between Winchelsea and Rye, Sussex, was on a dry bank which had a dyke on one side and a river on the other with no cover whatever. In addition, there was a main road just beyond the river (E.D. Clements, pers. comm.).

Occasionally such setts may be flooded out by freak weather conditions. On Canvey Island, Essex, there was a thriving badger sett on the bank of one of the ditches. When the sea wall was breached and water flooded this area on 31 January 1953, it was thought to have drowned all the badgers. However, at the end of March, a farmer, F.J. Leach, noticed that some mounds of fresh sand had been excavated from this sett and there was a trail of hay from the nearby haystack. In fact, cubs were reared successfully in this sett. How the badgers survived the flooding is not certain. They may have climbed up amongst the woodpiles of a neighbouring woodyard or found shelter in a haystack, or on slightly higher ground nearby, but as the latter was very exposed, this is less likely. It is just conceivable that the sow survived in a chamber below ground, which because of its higher position relative to that of the tunnel, contained a substantial amount of trapped air.

Although, as we have seen, there is overwhelming evidence for preference of main sett site according to geological strata and soil composition, local conditions, particularly available food such as earthworms, have an important modifying affect on choice (Skinner *et al.* 1991).

Cover

Some kind of cover near a sett is an important factor in choice of site. Cover allows the badgers to emerge inconspicuously and young cubs to play near the sett entrance without being visible to people or potential predators.

This need for cover is probably the major reason why 50.7% of the setts investigated for the Mammal Society Survey were found in deciduous woods, mixed woods and copses. If setts in hedgerow and scrub (which also provide good cover) are added, this figure rises to 75.2% for England, Scotland and Wales combined, but for counties such as Surrey and Sussex it approaches 90%.

Where woods and copses were scarce, hedgerows and scrub were found to be the most commonly used alternatives. Hedgerow setts were much more common in Somerset and Devon where traditionally they are set on banks, and if there were disused farm tracks bounded by banks with overgrown hedges these were almost always appropriated.

Coniferous woodland in England contained relatively few setts (5.7%), but a higher percentage was recorded in Wales (14.2%) and Scotland (22.8%). In England, the majority had been there when the original deciduous woodland had been felled and replaced. It would appear that lack of ground cover and scarcity of suitable food are the cause of the unpopularity of coniferous woods when good alternatives are present. It is probably for these reasons that setts which do occur in coniferous woods are usually near the edge (pp. 85–86).

In the survey, 8.4% of setts were in open situations, but this surprisingly high figure should be treated with reservations because the amount of cover in an apparently open situation varies greatly throughout the year. In winter and early spring a sett may appear to be without cover, but in summer in some places it could be hidden in bracken, in others by nettles, docks and thistles which quickly colonise the excavated earth nearby.

An interesting aspect of this phenomenon is the seasonal movement away from setts for the duration of the exposed period. Thus badgers in some coastal regions in South Wales may use setts on cliff slopes where bracken and bluebells give cover in summer and autumn, but in winter and early spring use alternative setts in copses nearby.

This seasonal movement, however, is not typical of most bracken-covered setts, as time of emergence makes this unnecessary. From September to the end of April badgers come out after dark, so ground cover is less necessary, but from May to the end of August when they often emerge before dusk, bracken gives them cover. Moorland setts also come into this category, because although open, they often have good heather or long grass cover.

Setts in truly open situations are found more often at higher altitudes where disturbance is more unlikely and cover less important. However, setts are sometimes made in surprisingly open situations, even in flat fields. One was in an open field which had recently been ploughed, and was invisible from the edge since the excavated earth had been levelled by farm instruments; six holes were in continuous use (G.P. Knowles, pers. comm.). The farmer had been trying to get rid of the sett for 20 years but gave up when it was discovered that the tunnels led far down under the remains of a Roman villa. When the crops came up, some cover was available.

Quite often, setts in open situations have their origin in hedgerows. When these have been removed to enlarge the fields, well-established setts may remain. Other hedgerow setts also have entrances some distance out into the field; they are seldom used for emergence but often for re-entry.

Other setts found on downland usually have some cover but a few may be in exposed situations. One sett on a Derbyshire hilltop is situated within the stones of a megalithic circle.

Slope

Thornton (1988) showed that main sett density increased with the hilliness of the district. This is likely to be a reason why in the Mammal Society survey 92% of setts were dug into slopes. This is advantageous to the badgers in various ways.

A slope facilitates the removal of the excavated soil which spills down it. It is also easier for a badger to find a particularly favourable stratum of soil for digging since it is more likely to be exposed. Also, sloping land is usually well drained, is more likely to be dry and warm and, in colder parts, a depth below ground is quickly attained which is frost proof.

The mound which forms outside an entrance on a slope builds up to form a platform where cubs and adults can socialise after emergence. With continual excavations, the height of this platform increases above the level of the entrance so the latter becomes the lower point of a cone. This formation catches wind eddies from any direction so a badger can detect danger without exposing itself fully.

FIG 4.5   *Sett on slope showing built-up spoil heap.*

Very steep slopes are often chosen when available. For example, chalky, downland setts in Sussex are usually found near the top of steep slopes (Clements 1974), and the sides of ravines are popular sites in mountainous country as in North Wales, especially when these are wooded. Such setts provide greater protection from both weather and interference. Also, badgers greatly dislike cattle stamping around their setts and steep slopes tend to deter them from doing so.

The direction the slope is facing seems to have little significance in most inland parts of Britain, but in exposed situations a preference is discernible. In Cornwall, 77% of the setts faced away from the wet and prevailing wind (Bere 1970), and in Sussex within about 15 km of the sea, there is a tendency for them to face away from the prevailing wind which is strongest near the coast (Clements 1974). In northern parts of Britain there is a tendency to choose the warmer south-facing slopes, as is the case in Russia (p. 73).

Altitude

In Britain, most setts are found at altitudes between 100 and 200 m. Several factors seem to be operating in determining this preference. Land below 100 m tends to be heavily culti-vated or occupied by people. At much higher altitudes, disturbance is much less but food supply becomes restricted, so medium heights are the best compromise.

Setts may occasionally be found at sea level if the site is not liable to flooding and is secluded. One sett in north Somerset is in a shingle ridge not far beyond high tide mark and another in Argyll is in a sand dune a few metres above a sandy beach. Some setts are also found at high altitudes. In the Yorkshire Dales many moorland setts are above 400 m, the highest reported, at Buckden, being at 538 m (Paget & Middleton 1974b). In Grampian a small number of main setts have been found above 600 m with a few in excess of 750 m, while one in the Highland region was discovered at 900 m. In this region there have been several records of badger sightings between 600 and 700 m throughout the daylight hours by shepherds, stalkers and hill-walkers (M. Harris, pers. comm.). Setts are also found at high altitudes in Cumbria and in south-west England near the tops of Exmoor and Dartmoor. In southern latitudes setts have been recorded up to 4000 m (p. 241).

Scarcity of food seems to be the main reason which prevents badgers going very high, although in Scotland and Cumbria badgers are known to make nightly treks to lower levels where the food is easier to acquire and, in parts of Russia, there is a seasonal migration downwards which may be related to available foraging as well as avoidance of harsh condi-tions (Novikov 1956).

Food supply

The presence of a plentiful and varied food supply at all seasons is undoubtedly one of the most important biotic factors influencing choice of sett site.

The diet of badgers will be discussed in detail in Chapter 6 and its relation to population density in Chapter 9. However, it should be explained here that although badgers are omnivorous and their tastes catholic, there are certain key items which are of vital impor-tance. The most significant of these in Britain is the earthworm (*Lumbricus terrestris*) found abundantly in pasture. However, this major source of food needs to be supplemented by a wide range of other items and these are obtained from a varied, rather than a uniform coun-tryside (Neal 1972a). It is therefore not surprising that so many setts are in places where woodland, grassland and arable are found nearby, and in larger areas of woodland they are usually situated near the perimeter. In Shropshire, 44 out of 49 setts recorded in woodland were within 25 m of the edge (Russell 1967). This is generally true throughout Britain, although setts deep in large woods do occur; however, some of these border wide rides and most are found in places where population density is high, a factor which leads to the exploitation of less desirable sites. Thornton (1988) confirmed that there were more main setts in tetrads containing many small units of woodland than in those with large blocks.

Copses, scrub and hedgerows bordering fields combine similar advantages of adequate cover and a varied food supply and are all popular choices of site. The widespread availabil-ity of such habitats due to agricultural practice is likely to have contributed to the wide dis-tribution of badgers in Britain and affected their population density.

Proximity of water

In Britain, there are not many places where there is no source of water within about 1 km; most setts are therefore within easy reach of a supply, so it is difficult to gauge its importance to badgers. Some setts are certainly situated very near to water but in most cases this choice can be explained by other factors. In drier country, such as upland calcareous pasture, badgers are known to visit cattle troughs and drink from the rain-water which collects in the crotch between tree trunks (Fig. 6.15). However, they are able to obtain much of the water they need from their food, especially earthworms; they will also eat green vegetation such as grass during droughts, presumably for its water content.

Nearness to a source of suitable bedding

This may be an important factor in the siting of some setts, although in most cases suitable material for bedding is easily available. For sleeping quarters many kinds of bedding will do, but it is probable that for successful cub rearing only certain kinds, especially hay and bracken, will provide the necessary insulation from loss of heat in colder climates. Thus for a breeding sett to be near a source of hay or bracken is an advantage. This could be another reason why setts in woods, especially coniferous ones, are near an edge; conifer needles make very poor bedding. Badgers living deep in deciduous woods are better off as the rides are often grassy and various herb-layer plants and leaves make possible alternatives.

Seclusion

Setts are usually found in secluded places if the badgers have any choice, but nearness to habitation does not deter them from using an otherwise desirable site; it is human interference that disturbs them (Gillam 1967). For instance, if a sett is repeatedly or drastically interfered with by people, badgers will leave if they have an alternative sett to go to.

It is obvious that badgers will become tolerant of human encroachment as 164 setts have been recorded within 30 km of the centre of London (Teagle 1969). Under semi-urban conditions they have an almost commensal relationship with people. This aspect will be discussed further in Chapter 11. Meanwhile it is enough to quote from Clements concerning the badgers in some Sussex towns. 'Hastings, especially, is well populated by badgers, with one sett which has trebled in size in the last ten years being in the centre of the town and only 150 m from the sea. Little wonder that a badger was seen walking along the promenade one night. In Eastbourne, badgers dug the 19th hole of the promenade's putting green! There is also a 50-hole sett within the built-up area of Brighton.' (Clements 1974).

Analysis of the reasons for badgers leaving their setts in country districts illustrates this desire for seclusion and freedom from human interference. The first of these is tree felling. If woodland is clear-felled, the resulting disturbance and lack of cover usually cause sett desertion. This happened in Gloucestershire in Conigre Wood after Ernest had done his original work there. Although the badgers periodically returned to prospect they did not live there permanently until sufficient cover had once more built up. The same is true at Woodchester Park in Gloucestershire where clear-felling usually caused main setts to be vacated, either during or shortly after the process of timber extraction. In these circumstances another sett within the territory, usually a subsidiary sett (see p. 42), then becomes the main sett, although the original main sett will eventually become recolonised. This might be within as short a period as a year if the ground cover regenerates quickly. The fact that badgers reclaim the main sett in this way illustrates that the sett location probably possesses a combination of environmental advantages not found elsewhere in the territory. In Britain, the Forestry Commission recognises the importance of sett sites and has drawn up guidelines for forestry management which aim to minimise the disturbance of badgers.

Second, earth-stopping by the hunt to prevent foxes sheltering in setts, if done too often, may cause abandonment. This applies more to subsidiary and outliers than well-established setts where interference is more likely to make the badgers wary rather than cause them to leave. The practice of earth-stopping is now governed by legislation which sets out precisely which methods should be adopted (see Appendix 1).

Third, repeated disturbance by cattle stamping around a sett may lead to temporary abandonment.

DISTRIBUTION IN BRITAIN

From the foregoing discussion it is clear that the distribution of badgers in Britain will to a large extent be determined by how well a particular area fulfils the following ecological requirements:

(1) a soil which is well drained, easy to dig and firm enough to prevent the roof collapsing;
(2) the presence of an adequate food supply at all seasons of the year;
(3) sufficient cover to allow the animals to emerge and leave without being conspicuous;
(4) a region in the immediate vicinity of the sett which is relatively free of disturbance from people and domestic animals.

The type of country which fulfils these requirements best is one which is hilly, has a sandy soil and contains a mosaic of habitats including a high proportion of deciduous woodland interspersed with fertile grassland containing a high density of earthworms. Many counties have some areas where this type of terrain occurs but they are more frequent in the southern half of England, particularly the south-west, in the border counties between England and Wales, in parts of Wales and some of the northerly and north-western counties of England. These are the areas where badgers are most common.

However, there are very few parts of Britain where badgers cannot exist at all apart from large conurbations, regions of very high altitude and extensive lowlands which are too wet or liable to flooding. Being remarkably adaptable to a great variety of habitats their distribution is therefore very wide. While they are almost certainly present in every county in Britain their density is very variable and this aspect will be discussed more fully in Chapter 9. The reader is also referred to the map (Fig. 9.1) in that chapter.

CHAPTER 5

Activity Patterns

BADGERS are largely nocturnal or crepuscular, although daylight appearances are by no means unusual in secluded places. Typically, in country districts, adult badgers emerge from their setts between sunset and darkness during the summer months but only after dark from October to April.

Those who have watched badgers regularly at a particular main sett can often predict the time of emergence of the first badger with remarkable accuracy, especially during spring and autumn, but there are many exceptional evenings when the watcher's forecast is widely out. Badgers like humans are sometimes fickle over keeping appointments!

By noting the time of first emergences throughout the year it is possible to produce an 'average emergence time' graph which for most evenings from March to November would enable the watcher to predict roughly first emergence. A number of such graphs have been published for different parts of Britain and Europe (Neal 1948, Lloyd 1968, Göransson 1974 and others) which roughly tell the same story. However, special attention will be given here to a comprehensive 4-year study (Neal & Avery 1956) because all data relate to the same main sett and any variation from year to year will reflect other factors, particularly the presence of cubs and changes in weather conditions.

The sett was in a relatively undisturbed area of the Quantock Hills, Somerset. Observations were made from a tree where possible disturbance through scent was highly unlikely. All the main holes were visible from the tree. Occasions when the badgers appeared to be suspicious were not included in the data. Emergence was defined as the first time a badger came completely out of an entrance. The graph, Fig. 5.1, shows the results to

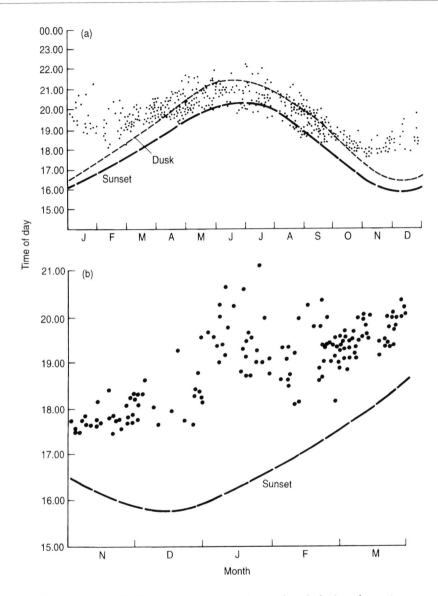

FIG 5.1 *Times (GMT) of first emergence when undisturbed (432 observations at two setts in Somerset (a) throughout the year; (b) during the winter. Source: K.R.C. Neal, R.A. Avery & F. Vaughan (unpubl. data).*

which have been added data sent by F. Vaughan who watched a rather similar sett near Yeovil, some 56 km away. These additional observations increased the data during the difficult watching months of December–February.

Certain generalisations can be made from this graph. First, the curve showing the average time of first emergences is a smooth one which runs roughly parallel with sunset times between March and September, except for a flattening during midsummer. This suggests that emergence is to a large extent affected by seasonal factors, particularly daylength. Second, there is much variation during every month but more so at certain seasons. So one must infer that there are other factors which influence the pattern from one night to another.

One can also derive from the graph certain seasonal characteristics. In January and February, emergence took place after dark and was largely unpredictable as there was as much as 3 h difference between one night and another. In March emergence was much more regular and occurred soon after dark. In April a very similar pattern was shown, but towards the end of the month some were well before dark while others were much later. From May to August, the majority of first sightings were before dark, many of them in excellent light and some before the sun had set. However, in July and August especially, there was a much wider range of times with occasional very late emergences as well as some particularly early ones. In September, times were very regular around late dusk. In October and November, emergence also followed a regular pattern but it occurred nearly always after dark — in November, nearly an hour after. In December times were unpredictable, and on a few nights no badgers emerged at all.

FACTORS INFLUENCING EMERGENCE TIMES

It is evident that the factors influencing emergence times in various parts of Britain are complex and often inter-related; these include daylength, light intensity, the amount of cover around the sett, disturbance by people or animals, the weather, the amount of available food and the social composition of the sett residents.

Daylength and light intensity

The graph of emergence times shows good correlation with daylength between March and October especially in spring and autumn. This was confirmed for an urban habitat by Cresswell & Harris (1988) from radio-tracking data from their Bristol studies. Obviously, the degree of light intensity is an important aspect of daylength, but it differs locally from day to day because of variation in cloud cover, moonlight and from one sett to another caused by the screening effect of vegetational cover. Let us examine these factors in more detail.

First, it is evident that light intensity and daylength are not critical factors affecting emergence between November and March when badgers come out well after dark under normal circumstances, and in December and January in particular, most erratically. Second, it is obvious that not all the residents come out at the same time. For example, on the night of 18–19 April 1955, during an all-night watch, Neal and Avery saw the first adult emerge at 20.20 at late dusk, but seven other resident adults and yearlings came out at 21.15, 22.15, 00.15 (2), 00.22 (2) and 00.55! This was certainly exceptional, but on a great number of other occasions emergence of adults was spread over a period of well over an hour. Those which emerged later were obviously not affected by these factors alone.

One could argue that if light intensity or daylength were the main factor in summer, average emergence times would vary in different geographical localities according to sunset times. On the whole this expectation is not fulfilled. If you compare records of average emergence times in Somerset with Essex, with a difference in sunset times of 15 min you would expect earlier emergence in Essex. However, data provided by W.W. Page (over 700 observations by a number of observers over several years) show a very similar graph to Somerset, but from April to October emergences were *later* by about 15 min (rather less in June) (but see p. 94).

Similarly, you would expect as you go north, emergence times in summer to be later with nights becoming shorter. However, Mary Marsh (pers. comm.) who watched regularly throughout the year in the Inverness region of Scotland, found that first emergence compared with Somerset was *earlier* on average between May and August, in June by about an hour. P. Skoog's data from Sweden (pers. comm.) also suggest that other factors are operating as emergence there in July is often as early as 19.00, many hours before dusk.

With this evidence against the light intensity/daylength theory, let us now consider evidence in its favour.

All emergence graphs, whatever the geographical location, show the greatest correlation between first emergence and light intensity in spring and autumn when it occurs around dusk. If you watch a sett at these times, variation from one evening to another can often be related to other factors which indirectly affect light intensity such as cloud cover and moonlight. Watches on a single night by around 140 observers on 23 April, 8 May and 16 May, showed that at that time of year cloud cover significantly modified emergence times and that the greater the cloud cover, the earlier they emerged. It was concluded that more cloud cover in the west and clearer skies and hence more moonlight in the east explained the difference in emergence times in these regions (Lloyd 1968). However, it should be borne in mind that cloud cover is usually associated with greater humidity and a higher temperature and these in turn influence such factors as earthworm availability. Radio-tracking studies in Bristol confirmed that there was a strong correlation between moonlight and absence of cloud with delayed emergence (Cresswell & Harris 1988). We have also noted many times that moonlight falling on a main entrance has caused delayed emergence, and Norah Burke (1964) stated that a favourite exit was not used on particular nights when moonlight shone down it.

It has often been noticed that emergence times in the same neighbourhood may be consistently different by as much as 30 min. In some of these instances, light intensity appears to be the most probable reason. In one study near Yeovil, Somerset there was a hill on which there were two main setts, one on the top and the other on the north-facing slope (M. Harrison, pers. comm.). Both were large with many entrances and had good cover from a number of elder trees. However, the sett on the top of the hill received the rays from the setting sun, the other did not. Emergence from the hill-top sett was consistently about half an hour later than the other over the three years, 1956–1958. However, in spring 1957, the badgers emerged significantly earlier at both setts. Nineteen fifty-seven was a particularly mild spring and elders were in leaf by early April, thus reducing the light level, but in 1958 they had not reached a comparable stage of leafage until about the end of May. However, after full leafage, the records for all three years merged indiscriminately.

These instances provide good circumstantial evidence that light intensity plays an important part in influencing first emergence, especially in spring, but other factors often override this factor.

Cover

Tree and cloud cover have already been mentioned as factors which may affect light intensity and hence the time of emergence. Let us now consider the vegetational cover near a sett
which allows badgers to emerge, socialise and go off unseen. In Chapter 3, comment was
made of the importance of this factor in choice of location of setts. There is strong evidence
that this allows earlier emergence at certain times of the year.

A comparison between emergence times from three setts in south-west Essex was made
by D.R. Scott (1960). Calling the setts A, B and C, he found that the latest emergences
were at A, the earliest at C, B being intermediate sett. A was in high beech forest without
much undergrowth and with a carpet of dead leaves, the nearest ground cover being
bracken some 50 m from the sett. Here there was little disturbance except the noise of distant traffic, but the sett was close to several well-used footpaths. Sett B was on private land
and not subject to any human disturbance in the evening; cover was better than at A as
there were a few bushes near some of the entrances and the ground was grassy. Sett C, where
emergence was earliest, was in forest land, traffic noise was considerable and a footpath used
by many people in the summer months ran alongside the sett. However, cover around the
sett was excellent consisting of holly bushes and brambles which extended some distance.
Scott concluded that good cover was by far the most important factor; when that was present, badgers would tolerate noise and human disturbance and slip away quickly after
emerging, lying low temporarily if people passed near.

A similar conclusion was reached concerning six setts at Old Winchester Hill,
Hampshire. The average times of emergence during August and early September were
20.12, 20.32 and 20.35 at setts where cover was good; 21.10 and 21.20 where there was
some cover but more disturbance, and 21.15 at a sett in a yew wood where there was a total
lack of ground cover and the sett was also subject to considerable disturbance (G. Barker,
pers. comm.).

Under urban conditions Stephen Harris (1982) found that emergence was delayed by
about an hour compared with rural situations, suggesting that cover and disturbance were
the main causes of this discrepancy. It was also discovered that earthworms were not utilised
nearly so much although there were many short-grass open spaces available such as lawns
and commons where they were abundant. Harris concluded that lack of cover in such situations as well as alternative food supplies were likely explanations.

Disturbance

Disturbance is a term which is difficult to define as it includes many forms of interference.
At a sett where disturbance of any kind is minimal, badgers are likely to emerge earlier in
the summer than at comparable setts which are disturbed. So it is wise when watching at
very isolated and undisturbed setts in summer to get there well before the 'expected' time of
emergence. 'Inexplicable' blank nights are often due to the watcher arriving after the badgers have left.

Continuous records by N.B. Palmer (1959) were made over a period of 9 months at two
setts in the Cheltenham district, Gloucestershire. Both were in similar types of deciduous
woodland, but whereas sett A was subjected to regular blocking by the hunt in winter and
spring, pigeon shooting, children playing in the wood, especially in summer, and occasional

gassing or shooting of badgers, B showed no sign of human disturbance. Palmer found that during the 3 months when A was relatively undisturbed, emergence was more comparable with B, but at other times it was 1–1½ h later. During one week's intensive watching at sett A during September, he showed that emergence was much later on Saturday and Sunday evenings — when children had played around the sett during the day.

Palmer also showed that behaviour varied considerably at the two setts. At A the badgers went off quickly and started to forage almost at once; they were also very quiet and there was little play near the sett. At B they stayed close to the sett for up to an hour, there was much play between the cubs and considerably more vocalisation.

Regular disturbance caused by background noise seems to have little effect as badgers quickly become habituated to traffic and human voices. However, any sudden or unusual disturbance has a considerable effect especially if it involves the sett itself. For instance, trampling by cattle over the sett area or the blocking of a sett by the hunt will usually cause very late emergence on subsequent nights. Late emergence on a particular night is, of course, also due to suspicion caused by human scent or movement, unusual sounds or the proximity of dogs or other domestic animals.

Weather

The effect of cloud cover and moonlight has already been discussed (p. 90), but other weather factors are also important. Badgers dislike emerging into heavy rain, although once out foraging, they seem to take little notice of it. In a detailed study of emergence times and activity periods during September in Sweden, it was found that emergence times were extremely regular at a particular sett, except for one night when there was heavy rain associated with a drop in temperature when emergence was 1½ h later (Göransson 1974). In Bristol, it was also found that nights of heavy rain were correlated with decrease of activity and range of movement in autumn (Cresswell & Harris 1988). However, slight rain and wet or humid conditions often brought badgers out earlier, almost certainly because these conditions, when temperatures are not too low, are ideal for worming.

Windy nights may delay emergence. Badgers are easily frightened by strong winds and may panic if there is a sudden gust with attendant noises. It is likely that under very windy conditions the sense of smell becomes unreliable and the animals are nervous in consequence. Cresswell & Harris (1988) found that under windy conditions badgers were more restless while foraging. They also suggested that in winter, the chill factor caused by strong winds probably explained why the speed of badger movement was increased under these conditions.

There is little evidence that ambient temperature has much effect on emergence except indirectly by affecting foraging conditions. However, in the north where conditions are more severe, emergence during the colder months is earlier than in the south possibly because earthworms are more easily obtained before the temperature drops too much.

Badgers will sometimes emerge under extremely cold conditions. The late James Fisher tracked badgers in the snow in Northamptonshire after a night when the temperature fell to -18°C (-2°F). They often come out when snow is on the ground and have been seen to emerge when snow was actually falling. Donald Bradnam recorded an emergence during a snow blizzard in February 1969, and Graham Moysey (1959) recorded on an automatic device the emergence of two badgers at 03.00 at a Devon sett, following a fall of snow, remaining outside for 30 min. By contrast, on the same night at a nearby sett, one badger emerged at 19.00 and another, 8 h later. So there is much variation under snowy conditions.

Availability of food

This is one of the most important factors affecting emergence. It is particularly evident in summer when short nights limit foraging time. When there is plenty of food about as in a wet season, emergence may be near to the expected time but given a severe period of drought in June when the earth is hard and cracked and earthworms impossible to reach, badgers will be out much earlier. During the hot dry summer of 1975 at a sett in the Brendon Hills in June, the badgers were out by 19.30 night after night — a full hour earlier than the average for that time of the year. Similar behaviour was reported from many other parts of the country during this drought.

These early emergences in summer also take place commonly in regions where food is comparatively scarce every year during particular months. This is so in Scandinavia and the Highlands of Scotland where emergence in June may be as early as 19.15. This early emergence coupled with the long daylengths in these latitudes has enabled photographers to make excellent films of badgers under good light conditions.

FIG 5.2   *Returning after a forage in the snow.*

Periods of food glut may have the opposite effect, so that after a night of abundance, a particular badger may not emerge the following night until very late — sometimes not at all.

Social composition of the sett residents

This factor affects emergence considerably at certain periods of the year. Neal & Avery (1956) found that from about a fortnight from the birth of cubs until the end of April, it was almost invariably the sow that emerged first, sometimes particularly early, presumably to find enough food to keep up her milk supply. However, once the cubs had been above ground for several weeks, they were usually the first to emerge and this was so for most of the early summer months. It was curious that one cub regularly emerged much earlier than the others, but when all had come out, the sow usually followed quickly. There is no doubt that when the family is large the cubs stimulate each other to come out earlier, play being a compelling reason for emergence. For setts where there are no cubs, emergence is often much later during the summer; it can be well after dark. This may be one of the causes of variation in emergence times from one year to another at a particular sett.

GENERAL CONCLUSIONS

It is clear that a number of factors, many of them inter-related, influence the time of emergence. Some factors stimulating earlier emergence are hunger and social activities such as playing, mating, marking territory, digging and bedding collection. Factors retarding emergence include lack of cover, strong light intensity, disturbance and certain weather conditions. It is probable that the approximate time of emergence is primarily determined by the animal's biological clock. This is a physiological mechanism which roughly determines the periodicity of such functions as sleep and activity, hunger being an important component. But variations of this generalised pattern are due to the differences in strength of the factors advancing or retarding times of emergence. In other words the time of emergence is the resultant of opposing forces on any particular night (Neal 1977).

If the problem is considered from this point of view, most inconsistencies and variations are explained. Referring once more to the graph (Fig. 5.1), the random nature of emergence in January is probably due to several factors. There is less urgency to feed as the badgers have considerable reserves of fat and often the weather limits the opportunities for finding food. This may be due to a succession of frosty nights or to a sudden drop in temperature on a particular night. Towards the end of the month activity is more pronounced owing to the proximity of the breeding season.

During February, with the birth of the cubs, there is greater need for the sow to feed, but she does not leave her cubs for long periods. However, the adult boars may be very active as this is the start of the main mating season and territorial activity is considerable. These factors probably account for early first emergences during this month.

March is a very busy month for sows with cubs. There is an urgency to find enough food for adequate lactation and much time is spent on cleaning out the sett and bedding collection. These factors exert pressure on the sow to come out as early as possible. However, other factors deter her from doing so, at any rate before dark, as at this time of year there is far less vegetational cover available and darkness becomes an essential substitute. So light

FIG 5.3   *Cautious emergence at dusk; three adults and a 12-week-old cub.*

intensity becomes the governing factor and she comes out as soon as it is dark enough; hence emergence times are very consistent during March. However, adults, apart from lactating sows, may not be in such a hurry to emerge. For example Neal & Avery (1956) found that while the sow emerged regularly around dusk, the next adult to come out on some evenings was more than an hour later and others came out later still.

This pattern of behaviour continues into April, but by the end of the month and into

May, more cover is available because of the growth of vegetation and the cubs are bigger; play now becomes an important reason for early emergence, and if there is little disturbance and cover near the sett, it will take place before dark.

By June the cubs are weaned and more independent. Once more the driving force is food. Only disturbance will prevent an early emergence as there is usually plenty of cover to counteract the disadvantages of being out in daylight. If food is scarce, emergence can be extremely early.

In July and August, the need for food by all members of the social group is paramount. The cubs are growing fast and the adults have the opportunity to make up for the loss in weight during lactation and, to a lesser extent, as a consequence of the mating season's activities (see Fig. 2.7).

From September to mid-November the main preoccupation is again feeding. Food is usually abundant now and badgers put on most of their fat in preparation for the leaner period of winter. As feeding is the main pursuit of all members of the group, emergence times are very consistent once more. For example, Neal & Avery (1956) found that all seven badgers present in October emerged each night within a period ranging from 27 to 56 mins. As the season advances and the nights get longer there are more hours of darkness in which to feed, so emergence, well before dark in September, becomes after dark in October and even later in November.

By the second half of November and during December, adults emerge very irregularly, although cubs of the year may continue to come out soon after dark especially if the nights are damp and mild. This is probably because there is usually a greater need for younger animals to put on more fat, especially if food has been scarce in the summer and autumn. December is the period of least activity for the adults; occasionally they may be out for several hours but on some nights may not emerge at all and on others only for a few minutes.

So it appears likely that it is the badger's biological clock that sets the general pattern throughout the year, the necessity for obtaining enough food according to season and daily requirements (which differ markedly in individual badgers) that regulates the time setting, and that other factors such as strong light intensity, disturbance and lack of cover on the one hand and the urge to play, collect bedding, mate or mark out territory on the other, modify the time slightly during the badger's year and from evening to evening.

TIMES OF RETURN

The results of 42 watches in Somerset are given in Fig. 5.4. Each dot represents the return of a single badger and illustrates the independent nature of individuals during their nightly activities. On one occasion in September seven badgers returned over a period of 2 h. Returns during winter were well before daylight but in the period April–September were mainly spread out during the 1½ h before sunrise. Occasional returns were long after dawn, particularly so for cubs in August and September.

THE PERIOD OF ACTIVITY

When emergence and return times are plotted on the same graph, you find that the active period varies seasonally from an average of 6½ h in midsummer to over 11 h in November.

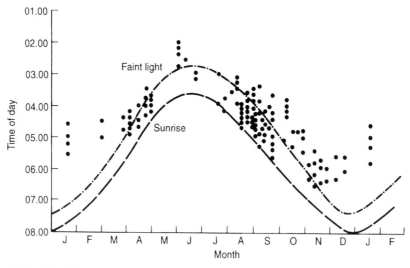

FIG 5.4 *Times (GMT) of return to the sett in early morning. Each vertical row of dots represents the return times of the various resident badgers. Source: A.M. Milburn (Wiltshire and Worcestershire) and K.R.C. Neal and R.A. Avery (Somerset) (unpubl. data).*

But such a graph takes no account of what happens in the interim period or of variations in behaviour among individuals. To get a clearer picture, it is important to know whether periodic returns are made during the night, whether the behaviour pattern changes throughout the year and how much time is spent in such activities near the sett as digging, bedding collection, grooming and play compared with foraging away from the sett. Attempts to answer these questions have been made using automatic devices placed in sett entrances which recorded comings and goings (Moysey 1959, Göransson 1974, G. Barker, unpubl. data); also by radio-tracking (Kruuk & Parish 1977, Harris 1982) and by spool-and-line techniques (Brown *et al.* 1993).

Activity near the sett

The time spent by badgers near the sett varies considerably according to season. This period usually includes a time after emergence when there is grooming, play and general exploratory behaviour, often with a similar period on return before they retire. However, at certain seasons various activities may cause them to be around the sett much more and return visits to the sett may occur throughout the night.

Typical activity at main setts in south-west England where breeding takes place can be summarised as follows. The period when most prolonged activity near the sett occurs is from mid-January (in a mild winter) or early February until mid-May. During this period most activity is connected with breeding, mating and socialising. Breeding accounts for many bouts of bedding collection, some in preparation for cubs, some when they are growing, but still below ground. A lot of digging activity may also occur as setts are cleaned out.

Defence of the young cubs also causes the sow, in particular, to remain near the sett. For the first few weeks after giving birth, she often waits near the entrance until other members of the social group have gone off before leaving for a spell of foraging herself, but she quickly returns. During 10 consecutive all-night watches in early April when we were filming, the sow made four sorties each night to forage, returning to be with her cubs and suckle. Also during this period there is much rutting behaviour by boars as breeding sows usually have an oestrus soon after birth and yearlings may also come into heat around this time. In late April and May, the cubs are above ground and becoming increasingly active; there is much play and socialising. Up to about the middle of May when the adults leave, the cubs remain in or around the sett, but when about 12 weeks old they leave with the adults. In June, much depends on food availability. When plentiful, there is often a long period of boisterous play and socialising around the sett, but they soon go off, if hungry. By July, less time is spent by the sett after emergence and even less during the August–November period. Then they leave soon after emergence and are away for most of the night.

After leaving the sett

There is great diversity of activity patterns as each badger acts as an individualist as soon as it leaves home; boars, sows and cubs may behave differently throughout the year. However, some seasonal generalisations can be made. For example at a sett in Sweden, on 19 consecutive nights in September, after a short period by the sett all the badgers spent the remainder of the night foraging — averaging about 10 h per night (Göransson 1974). In Britain the pattern is similar during the autumn months, but foraging is seldom continuous as badgers have periods of rest during the night. Chris, following badgers on wet nights, found that after an hour or two's foraging on earthworms, they became satiated and then curled up, usually in a hedgerow couch, and slept for several hours; they then had a further protracted forage before returning to the sett shortly before dawn.

When radio-tracking badgers in Bristol, Harris (1982) found that periods of rest between bouts of foraging were common; they sometimes used couches and at other times returned to the sett for a time. He found individual activity periods were longest in July–September and shortest from November to April. Individual rest periods were shortest from May to July and longest from December to January. In the latter period, badgers were only active above ground for 8.4% of the night compared with 65% in July. He also found that in March–April there were two peaks of activity, one, 2–3 h after emergence, and a larger peak about 3 h before the final return to the sett. However, between May and October, greatest activity occurred 2–3 h before and after midnight.

The night activities of individual badgers have been recorded using a spool-and-line technique (Brown *et al.* 1993). A spool carrying 4 km of fine polypropylene thread is attached to the collar of the badger, and as the animal wanders through its territory, the line unravels showing the exact route the badger has taken (for full details of techniques see Chapter 12). By so doing it was shown how cubs from the same social group extend the range of their activities as the year progresses and to contrast the nocturnal activities of an adult male and female in September highlighting the patrolling of the perimeter of the territory by the male at this season (Fig. 5.5).

Brown *et al.* (1993) found that an average badgers of all age and sex groups travel rather similar distances each night, although adult males go slightly further and spend

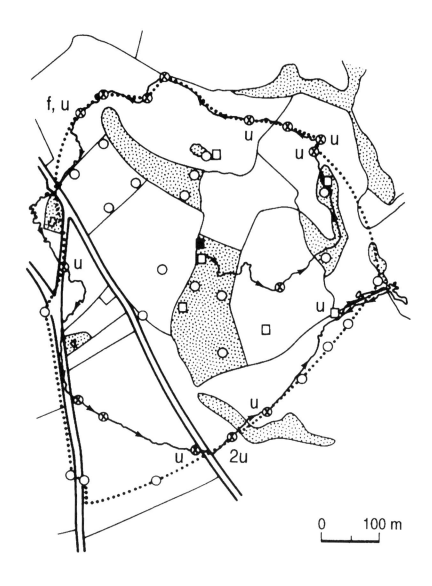

FIG 5.5 *Spool and line trace showing an adult male in September. Arrows denote the direction of travel. Woods, roads and gardens (stippled), all other areas are pasture. A solid square marks the main sett, open squares, other setts, the thicker dotted line, the territorial boundary, and circles, latrines. Latrines that were visited, marked with a cross, as are setts where the animal went below ground and re-emerged. f = faeces, u = urine. (Julian Brown, 1993).*

TABLE 5.1   *Total distance travelled by different age and sex categories throughout the year, and distance travelled along the territory boundary.*

Category	Number traced	Total distance	Distance along territory boundary
Adult males	5	1597	422
Adult females	15	1202	67
Yearling males	7	1242	59
Yearling females	4	1211	95
Male cubs	6	1028	8
Female cubs	7	1301	0

Values are the mean distance (m) travelled per badger per night.
Source: J. Brown (unpubl. data).

proportionately much more time on the territorial boundaries than others. However, numbers traced are small and more work needs to be done to amplify these findings and bring out seasonal differences.

Winter activity

In winter, particularly between mid-November and mid-January activity is considerably reduced, December being the month of least activity. There is a corresponding drop in body temperature during this period (p. 27). Using an automatic device, George Barker (unpub. data) showed there was not only erratic emergence at this time, but also under extreme weather conditions badgers were sometimes only out for half an hour and occasionally no badger emerged at all. During one cold spell, when snow was on the ground, the badgers spent several consecutive nights below and when they did emerge, did not go far. Exceptionally, a single animal travelled 3–4 km in the snow. When monitoring a group of badgers under semi-natural conditions in Aberdeenshire (57°N), Fowler & Racey (1988) showed that heavy snow cover in 1983/4 compared with 1984/5 almost certainly accounted for no activity being recorded on 12 nights in the former winter compared with some activity on all nights in the latter. In a study by Maurel & Boissin (1983) much further south in France (46°N), minimum activity occurred over a much shorter period, mainly in January. Fowler & Racey (1988) considered that the much longer period of reduced activity in Scotland reflected an adaptation of badgers to severe conditions. They postulated that when severe conditions cause shortage of food and greater heat loss, winter lethargy, involving a reduced body temperature and confinement to sheltered setts, confers considerable economy of energy and reduces demand on reserves of fat.

DIURNAL ACTIVITY

True daylight activity, as distinct from early emergence before the sun has set is not unusual; instances reported have involved cubs more than adults. In the June–August period, you may come across cubs foraging not far from the sett in the afternoon in deciduous woodland where disturbance is minimal. Once, when checking up on the best position for photography and focusing on the place where Ernest thought the cubs would play, he heard a familiar rustling, and looking up, saw a cub returning. It disappeared down the entrance without a glance or smell in his direction although he was only 3 or 4 m away. Cubs in secluded places undoubtedly make occasional forays during the day, perhaps to relieve the monotony of a very long spell below ground.

Adults, occasionally seen in the early morning, are usually making a late return after a night's foraging. A sow and well-grown cub were seen returning as late as 10.00 on a brilliantly sunny August morning in Hertfordshire, but this made no difference to their time of emergence the following evening (Soper 1955).

Sometimes badgers lie out away from the sett during the day in the shelter of bracken or bramble thicket. If disturbed they make their way back to the sett. This may have been the case when an adult was seen walking along a cliff on a sunny August day in mid-morning by the passengers of a launch plying off the south coast of Cornwall!

An adult was watched in mid-July on a very hot day, 'travelling through scrub, snapping at insects and chewing grass as it went' (J.F. Chapman, pers. comm.). However, the strangest case Chapman witnessed was on a sunny morning in Upper Nidderdale, North Yorkshire in winter, following a snow blizzard. The badger was ambling through a wood towards a sett which had shown no activity over the previous 8 days. Perhaps it was changing setts.

Shortage of food, as in times of drought, is commonly the cause of diurnal behaviour, but it is unusual for a boar to break into a hen run at 14.00 on a May afternoon and kill six hens! Neville Baker (pers. comm.) said that the killing attracted the attention of the gardener who followed the badger to its sett from which it was later dug out.

In more northern latitudes diurnal activity is more common during the long summer days especially at higher altitudes in secluded areas. On one occasion in Sutherland, Scotland, a badger was seen foraging on a hillside among boulders in early April at 14.30, and in September, an adult was watched at 10.00 for 20 min feeding on the carcass of a stag before running into a cairn on being disturbed. This occurred 650 m up in the mountains on a wet and windy day (R. Tweddle, pers. comm.).

Most instances of badgers seen in daylight are characterised by an apparent lack of awareness of the observer. This is well illustrated by an account given by R.R. Hershaw (pers. comm.) who noticed a badger at about 15.00 in bright sunshine loping alongside a hedge bordering a wood. He walked up to within 5 m to watch it.

> To my surprise it seemed quite oblivious of me, for it took not the slightest notice but nosed about like a scenting dog; in fact at one stage it picked up a stick in its mouth and ran backwards and forwards with it. I followed it for about 200 m before it was lost to view among some fallen masonry. It showed no sign of caution or awareness during the 20 min or so that I watched it.

Some daylight sightings may be due to the badger being poisoned or diseased. When dieldrin was used as a seed dressing there were several occasions when badgers were seen in daylight behaving strangely. It was subsequently proved that they had eaten pigeons which had died from eating the treated corn (Jefferies 1968). Tuberculous badgers have also been seen in daylight behaving oddly.

When very small cubs are seen above ground in late March or April, the probable reason is that their mother has met her death and the cubs are desperate for food. Although not yet weaned, they venture out instinctively and go through the motions of foraging.

CHAPTER 6

Food and Feeding Behaviour

EXAMINATION of a badger's skull reveals much about the diet of the animal (see Fig. 2.12). The incisors, canines and front premolars are typical of most carnivores but the molars are much flattened and broad — a characteristic of many herbivores. However, the jaw articulation allows very little sideways movement, so grinding is more limited than in rodents and ungulates. Thus it is not surprising that investigations concerning the badger's diet amply confirm that it is a true omnivore in the sense that it takes an extremely wide range of animal and plant foods. However, although its tastes are so catholic, it is obvious that it relies heavily on certain foods according to availability, thus its diet varies considerably both seasonally and throughout its range.

The diet reflects the badger's characteristic food-finding behaviour. It is primarily a forager, not a hunter. If a source of food is abundant on a particular night, it will concentrate on this, sometimes to the exclusion of all other items. This is a useful energy-saving device as many primary sources of food such as earthworms and cereals occur in patches, so that once discovered they can be exploited in a leisurely manner without moving far. Badgers gradually learn the food potentials of their territories and observations strongly suggest that on emergence, they choose certain areas for a particular food source from memory and according to favourable weather conditions and go straight to those regions. However, the badger is also an opportunist, taking other items it comes across accidentally during its foraging. When food is scarce, opportunistic foraging becomes more apparent and it may take many hours before sufficient food has been collected. Adults, and cubs after weaning, forage independently and show no signs of co-operation.

A badger's aposematic colouring and sometimes noisy foraging give early warning of its presence to the more active animals which can easily avoid capture in consequence. It is not adapted for pouncing and fast running although it is quite capable of sudden darts on unsuspecting prey, so active mammals and adult birds seldom appear in the diet, but dead or unhealthy ones, such as rabbits suffering from myxomatosis, are eaten.

FIG 6.1   *Cubs foraging below a flowering elder. Photo M. Chesworth.*

With such keen senses of smell and hearing, badgers are able to locate the nests of young rabbits and rodents and the presence of insects in leaf litter or under the bark of decaying logs. When foraging, they repeatedly stop and listen between bouts of probing with their snouts to discover any source of food by scent. Techniques used for obtaining different food items vary; these will be described later.

Much research has been done on the diet of badgers, notably by Andersen (1955) in Denmark, Kruisinga (1965) in Holland, Popescu & Sin (1968) in Rumania, Skoog (1970) in Sweden, Likhachev (1956) and others in Russia, Pigozzi (1988) in Italy, Stocker & Lups (1984) in Switzerland and Rodriguez & Delibes (1992) in Spain. In Britain research has been carried out by many workers, including Barker (1969), Hancox (1973), Bradbury (1974), Kruuk & Parish (1981, 1985), Harris (1982), Neal (1988) and Shepherdson *et al.* (1990). Results show that the range of food items taken is immense, but they can be grouped into a number of distinct categories which Skoog divided into primary and secondary. The main animal categories are earthworms, insects, mammals, birds, amphibians and reptiles; the main plant ones are cereals, fruits and green material. These categories will be discussed in detail later.

FOOD ANALYSIS

Two main methods have been used: dung and stomach analysis. Each has its advantages and disadvantages. The former is excellent as much material is easily obtained and provides a simple method of determining frequency of occurrence of most food eaten; also, by using more precise calculations percentage volumes of these items can be calculated. The main disadvantage is that some soft-bodied animals are almost entirely digested and some kinds of scavenged food leave only residues which are hard to identify.

Stomach analysis is ideal when little digestion has taken place, but this is seldom the case as the animals are often killed when the stomach is empty or digestion largely completed. Also, it is difficult to get sufficient material at all times of the year as the investigator is usually restricted to road casualties. However, over a long period of time or when culling has taken place for disease control, much useful information has been obtained. A combination of dung and stomach contents analysis produces the most comprehensive picture. Direct observations of feeding, particularly when radio-racking and using infra-red or light-intensifying binoculars, have also added much to our knowledge of foraging behaviour.

Dung analysis is time consuming but can be extremely interesting. It is not the messy process the term suggests and can be recommended especially to those who have a flare for detective work. However, it must be stressed *that faeces are a potential source of disease and necessary precautions must be taken.* Even a cursory examination of dung in the field can yield useful information; for example, if the faeces appear loose and muddy, you can be sure that earthworms have been eaten in large quantities. Also, by placing a sample on a piece of paper and spreading it thinly, undigested material such as cereal husks, seeds, grass, beetle elytra (wing cases), other insect remains and feathers will become apparent (Shepherdson *et al.* 1990). However, for a more detailed analysis, the faeces should be carried back in a polythene bag, labelled, frozen (not in the household fridge!), or better, preserved in 10% formalin which kills off any TB mycobacteria if they should be present. Analysis can then take place when convenient.

FIG 6.2   *Faeces on surface of ground showing remains of yew berries (stones), cereal husks and beetles. Dorset.*

Keith Bradbury (1974) analysed 3846 dung samples from England, Scotland and Wales to determine the frequency of food items throughout the year. He placed them in six main categories (Fig. 6.3). However, frequency taken alone gives a misleading picture. For example, a badger may pick up the odd beetle during a night's foraging at most seasons of the year, so in terms of frequency, beetles appear to be an important food item; but it is only over a comparatively short season that beetles are eaten in large numbers.

To analyse the contents, each dropping is first defrosted, and if too hard, soaked overnight in water; it is then broken up in a 1-mm-mesh sieve (a gravy strainer is admirable) and thoroughly washed under a running tap; the first sample of filtrate is collected and put aside for examination for the chaetae (bristles) of earthworms and radula teeth of molluscs. The clean remnants left in the strainer are then placed in water in a white dish and the contents sorted with forceps into food categories. To help identification, a reference collection of hairs, feathers, skeletons, insects and seeds is invaluable.

The remains of plant material are often little affected by digestion as badgers are unable to deal effectively with cellulose, lignin and suberin. So husks of cereals, fragments from shells of acorns or nuts, seeds or skins of fleshy fruits or pieces of bark and skins of pig-nut

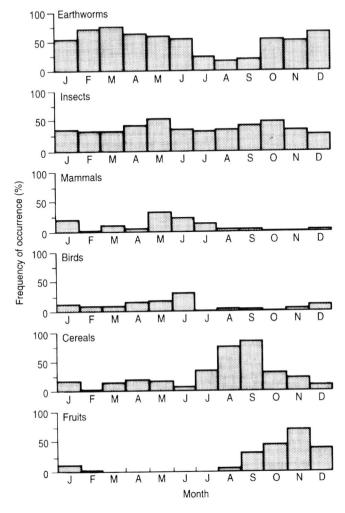

FIG 6.3   *Frequency of occurrence (%) of main food categories throughout the year in 3846 dung samples. Source: Bradbury (unpubl. data).*

tubers can easily be recognised. Mammalian fur is not digested; with large prey such as rabbits and hedgehogs, few hairs or spines are swallowed as most of the skin is not eaten, but sufficient guard hairs are usually found to make identification possible. The recently born young of rabbits, voles and rats are eaten whole, but the hairs are so fine they can usually only be detected under the microscope. Fragments of bones and teeth also help with identification but with very young animals they may be completely digested. Feathers and claws of birds pass through the gut unchanged and may often be recognised as belonging to a particular species. Insects, with their indigestible exoskeletons, leave more obvious clues such as the wings, legs and elytra of beetles and the bodies of bees, wasps and wireworms. When caterpillars and other insect larvae are eaten, their bodies are seldom fragmented so they too may be identified accurately. Surprisingly, the eggshells of birds are not usually dissolved by the stomach acids and fragments retain their characteristic markings. The same applies to snail shells. The gizzard rings of earthworms (one to each worm and approximately 5 mm long for *L. terrestris*) also escape digestion but are easily overlooked as they are transparent. A low-powered binocular microscope (× 35) is very useful.

To test for the presence of earthworms and molluscs, a small sample of the sediment that has settled on the bottom of the filtrate, put aside earlier, is removed with a pipette and spread thinly over a petri dish. If a few drops of picric acid solution are added, any earthworm chaetae and radula teeth of slugs and snails are stained yellow, making them more obvious when examined under the binocular microscope.

This method of dung analysis can be adapted so that the percentage volume of the contents of each dropping can be calculated. This entails counting and/or measuring the volume of each food item and calculating the volume of each before digestion by multiplying by the appropriate factor previously worked out by Kruuk & Parish (1981). For serious investigations at least 20 samples should be taken each month from the same area over a

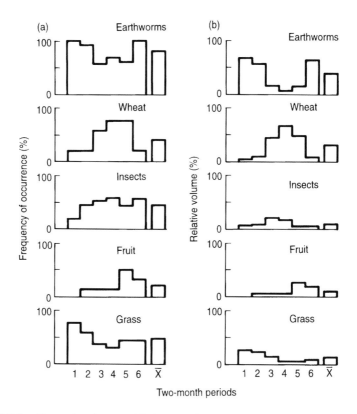

FIG 6.4   *Comparison between (a) the mean frequency of occurrence of different foods in badger faeces and (b) estimated mean volume; during two-month periods over 2 years. (Modified from Shepherdson et al. 1990).*

period of not less than 3 years. For details of the full standard procedure, see Harris *et al.* (1989b). Typical results expressed as a volume may be seen in Fig. 6.4.

EXPLOITATION OF THE HABITAT

The quantity of food obtained in each of the main categories varies enormously. In Britain, Ireland and much of Western Europe when earthworms are readily available badgers primarily forage for these, but when scarce or unobtainable, they are very adaptable and quickly exploit whatever food is in sufficient quantity to justify the search. Also, the scarcer the food supplies, the more opportunistic their foraging becomes. For this reason their diet, although consistent for most of the main categories, differs markedly in detail according to the broad geographical region in which they are living, the type of habitats that occur on their territories, the season of the year and in the shorter term, the weather conditions prevailing at any particular time.

Variation with geographical location

In general terms, the further north the habitat, the longer and more severe the winter becomes; hence winter feeding in these regions becomes minimal and the badgers lie up in a state of semi-dormancy for long periods without feeding. This applies particularly to northern Scandinavia, much of Russia and Siberia and in areas of higher altitude further south. In contrast, those in milder and damper climates feed actively during much of the winter and are less dependent on stored fat for survival.

For Britain, Bradbury (1974) considered from his data that the diet in lowland areas becomes more variable as you go north. This is probably related to the number of nights when temperature and humidity are high enough for earthworms to appear on the surface of the ground. When earthworms are available, other items become less important; when not, badgers become more opportunistic and exploit a wider range of food.

In Denmark, where badgers have access to wetland, it was found that frogs (*Rana.* sp.) and toads (*Bufo* sp.) figured largely in the diet, especially in June and July (Andersen 1955). This is in contrast to most parts of Britain where they are relatively unimportant.

In southern Europe, drier conditions over long periods make earthworm exploitation spasmodic or impossible. Here, badgers show how remarkably adaptable they are in exploiting any food available. In northern Italy it was found that worms were eaten in alpine meadows in summer but their main foods were fruits such as olives (*Olea* sp.), figs (*Ficus sp.*), plums (*Prunus* sp.), grapes (*Vitis vinifera*) and many kinds of insects (Kruuk & Kock 1981). In the Maremma National Park on the west coast of Italy, the diet consisted mainly of fruits between late summer and midwinter and insects from late winter to early summer, all other categories being of minor importance (Pigozzi 1988). In the semi-arid Coto Doñana in southern Spain, rabbits formed the main food (over 50%), with other items, particularly insects, being taken opportunistically (Martin-Franquelo & Delibes 1985). In another arid area of Spain where there was some irrigation which allowed fruit cultivation, 76% of the biomass eaten was fruit and 11% insects although the latter represented 44% of the total volume.

To get an over-view of the diet of the species it has to be remembered that much of its range is within the former Soviet Union. A review by Roper & Mickevicius (in press) of the considerable Russian literature on this subject is very useful as it covers areas from Moscow to eastern Siberia and many locations in the southern states. Speaking generally, animal food (62% on average) was more frequently taken than plant food and the general picture confirms the view that badgers are opportunistic foragers on a wide variety of animal and plant food with a preference for the former. The most important animal categories were (1) insects (30% by volume) including dung beetles (*Scarabeidae*), cockchafers (*Melolontha* sp.), locusts (*Locusta* sp.) grasshoppers (*Saltatoria*), ants (*Formicoidea*), bees (*Apidae*), wasps (*Vespidae*) and lepidopterous larvae and (2) small mammals including mice and voles (*Muridae*) (varying greatly from year to year according to abundance), rats (*Rattus* sp.), rabbits (*Oryctolagus cuniculus*), hares (*Lepus* sp.), hamsters (*Cricetinae*), moles (*Talpa* sp.) and hedgehogs (*Erinaceus* sp.). Most small mammals were taken as young. Earthworms were mentioned in only a few studies. Other categories of minor significance were birds, amphibians, reptiles and fish. Plant material of importance were roots, tubers and, above all, fruits. Cereals did not figure largely in the reports.

In Japan, the subspecies *M. m. anakuma* has a rather similar diet to badgers in Western Europe. Earthworms are the most important item, with insects, small mammals, seeds and fruits also taken according to availability (Yamamoto 1991).

Variation in relation to habitat

Badgers, being so adaptable, exploit many types of terrain, but they thrive best where there is a mosaic of different kinds of habitats within their territories giving them greater choice throughout the year. This is one reason why setts near the edges of deciduous woods bordering arable and grassy meadows are so popular, and generally speaking, it is farming practice that brings about this variability. Thus badger density is closely related to the manner in which land is managed. When habitats are more uniform, population density tends to be lower and territories larger, as in moorland and fenland situations.

Radio-tracking studies, coupled with food analysis and studies of the distribution of different foraging habitats within badger territories, have shown that badgers select habitats for foraging according to the availability of certain types of food (Cheeseman & Mallinson 1981, Kruuk 1987, Hofer 1988, Shepherdson *et al.* 1990). In particular, in Britain, whenever earthworms are readily available in certain habitats such as pasture and deciduous woodland, these are selected for foraging. For instance, it was found that badgers in Woodchester Park, Gloucestershire do not use the various habitats in their range in proportion to their size (Cheeseman & Mallinson 1981). Although permanent pasture comprised only 25% of the area of each social group's territory, in every month of the year they actively selected permanent pasture as a preferred foraging habitat, spending more than 50% of their time foraging there. Arable land was visited in August and September when cereals ripened, but for the rest of the year was not a preferred habitat. Deciduous woodland was selected in spring and autumn whereas coniferous woodland was little used at any time of the year. However, in places where other foods are readily available in quantity because of geographical location or season, badgers opportunistically exploit these sources in the habitats where they occur.

The foraging area of a social group is often markedly circumscribed for territorial reasons, especially in high density areas (p. 148), so neighbouring groups may have very different sources of food available to them. Analysis of the dung from six territories in Wytham, showed clearly that apart from earthworms which were common to all, there was a link between species composition in the diet and availability, particularly for wheat, acorns, blackberries and dor-beetles (*Geotrupes* sp.). The latter were found commonly in dung from territories which included pastures with plenty of cow-pats, but they were virtually absent from those which were mainly woodland (Hancox 1973). Hofer (1988) working in the same area made a more detailed study showing the proportion of food taken throughout the year in six territories (Figs 6.5, 6.6).

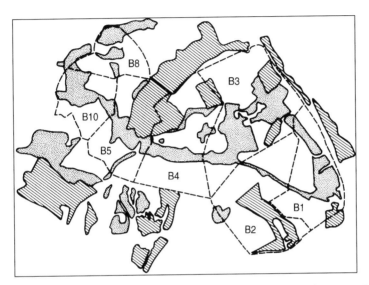

FIG 6.5   *Configuration of badger group territories in relation to the dispersion of pasture field* ▦ *and mature deciduous woodland* ▨. *Dashed lines = boundaries of group territories. (Hofer 1988).*

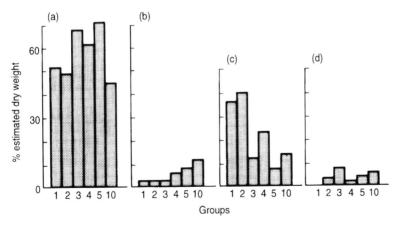

FIG 6.6   *The diet of six different badger groups (as in Fig. 6.5) as indicated by the occurrence of the four most important food categories, expressed as percentage of estimated dry weight: (a) earthworms; (b) invertebrates other than earthworms; (c) cereals, almost exclusively wheat; (d) fruits, mainly blackberries. Source: H. Hofer (1988).*

Moorland and mountainous habitats often deprive badgers of food items which are of major importance in more favourable places, but usually there is a part of the territory where earthworms are locally abundant and large numbers of slugs, beetles and crane-fly larvae (*Tipula* sp.) may compensate for the absence of other items. Carrion becomes an important source of food in such areas and fruits, such as whortleberries (*Vaccinium myrtillus*) and rowan berries (*Pyrus aucuparia*), are of great value in late summer.

Where food is relatively scarce and territories large it is not unusual for badgers to exploit a particular food which is seasonal. For instance, they will move from woodland setts to those in hedgerows in August to be nearer supplies of cereals, and those in mountainous districts may descend to lower areas periodically where foraging is more productive (see also p. 85).

Variation with season and weather

The effects of season and weather conditions cannot easily be separated as they are obviously inter-related. This is specially true of Britain where some winters may be mild and damp and provide plenty of food, while others may be severe and little food, apart from carrion, is available. However, as a broad generalisation, food of animal origin is of greater importance than plant food over most of the year except from mid-July to October when cereals and fruits of many kinds are of major significance. Also, the maximum intake of food occurs during the period September–November and the minimum between December and February (Andersen 1955, Stocker & Lups 1984).

In southern England there is a general tendency for fewer earthworms to be eaten during the summer and early autumn, no doubt because good worming conditions are less frequent at that season in an average year. In Wytham Wood, near Oxford, badger diet was

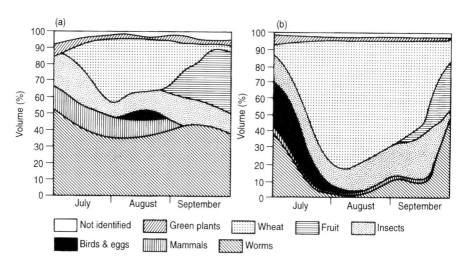

FIG 6.7   *Comparison (expressed in % volume) between (a) the diet of badgers in lowland Britain in the wet summer of 1963 with (b) the dry one of 1964. (G. Barker, 1969).*

analysed during the period July–September in two successive years. It was found that in 1963 which was a very wet summer the volume of earthworms eaten was many times greater than in 1964 which was very dry; then there was a marked compensatory switch to cereals (Barker 1969; Fig. 6.7).

This preference for earthworms over cereals whenever the former are easily available was demonstrated during a dry spell in August in Somerset when the badgers were eating oats from a field near their sett night after night. Then came a short wet spell and they switched at once to earthworms although the oats were still available to them (Neal 1977).

Under very severe drought conditions, especially in June, badgers may become desperate for food. This happened in many parts of England in 1975, 1976 and 1984. Earthworms were unavailable and cereals were not sufficiently advanced to be exploited. Consequently there were many instances of unusual behaviour, including raids on poultry, scavenging in gardens and much earlier emergences to lengthen the foraging period.

There is also a seasonal fluctuation in the exploitation of mammals, birds and insects, again correlated with availability. More mammals are taken in spring and early summer when their young are numerous, and insects such as beetles become more important in the late summer and autumn.

THE MAIN FOOD CATEGORIES AND RELATED FEEDING BEHAVIOUR

The main food categories will be described roughly according to their importance in Great Britain for both animal and plant items.

Earthworms

The importance of earthworms in the diet of badgers in Britain, Ireland and much of western and central Europe cannot be overestimated; they are the most important single item of food. Only in extreme habitats where badgers are sparse and earthworms scarce or unavailable is this not the case (p. 109). In Britain, there is a strong case for concluding that the density of the badger population is largely determined by the degree of availability of earthworms arising from habitat (including land use) and local climatic conditions.

Of 214 stomachs analysed in Somerset, 159 (74.3%) contained food. Of these, 75% contained some earthworms (*Lumbricus terrestris*), 68% had more than 50% and 57% virtually nothing but earthworms (Table 6.1; Neal 1988). The maximum volume of earthworms showing little sign of digestion exceeded a litre; the maximum weight was 642 g and the largest number 203. The majority had been swallowed whole, a few chopped once and a small minority chopped into several pieces. One sample came from a badger killed following a frosty night when earthworms would have been unavailable on the surface; it contained two moles and 165 earthworms. This suggested a cache of worms had been discovered when excavating a mole run.

In Yorkshire, of the dung samples collected from setts in every situation visited, including those at high altitude and on every type of soil, 82% contained earthworm chaetae and in at least 40%, earthworms were the predominant food (Bradbury 1974).

The most suitable worming nights are those which are mild and damp. *Lumbricus*

FIG 6.8   *The stomach contents of a single badger — over 200 earthworms.*

TABLE 6.1   *Percentage of earthworms in badger stomachs according to season.*

Month	Stomachs		Percentage of stomachs with			
	Total number	Number with contents	>95%	50–95%	<50%	0%
					earthworms	
Jan–Feb	57	36	69.4	5.6	8.3	16.7
March–April	52	44	72.7	11.4	6.8	9.1
May–June	42	32	50.0	12.5	3.1	34.4
July–Aug	21	18	22.2	0.0	16.7	61.1
Sept–Oct	36	24	58.3	16.7	8.3	16.7
Nov–Dec	6	5	0.0	40.0	0.0	60.0
	214	159	57.3	10.7	7.5	24.5

Source: Neal (1988).

terrestris lies on the surface to feed when the ground is damp and temperatures are above 2°C (optimum about 10°C, Satchell 1967). In many badger territories there are some patches which, because of their situation, are warmer on certain nights, and these are selected for foraging (Kruuk *et al.* 1979). Kruuk *et al.* (1979) also showed that badgers preferred short-grass pasture for foraging as they are more easily captured there. As the biomass of earthworms in pasture can range from 1000 to 4000 kg ha^{-1} (Tischler 1965) there is an abundance of potential food in good pasture if this habitat is included in the territory.

In western Scotland, *Lumbricus rubellum* was found to be the main species eaten. They occurred commonly in areas where sheep droppings were abundant; these patches were evidently selected by the badgers for foraging as 81% of the pits made during capture were near to sheep droppings (Kruuk 1989). These worms are also found under cow-pats in other areas. Other species of earthworm are eaten, including those of the genus *Allolobophora*, but in most places these are far less important since they do not lie on the surface. Occasionally other species are discovered under the bark of logs.

In Kent some farmers use irrigation sprays run on cables. They are used at night and travel the length of the field, rotating as they go. Both badgers and foxes were seen to make use of the wet conditions for worming when surrounding fields were dry, but whereas the badgers did not mind getting a soaking in the process, foxes learnt by the clicks made by the sprayer as it changed direction to avoid getting wet (C. Ferris, pers. comm.).

When foraging for earthworms, a badger will walk slowly forwards until its snout is just above one which is lying on the surface with its 'tail' in its burrow, grip it with its incisors and pull it out of the ground. When fully extended, the worm seldom breaks; otherwise a steady pull is usually successful. However, some worms grip their burrows too hard and break; the badger may then quickly burrow after the remainder. Examination of stomach contents shows that badgers are not always successful as there are more heads than tails. On a good night a worm is caught every metre or so. Chris watched one badger in rich pasture eating worms at the rate of six or seven a minute without much pause for 2 h, after which the badger curled up in a nearby couch and went to sleep!

Insects and other arthropods

Insects are an important food source, being eaten as adults or larvae in every month, but only during periods of abundance are they eaten in quantity. Only a few groups are of importance in the badger's feeding ecology; they are almost all of large size and spend much time in or on the ground while feeding or breeding. The most important are the dung beetles (Scarabeidae), wasps (Vespidae) and bumblebees (Apidae). Those of secondary importance include the ground beetles (Carabidae), the caterpillars of moths, especially (Noctuidae), and the larvae of crane-flies (Tipulidae).

Of the dung beetles, the large dor-beetles (*Geotrupes* sp) are by far the most important. They are very active at night, visiting the dung of cows and other herbivores. Badgers, when foraging, break up the cow-pats with their claws or turn them over to find them. Pits excavated beside or under the pats indicate where they have followed beetles which have burrowed into the ground (also earthworms). In May and August, especially, large numbers may be consumed. In Denmark over 800 were recorded in a single stomach in May (Andersen 1955).

The other dung beetles commonly eaten belong to the genus *Aphodius*. As their larvae feed near the surface of the ground in quite large aggregations they are often consumed in greater numbers than the adults (Skoog 1970).

Other beetle larvae which are favourites with badgers are the juicy cockchafer grubs (*Melolontha melolontha*) which feed on the roots of grasses and in some years may be very numerous in old pasture. Badgers may make visits to such areas and consume large quantities, night after night. Sometimes cockchafer grubs appear in lawns and golf courses, and if discovered by badgers, the shallow pits made when digging for them may bring wrath on their heads. Under these circumstances it is little comfort to the owner of the lawn to be

FIG 6.9   *Pit made by a badger when digging for invertebrate prey. Note pad-marks.*

told that the badgers are merely ridding the turf of insect pests! However, that is the case, and the best way of preventing such damage is to tackle the primary cause which is the presence of the grubs. A species of *Melolontha* is common in some of the pine forests in the former Soviet Union; they are an important food for badgers. Dung analysis from one area in the Volga-Kama area showed they were present in 96% of the samples (Roper & Mickevicius, in press)

Occasionally a smaller chafer (*Phyllopertha horticola*) may reach plague proportions (especially in upland pasture) and provide abundant food for badgers. Considerable damage to grassland over an area of 2000 m² occurred in Snowdonia, North Wales, which was described as similar to that made by rooting pigs. It was not established for certain whether the badgers causing the damage were after chafer larvae or wireworms (*Tipula* sp.), but the former appeared to be the more probable (Milner 1967).

Ground beetles are regularly taken opportunistically when foraging, usually in small numbers.

Some idea of the variety of beetle species eaten may be gained from those identified in the stomach of a single Danish badger in June; it contained 452 individuals representing 35 genera (Andersen 1955).

Wasps' and bumble bees' nests become important items in the diet from July to September in some districts. They are probably located by scent although hearing may play a part. Wasps are an important food because they are common, of a reasonable size and are to be found in large numbers within a small area. A large nest is a complete meal for the taking (Skoog 1970). Badgers are extremely fond of wasp grubs. On finding a nest a badger shows great signs of excitement, fluffing up its coat and darting here and there as it investigates its position. There is an old country saying that 'a badger never goes in where the wasps come out'. This is certainly true, as a badger will always dig down to the nest from above, not expand the entrance used by the insects. This is just as well as the one vulnerable spot where a badger may be stung is the end of the snout, the wasps being unable to reach the skin in other places when the hairs are erected. A badger will dig down very quickly with its powerful claws and make short work of adults, pupae and larvae as well as quantities of nest material. By morning, all that remains is a large hole in the bank, remnants of nest scattered about and a few desultory wasps huddled pathetically in the ruins of their home. It is surprising how many adults are eaten during such a raid. Skoog records up to 300 in a single stomach. With such numbers it would seem almost inevitable that some stings would be received, although the quick chopping action of the teeth would kill the majority. Partially destroyed nests are sometimes found; this could reflect unusually effective defence (Hancox 1991). We know of no evidence that badgers are immune to wasp venom.

Large numbers of wasps' nests are destroyed by badgers each season — one reason why badgers are popular with foresters, who are often plagued by them when clearing brush in autumn. The record for nest destruction probably goes to the badgers of Beaufort, Sussex 'which devoured between them 30–40 nests during two ensuing nights' (Butterworth 1905). Badgers occasionally pick up queen wasps during the early months and so prevent the subsequent formation of nests. The most common species taken are *Vespa vulgaris* and *V. germanica* (Andersen 1955, Skoog 1970, Schmid & Lups 1988).

Bumble bees' nests are also destroyed in large numbers. These have the added attraction of honey to supplement the larvae and pupae. Fewer adults are eaten than with wasps and they are chopped up more thoroughly before swallowing. The commonest species recorded in the dung were *Bombus terrestris* and *B. leucorum* (Skoog 1970).

Sometimes honey bees from an apiary may swarm and make a nest in a hollow tree. If discovered by a badger in an accessible situation, it will tear the bark away with teeth and claws and in an incredibly short time devour much of the honeycomb. Occasionally badgers attack beehives in isolated situations. Several instances were recorded when hives had been overturned to get at the honey, the badgers destroying or reducing some colonies in the process (L. Webb, pers. comm.). On another occasion, four strong colonies were devastated one June. The badgers appeared to have nosed off the lids of the hives; abundant claw marks on the sides showed how they had separated the supers (boxes containing the honeycomb) from the brood chambers below (Dines 1981).

The larvae of crane-flies (*Tipula* sp.) may occur in sufficient density to reward persistent searching in the humus layer of woodland where the moss layer is turned over in the process (Skoog 1970). They may also be present in large numbers in damp pastures and grassy upland moors. They are eaten largely in late autumn, winter and spring when they have attained sufficient size to make the search productive. The adults are also eaten at the time of a hatch. Chris saw a badger snapping them up from a pasture at the rate of 20 a minute!

Caterpillars of various moths which feed at ground level are eaten in fair numbers, although it is unusual for a badger to find many in a single night. A common species taken is the large yellow underwing (*Tryphaena pronuba*), but many others are eaten occasionally including those of the swift moths (*Hepialus* sp.) which feed on the roots of grasses.

Ants are sometimes eaten when other food is scarce. Ernest has seen ant-hills partly destroyed by badgers which had presumably been going for the larvae and pupae. Badger hairs left behind provided the evidence.

In the former Soviet Union with its great variety of climates and habitats it is not surprising that unusual insects to us are taken in large quantities when they occur in great numbers locally. Thus in Buratia, locusts (*Locusta* sp.) were present in 80% of faecal samples, and mole crickets (*Gryllotalpa* sp.) occurred in 96% of samples from Uzbekistan (Roper & Mickevicius, in press).

Other arthropods in the diet include woodlice, centipedes and millipedes, but they are of little significance.

Mammals

Although the frequency of mammal remains in the dung and stomach contents is not so high as insects, mammals constitute an important food source. A single mammal is the equivalent of a much larger number of small prey, and a nest of young rabbits, for example, can provide a substantial meal in a very short space of time.

The most important species taken are rodents (voles, mice and rats), insectivores (moles, shrews and hedgehogs) and lagomorphs (rabbits and hares). Badgers are not adapted for catching larger mammals unless they are injured, old or diseased, and even with smaller species, more young than adults are taken. Unexpected items occasionally recorded are squirrels, lambs, foxes and deer but these are nearly always taken as carrion (p. 126).

Mammals may be eaten during any month but the main peak is in spring and summer when most of the prey species breed. There may be a further peak in winter, particularly if the weather is severe, but this almost certainly points to carrion.

The commonest rodent taken is the short-tailed vole (*Microtus agrestis*). Even in situations where the bank vole (*Clethryonomis glareolus*) is common (Bradbury 1974), *Microtus* is taken in greater numbers, probably because it is more easily caught. In fields, badgers can easily expose the runs of *Microtus* which are rather superficial, or dig down further to find the nest. A conical pit and a few badger hairs are tell-tale signs. In woods and hedgerows where *Clethryonomis* is more common, their nests are often in places where digging is more difficult, such as under tree roots.

Badgers occasionally catch water voles (*Arvicola* sp.) by digging out their runs. One excavation in Sweden was several metres long, 200 mm across and 300 mm deep. Badger hairs were found at one end where the vole had been captured (Skoog 1970). In western Switzerland, the subspecies *Arvicola terrestris scherman* shows cycles of abundance every 4–8 years and during peaks becomes a major source of food for badgers. They are easy to capture, and, when numerous, are preferred to earthworms (Weber & Aubry 1994).

Wood mice (*Apodemus sylvaticus*) are eaten spasmodically. The adults are usually far too agile to catch, but when numbers are high they are taken quite frequently; at other times the nestlings only are captured (Skoog 1970).

Rat nestlings (*Rattus norvegicus*) also figure occasionally in the diet but adults are seldom caught unless cornered.

Of the insectivores, moles (*Talpa europaea*) are probably the most commonly eaten, both adults and young being taken. Mole runs are sometimes opened up as when hunting voles; caches of worms may be discovered in this way and adults captured (p. 113); badgers may dig into mole fortresses to get at the nestlings. In 1983, a badger was watched making for a cluster of mole hills; 'it passed by some, deliberated at others, then coming to another, dug swiftly down and brought up a store of worms'; presumably the worms were discovered by smell (C. Ferris, pers. comm.).

Shrews do not appear to be a favourite food. The common shrew (*Sorex araneus*) is the most usual species caught but pygmy shrews (*Sorex minutus*) and water shrews (*Neomys fodiens*) have been recorded.

Hedgehogs (*Erinaceus europaeus*) are eaten occasionally. Four were found in the stomach of a single badger killed near Oxford (Middleton 1935) and remains have been recorded by Bradbury and others. All accounts agree that very few spines are swallowed.

There have been conflicting reports of how a badger succeeds in killing and eating a hedgehog without being damaged by the spines, but the most detailed eye-witness account was given by Chris Ferris (pers. comm.). She was watching a female with four young foraging among leaves when some badgers approached — two adults and three cubs. The hedgehogs all rolled up, the adult into a prickly ball but the young making a poor job of it. The sow and her cubs promptly ate the young ones which presented no problem at all, while a boar took over the ball of spines. To quote from her diary:

> When the hedgehog was on its back with the 'join' between head and hind quarters uppermost the boar made one swift movement of its left front paw and ran the claws straight down and into the 'join'. The hedgehog gave a sort of bounce and emitted a high-pitched cry that continued for some seconds. Then the right paw descended on the 'join' which was now open and raked sideways along the belly of the prey. The hedgehog was now opened flat and pinned at both ends by the formidable claws. The boar then lowered its head and began to eat.

On returning the next morning the skin was found to be flat, spines downwards, and apart from a tiny piece of head was quite clean.

When we have found the remains of hedgehogs, some skins had been turned inside out, others were flattened and a few looked like prickly balls with the spines outwards and no flesh remaining. Chris Ferris suggests that the curling of the skin may be due to differential drying of the two surfaces.

Another observer maintains that 'the skin is curled up in the normal manner of a frightened hedgehog and the spines are erected. The skin of the legs is sometimes turned inside out and sometimes absent; the jaws are invariably present and the cranium sometimes. The skins form a complete ball and yet everything has been removed from the inside and no trace of blood or viscera is left lying about' (R.W. Howard, pers. comm.).

Very few hedgehog remains were found in Bradbury's (1974) material. He makes the point that badgers and hedgehogs forage for rather similar prey and hunt in similar situations so are bound to encounter each other many times, yet relatively few appear to be eaten. He suggests that badgers either eat them reluctantly, or only certain individuals develop the necessary skill for dealing with them. On the other hand, the skins of hedgehogs are not uncommonly found, and the question must be asked critically whether the majority are killed by badgers or foxes, and if by the latter, how? Their claws appear to be unsuitable.

Rabbits occur frequently in the diet, although not in such numbers as formerly (Neal, 1945). In pre-myxomatosis days in Britain nests of young rabbits formed a staple part of a badger's diet in spring. Normally an adult cannot be caught, but in those days snaring was a common practice and badgers undoubtedly took their chances when they came across them in snares.

Since then, rabbits have increased once more in many parts of Britain, and Bradbury (1974) showed that nearly 7% of his samples contained rabbit hair. In mild winters the fur appeared in the dung in January due to early breeding but the peak was reached in April. Unweaned litters accounted for the vast majority.

Field evidence for this preference was given by the late Professor Niko Tinbergen (pers. comm.) who said that each year a badger used to visit the Ravenglass sand-dune region of Cumbria to feed on the rabbits. It dug up a number of rabbit nests but always seemed to choose the time when the young were near 'fledging'.

A badger locates a rabbit's nest by scent or hearing — probably both. It digs down vertically in preference to opening up the tunnel.

Leverets are occasionally eaten but they are far less important to badgers than rabbits. In Sweden, a sow and cub, which were shot, were found to have eaten four young hares; three were in the sow's stomach, one in a cub's stomach (Skoog 1970). An interesting point was that the sow was carrying the leg of a leveret in her mouth when she was shot.

Badgers typically eat their prey on the spot as most prey is small, but under very unusual circumstances prey of relatively large size may be carried back. One such instance was photographed by E.C.D. Darwell (Fig. 6.10). He described the event as follows:

> On the evening of 17 June the boar went off into the woods surrounding the sett leaving five cubs playing around the entrance. Ten minutes later it returned with a dead rabbit and I photographed it near the entrance. After the flash it took the rabbit into the sett. The rabbit appeared to be an adult or at any rate nearly fully grown. I think I heard sounds suggesting that the rabbit was being eaten, but I was distracted by the arrival of a fox which had obviously been following the scent of the rabbit, but that may only have been my imagination.

However, it is quite possible that it was the fox that had first caught the rabbit and the badger somehow robbed it and brought it back to the sett, followed by the fox.

Other instances of food being carried into the sett include a sow, accompanied by two cubs, carrying a rabbit (J. Vinck), badgers carrying pigeons (*Columba* sp.) (C. Ferris), and a sow with cubs below carrying two dead chickens (*Gallus* sp.) and, later in the year, a pheasant (*Phasianus*) (C. Ferris).

A strange case of food carrying occurred on a farm in Oxfordshire (Orchard 1958). A newborn calf was missing. Investigation by torchlight at a badger sett in a wood bordering the field revealed a cloven hoof sticking out of the main entrance of the sett. On pulling the leg, the body of the calf was revealed. On returning with the calf to the cow shed, artificial respiration was given and the calf recovered. When it was daylight, on going back to the spot where the cow had calved, it was possible 'to follow the tracks of two badgers moving backwards as they dragged the calf across 200 m of frosty grass, under a barbed wire fence to which a few calf hairs still clung, and over 20 m of woodland to the main entrance of the sett'.

Suspected lamb killing by badgers has been reported from time to time but very few instances have stood up to careful investigation. Usually, other animals have been the culprits. A Pest Control Officer reported two instances he was asked to investigate in Somerset. On one, he set traps for the killer and caught an Alsatian dog, and on the second, when

FIG 6.10   *It is unusual for a badger to bring back food to the sett; this one is bringing back a rabbit (see text). Photo E.C. Darwell.*

going with the farmer to the orchard where the lambs had been killed, they caught the culprit in the act of repeating the crime — it was the farmer's own sow! Usually the circumstantial evidence for suspecting badgers is that lamb remains are found outside a sett, but when this happens it is almost certainly the work of a fox living there. Foxes habitually bring back prey for their cubs, but badgers seldom need to do so since they suckle their young for 3–4 months, by which time they are able to forage for themselves. However, still-born lambs are occasionally eaten and also dead sheep.

Having said this, it does not follow that no badger has been a lamb killer. Ernest knows of about seven instances over 50 years where the evidence is either certain or highly probable. In all cases it appeared to have been the work of a single individual, usually an old boar.

A Pest Control Officer for Gloucestershire described how lambs were apparently being taken by badgers. A lamb was penned on the scene of the tragedies and an old boar badger was shot when about to attack it. There was no more trouble, so it seemed that one 'rogue' was responsible (F. Baty, pers. comm.).

There was another instance on the Worcester/Hereford border where a farmer lost 21 lambs — usually one of each twin. Snow on one occasion showed up nothing but badger tracks. A badger was dug out and killed and there was no more trouble (S.P. Clark, pers. comm.). A further instance was recorded in North Wales (Batten 1923).

The method of lamb killing by badgers is distinctive. Badgers usually go for the hind quarters, especially the back region just above the root of the tail. This is also the position attacked when badgers are fighting between themselves during territorial disputes. Badgers are also said to crack the ribs, which a fox is claimed not to do. When eating a lamb, a badger goes for the guts and liver first, and if a complete meal is made of the lamb, the skin is left inside out and often thrown over its head.

One can say with conviction that lamb killing is extremely rare, and if it does occur, is usually the work of a rogue animal which finds normal food difficult to get. It is not usually a hazard for a farmer and no action to destroy badgers on a farm is justified as a preventative measure.

Extremely rarely a badger may attack a cat. Ernest knows of two instances when the deed was actually witnessed. However, cats are normally in no danger from badgers. There are many instances when food has been put out for badgers in gardens and cats have shared the meal, even eating from the same plate at the same time (E.N. Watts, pers. comm.).

Cannibalism

Cannibalism occurs occasionally, but in most cases the evidence is circumstantial. The late Lord Knutsford told how he came across two very small cubs outside a sett which had just been killed and eaten out except for their feet and heads. On digging out the sett, he found two old badgers, a boar and a sow, which he was sure were the culprits. The sow was not in milk, so could not have been the mother. He came to the conclusion that the old pair had for some reason required the sett which had been occupied by a young sow and her cubs. There have also been other instances of dead cubs being found outside setts with the skin completely cleaned out except for some of the distal bones of the limbs.

One case involved a senile sow and her small cubs, all of which were killed and partly eaten by a rogue badger (Hancox 1973). Nearby was a pit containing dung with cub hair and claws in it. It was thought that the killer may have been a half-tame sow which was released into the area previously. A second instance was recorded in Switzerland (Lups & Roper 1990). This was a road casualty killed on 23 March 1981. The stomach contained 25 g of earthworms, 17.5 g of plant material, 1 g of insect remains and 57 g of bones, muscle and fur from a badger cub. The sow was in good condition and by the state of the uterus had had cubs earlier in the year, but it was not known whether she was lactating.

Sows in captivity have been known to eat their own cubs if disturbed. It is probable that cases of infanticide in the wild may be either the action of a dominant sow involving the litter of a subordinate, or young cubs killed and eaten by an adult boar which has discovered them when the sow was away foraging. Normally, the boar is banished from the breeding part of the sett and the sow is careful not to leave her cubs before the boar has left the sett area, but accidents can happen. However, hard evidence is difficult to come by (p. 161).

Birds and eggs

Bird remains found through dung analysis are undoubtedly mainly taken as carrion (p. 127), but live birds are occasionally caught and eaten. During the breeding season, badgers sometimes come across the nests of ground-nesting birds and eggs or chicks are taken. However, during a dung analysis study, it was found that in only five instances out of 177 involving bird material were a batch of eggs and an adult bird present in the same sample, and only in 16 was there evidence of fledglings (Hancox 1973). It is highly probable that most young birds taken have not yet acquired the strength for adequate flight and are sheltering on the ground when predated.

It has been reported that badgers can sometimes rush birds and catch them successfully. This is possible with duck, especially during the moult, and sleeping waders such as oyster-catchers and curlews on the shore. Chris Ferris (pers. comm.) has witnessed badgers kill and eat ground-roosting birds on bitterly cold winter nights, the cold making these birds torpid and easy to catch. Larks (*Alauda* sp.) were among the victims.

What about game birds? In Britain, the Game Conservancy considers that damage by badgers in pheasant rearing is insignificant and calls for no repressive measures against the badger. Pheasant nests are occasionally robbed, but this is exceptional and with normal badger numbers this is no problem. Records of pheasant egg fragments were found in only two dung samples during Bradbury's (1974) research and when Hancox (1973) worked on an estate where pheasants were probably the commonest ground-nesting species, he found the remains of 24 eggs in 2000 dung samples. Adult material has been recorded in samples from Britain, Denmark and Sweden, but these are very rare events; in most cases they were probably birds that had been wounded by shooting since some were cock birds which do not incubate. However, some females may have been surprised on the nest as Skoog mentions instances where remains of both adults and eggs occurred in the same material (Skoog 1970).

It has been the experience of many naturalists and gamekeepers in Britain that pheasants have on numerous occasions raised broods successfully from nests very near badger setts. Mrs Fairfax, writing in the *East Anglian*, said that during one season she knew of 14 hen pheasants which brooded safely within 100 m of a badger sett. Also, a hen pheasant hatched her full clutch safely within the perimeter of an occupied sett (N. Burke, pers. comm.).

There is less information regarding partridges (*Perdix* sp.). Several instances have been reported of nests being destroyed by badgers when foraging beside hedgerows, but damage of this kind does not seem to be a usual hazard.

Poultry killing has always been a subject of some controversy and emotion. It is easy to be prejudiced about the species as a whole if you have just lost some valuable hens or ducks to a marauding badger. It is also just as easy to convince yourself that badgers don't kill poultry if you happen to love badgers and let your heart rule your head. Over the past 50 years Ernest has received many letters about poultry killing from various parts of Britain and has attempted to sift the evidence and analyse the factors concerned. In addition, those who have investigated the diet of badgers have contributed valuable factual data, so an objective judgement can be made.

It is indisputable that badgers do kill poultry occasionally. Apart from all the cases where foxes were clearly the culprits there are a number of eye-witness accounts and many others where circumstantial evidence was tantamount to proof. We shall cite a typical instance in some detail as the circumstances are significant. On 30 March in Hampshire, a farmer was woken at 03.00 by a fiendish noise and rushed out into the snow to find a badger in the henhouse. It had presumably raised the drop hatch by getting its snout under it, but after entering, the door had fallen shut, trapping it effectively. It had killed two hens. The farmer shot it and found it was an old boar with worn teeth. The next morning its tracks were followed in the snow. It had come from the local sett 300 m from the house, reached the garden and walked along the road. Its tracks then suddenly altered towards the henhouse as if it had suddenly got wind of the birds. The farmer then told me that although he had kept poultry there for the previous 7 years he had never before lost any birds to a badger although he had lost many to foxes.

A number of other rather similar instances are recorded where a badger has obviously been attracted by the sounds and warm smells from a poultry house and entered by the same method of nosing up the hatch. On one occasion, on hearing squawks from the poultry, the farmer got out of bed and grabbed a gun and torch. As the farmer was opening the door of the henhouse the badger rushed between his legs and escaped before he could fire a shot. To his surprise, he found no hens had been killed. Incidentally, it is worth making the point that if the hatch fits into a groove at the bottom of the door a badger cannot get its nose under to get inside!

Very occasionally, badgers have been known to go to considerable trouble to secure a meal of poultry. In one instance in Gloucestershire an adult boar gained access to the end of a chicken coop which was constructed of 12 mm plywood in sound condition by tearing with its teeth and claws a hole just big enough to squeeze through. Having killed and partly consumed the two occupants, the badger was too large to climb out through the hole it had made, and was found curled up asleep in a corner.

There were several other instances where badgers forced their way into dilapidated hen-houses by destroying the rotten wood, but usually where poultry are well housed and sensible precautions taken, little damage from badgers occurs. However, there have been a few instances of young poultry losing limbs when kept in 'arks' or houses which have a raised slatted floor. Sometimes a badger has been able to get underneath, get a grip of a bird's foot and pull with distressing results.

Normally, when badgers kill poultry they do so in a very different manner from foxes. Foxes usually go for the neck but badgers will attack the body. When badgers eat a carcass they often start at the vent, pull the guts out and eat that first; later they go for the more muscular parts such as the breast.

From all the evidence available certain deductions can be made. First, poultry killing is an unusual occurrence. Bradbury (1974) found few instances although his dung samples came from all over Britain. The exception was from those from a sett near Huddersfield from which traces were repeatedly recovered. He found these badgers regularly visited a refuse heap near a poultry farm on which dead birds were thrown. A similar paucity of evidence is characteristic of the data from other work in Britain and on the mainland of Europe. In many parts poultry killing is almost unheard of but in some areas, especially Ireland, South Wales and some counties with high badger populations, rather more instances occur.

Second, poultry killing is usually the work of an individual; it is not typical of badgers generally. In the majority of cases, if the badger is killed, there is no further damage although many other badgers may be in the district. When it does occur, it is often the work of a very old animal with much worn teeth or one in bad health which is unable to feed normally. If such an animal discovers an easy source of food such as poultry, it may acquire the habit and do quite a lot of damage.

Third, poultry killing becomes more prevalent at times of food scarcity. A particularly important time is February–March if this coincides with severe weather as the sows are then suckling cubs and their normal food may be unobtainable. The same applies to periods of drought. This was particularly evident during the severe summer droughts of 1975 and 1976 when many complaints were received, mainly from regions of high badger density. As soon as the rain came and earthworms were once more available, the trouble abruptly stopped.

To put poultry killing in perspective, Ralph Gibbons wrote about some badgers which had a sett under the floor of a garden shed in Watford. They had complete access to a hen run only a few feet away where there were four hens. There was never any damage to the hens and no eggs were lost!

Badgers will occasionally take ducks and we know of one instance when a goose was killed, but again these cases are the work of an animal which for some reason finds normal food difficult to get. In Staffordshire, 10 mallard (*Anas platyrhynchos*) nests were kept under observation in a paddock where a semi-wild badger was free to wander (Drabble 1969). They were all in places where the badger could easily find them. Nevertheless every single nest hatched out and the adult birds got the ducklings to the pool.

However, not everyone is so fortunate. M. Patterson, from Dyfed, Wales, described how a badger climbed over a low pigsty wall where 17 ducks were shut up. It killed and ate four and bit two others. It had evidently eaten so much that it was unable to climb back. It was found curled up asleep among its victims at 10.00 the next morning and shot.

On another occasion a badger was seen chasing mallard at dawn round and round a pond until it was empty. The few ducklings that escaped 'were covered in mud and looked more like chocolate ducks'. The owner ended her account somewhat heroically by saying 'Nevertheless I prefer badgers to ducks!' (D. Lucas, pers. comm.). Fortunately duck killing is exceptional.

Reptiles, amphibians and fish

Adders, grass-snakes (*Natrix natrix*), lizards (*Lacertidae*) and slow-worms (*Angius fragilis*) have all been recorded in the diet, but presumably badgers only come across them occasionally. E.D. Clements (pers. comm.) found a badger cub actually eating a slow-worm in daylight. At his approach the badger retreated, but Clements kept quite still and it soon re-emerged and for a full 5 minutes continued to eat it at his feet!

In Britain there are few records of live snakes being eaten by badgers, although tame ones have eaten dead adders with relish. However, in Sweden, remains of both adders (*Vipera beros*) and grass-snakes have occurred quite commonly in the dung (Skoog 1970). As far as we are aware no encounter between a badger and an adder has been witnessed, but Ognev (1935) states that the venom has almost no effect on a badger. In one study in Kazakstan, all species of snake known to be present locally were taken. Stomach analysis showed that they were eaten whole, and as remains of toads (*Bufo* sp.), small mammals and lizards were also present, it was thought likely that badgers catch them soon after the snakes have swallowed large prey, making them slower and easier to catch (Roper & Mickevicius, in press).

Amphibians are eaten more frequently, especially frogs (*Rana.* sp.) and toads; newts (*Tritura* sp.) more rarely. In Britain, amphibians are only of minor importance, but elsewhere in Europe they occur frequently in the diet. In one study in Denmark (Andersen 1955), 14% of the 190 stomachs examined contained frog or toad remains. Usually only one or two animals occurred in a single stomach, but on one occasion 17 toads were found. Frogs and toads were taken in every month from May to September, but were most common in July. In two instances about 500 young frogs (just after metamorphosis) were found in a single stomach.

Frogs and toads appear to be equally popular and are treated in the same way before swallowing. E.M. Cawkwell (pers. comm.) described how he used to feed his tame badger on frogs. It would seize the animal, bite it hard and throw it out of its mouth as the frog urinated. It would then scrape its claws on it rapidly and crunch it whole in the mouth. Others have commented on this claw scraping which is usually done very thoroughly. This would reduce the amount of obnoxious secretion which these amphibians, especially toads, produce from their skins.

Fish are usually eaten as carrion (p. 127). In Uzbekistan they were caught in dried-up river beds during summer droughts (Roper & Mickevicius, in press). However, there is some evidence that badgers will catch them alive. Mark Fisher (pers. comm.) regularly took his tame badger out foraging after dark and told how it found an eel in a ditch and ate it. He also watched it take minnows swimming in a bowl of water. Could badgers do this in the wild? The only eye-witness account we know of was graphically described by E.R. Brown in the Natural History Report for 1961 of Felsted School, Surrey on which the following account is based. After a prolonged badger watching expedition on 4 January, Brown decided to go home by a route which passed near the river in the hope of seeing an otter. It was 01.05. As he approached the river he heard a fox bark and crept in that direction in order to catch a glimpse of it. He moved towards the river, and suddenly saw a fish appear above the grass and heard it fall and flap about on the dry ground. On approaching the river silently, he was astonished to see a full-grown badger standing on a solid mud spit which projected nearly 2 m into the water. It had its right paw raised and was staring intently into the water at its feet. Suddenly it made a bear-like sweep with its paw and neatly flipped a small fish out of the water and on to the bank behind it. Brown watched fascinated for a few more minutes. Then the badger, apparently satisfied, turned and ate the fishes on the bank and wandered off.

Molluscs

Molluscs are frequently eaten in small numbers but they do not constitute an important part of the diet. A possible exception to this is in moorland where the large black slug (*Arion ater*) may be taken in larger numbers. Slugs are mainly eaten in wet weather. It was on such a night that Ernest watched a badger climb a tree, presumably to find slugs (Fig. 2.6). Before eating a large slug, a badger will roll it in the grass to remove the slimy exudation. Large snails are treated similarly although smaller ones are crunched up at once.

Snails most often taken in Britain are *Cepaea nemoralis* and *C. hortensis* (Hancox 1973). These are field snails of medium size. Garden snails (*Helix aspersa*) and Roman snails (*H. pomatia*) are eaten less frequently.

In coastal regions, sea mussels (*Mytilus edulis*) may also be eaten. In the Baltic, the badgers evidently search the piles of seaweed for these bivalves. One autumn after a gale had thrown up along the shore much seaweed with mussels attached, sea mussel remains occurred in large quantities in the dung (Skoog 1970). In a study in the Crimea, sea mussels were found in 81% of the faecal samples (Roper & Mickevicius, in press).

Carrion and refuse

Badgers will certainly take carrion. In Scotland, badgers have been known to feed on the carcasses of red deer (*cervus elephus*) returning night after night until little is left. There is an account of a dead hind calf in which poison had been inserted for the purpose of killing crows. It was placed on an island in a loch in the centre of a deer forest. The water around the island was deep and 20 m across, yet a badger had scented the carrion, swum over and was found dead after eating the poisoned meat (MacNally 1970). Badgers will also eviscerate calves if found dead and still-born lambs are eaten occasionally.

A tame badger used to be fed on grey squirrel (*Sciurus carolinensis*) carcasses; the badger's reactions to them was an interesting sidelight on how one would deal with a live animal of that size. It first approached it with extreme caution, then a quick grasp by the teeth, a sudden sideways flick of the head and the squirrel was dashed heavily on the ground. It was then skinned and by morning, nothing was left except the complete skin (C. Russell, pers. comm.).

The great majority of bird remains found in dung samples have almost certainly been eaten as carrion. The fact that gulls (*Larus* sp.), crows (*Corvus* sp.), pigeons (*Columba* sp.) and even sand martins (*Riparia riparia*) have been identified underlines this assumption. It was noted that pigeon remains in dung went up dramatically in October, no doubt because of shooting (Hancox 1973). Badgers certainly pick up wounded birds and those which have subsequently died. There are also instances of badgers dying after feeding on pigeons which had been killed through eating corn dressed with insecticide (Jefferies 1968).

Badgers visit starling roosts during the winter to pick up birds which have died during the night and will eat any species they come across which has died through severe conditions. They will also habitually search the tide-line around the coast and consume dead gulls and any other animal matter they can find, including dead fish.

Fish remains were often found in the dung of badgers which were living on islands in the Baltic as a result of shore foraging, and herring was used as bait very successfully when live-trapping badgers in Sweden (Skoog 1970). There is a nice apocryphal story of how to catch badgers. A kipper is attached to a string and put down the sett; after a few minutes it is pulled out again with the badger on the end! Perhaps there is an element of truth in it!

Badgers have also been known to scavenge salmon (*Salmo* sp.). On the middle reaches of the Tweed during 1968–1969 when salmon disease was prevalent, a number of carcasses were eaten by badgers (Cuthbert 1973). A large sett was situated about 200 m from the river and any salmon stranded within about 300 m up or down stream from the sett were rapidly disposed of. Frequently the badgers dragged the carcasses into undergrowth well back from the river bank and consumed them there. On two occasions skeletal remains of salmon were also found near the sett.

The importance of carrion in a badger's diet varies considerably with locality, but there is little doubt that a badger will usually take it if the opportunity arises, unless an abundance of preferred food is available. Carrion is of particular importance in times of food scarcity, especially during winter.

Cereals

Cereals can be regarded as a primary food, but the quantity taken depends on availability, weather conditions and alternative food supplies.

In Britain, in good cereal-growing localities, husks in the dung usually start appearing in early July, and appreciable quantities are consumed until October; some gleaning may go on even after that. Badgers will also take cereals put out for pheasants, visit cattle troughs containing supplementary feed and enter barns where grain is stored. On one occasion, badgers, which regularly visited a farm in Gloucestershire, walked up the outside steps of a building where cattle cake was stored to eat it (W. Simpson, pers. comm.).

Regions where less cereal is grown tend to have more pasture and a heavier rainfall, so the badgers eat less cereal and rely more on earthworms. For the same reasons less cereal is eaten during wet summers than in dry ones (Fig. 6.7).

Barker (1969) found that wheat appeared in dung samples much more often than any other cereals. However, wheat is the most important grain crop in southern England from where the majority of his dung samples came. In Scandinavia, oats are eaten far more than wheat (Andersen 1955), but there, oats are the main crop and wheat is only grown to any extent in the south. From observations in Somerset where both oats and wheat have been available Ernest has not been able to detect a preference, although badgers seem to start earlier on the oats. However, this could well be due to earlier ripening.

Barley is usually strictly avoided when other cereals are available; however, one badger's stomach Ernest examined was full of barley. In some districts, such as parts of Scotland, barley is commonly eaten when it is the main cereal grown, but again oats are preferred if present (Kruuk 1989). In 1967 at a sett near Taunton, there was a field of oats above the copse where the sett was situated and one of barley below. Badger tracks went into both, but in the barley they were merely pathways through it, very little was knocked down and there were no signs of it having been eaten, but in the oat field the tracks were more numerous and led to small areas where oats had been flattened and grain eaten.

In another sett in a hedgerow bordering a barley field, badger tracks among the barley were clearly defined, but on analysing the dung from the resident badgers, no barley was found, only earthworms. Presumably they had been foraging for these in the barley field.

The technique for eating the grain varies according to the height of the stalks. During the drought of 1975, food was so scarce that badgers went into the oat fields even before the grain had swollen. The stalks were only about 700 mm high. On 1 July, long before sunset, Ernest watched an adult boar feeding in the field. Sometimes it would rear up on its hind legs and snatch at the heads with its jaws; at other times, it would bend the green stalks with a fore paw to bring the head within reach.

When the oats are taller and riper, the badgers trample them down in patches, usually near the edge of the field, and the straws are typically left in bundles which criss-cross each other (Fig. 6.12). The reason for this was given by D. Kruisinga (pers. comm.) who watched badgers eating ripe oats in Holland. The badger would raise a front paw and take a sweep at some of the oats to pull the straws down, then pass the heads through its half-open jaws, sieving off the grain. It would then take a sweep with its other paw and do the same, so the straws appeared criss-cross. It would then move forward slightly, repeating the process, trampling the straws it had previously dealt with.

With wheat the heads are usually bitten off if they are still green, but when ripe the grain may be extracted, leaving some of the husks still attached. M. Plummer (pers. comm), after noticing husks in badger droppings near a wheat field in Kent, examined the crop carefully. Badger tracks went into it and some standing corn stalks were headless. At one place where a badger track from the wheat entered the adjoining wood, she found a broken-off piece of elder tree around which were piled husks from the wheat. Caught up in the cracks and crannies were husks and ears from the green corn. The amount of this residue increased for about a fortnight, by which time the wheat was ripe and the badgers had ceased to use the

FIG 6.11   *Badger foraging in an oat field. Cereals are an important source of food in some areas. Photo G.A. Pawsey.*

FIG 6.12   *When badgers feed on tall cereals, the straws usually lie in a criss-cross manner after trampling.*

stump. She concluded that the badgers somehow drew the heads of corn through the cracks and by this means separated the grain from the green husks. If badgers did use this technique it would be extremely interesting as it would be an instance of tool using. Ernest examined photographs of the stump which were most convincing, but confirmation of how the grain was extracted was not obtained. Further evidence is needed.

Damage done by badgers through eating cereals varies greatly according to locality. Only in the early stage when the crop is still standing is the damage significant; after that, it is a matter of gleaning.

In a study of three fields on a farm in Devon in 1988 and 1989 oats were first damaged at the early–late 'milk stage' of grain development i.e. 4–5 weeks prior to harvest (Wilson 1993). By August, the area damaged covered between 1% and 9.6% of these fields (the size of the social groups using the different fields varied considerably). Badgers were calculated to have eaten grain from about 15% of the flattened areas.

Skoog calculated that about 200 ml of oats was eaten per badger per night at the peak season in Sweden (Skoog 1970). In parts of Britain wheat or oats may be consumed in comparable amounts, but it is usually strictly limited to relatively small areas of the field.

Badgers are fond of maize, and if this crop happens to occur on their territory, some damage is likely to occur in the autumn. In Holland, badgers are said to select the earlier and sweeter varieties (D. Kruisinga, pers. comm.).

FIG 6.13 *Damage caused by badgers when eating oats is usually localised to an area near one edge.*

Fruits, seeds and storage organs

These form an important element in the diet especially in the late summer and autumn. At this time badgers are rapidly building up fat for the winter; in addition to earthworms, much of this fat is derived from plant food, especially acorns (*Quercus* sp.).

Badgers are very fond of succulent fruits, especially if they are sweet. In some localities they will switch their attention to blackberries (*Rubus fruticosus*) as soon as they start to ripen. Chris witnessed an incident during the drought of 1976. Most of the badgers picked off the ripe berries wherever they were within reach from the ground, but one individual had a better idea and jumped off a bank right on top of a blackberry bush and was spread-eagled across it. Then, it used a front paw to bend down the branches so that the berries were within its reach and could be picked off one by one! No doubt with such a thick hide it didn't need to worry about the prickles!

In northern Europe badgers will take wild raspberries, and in hilly districts, concentrate on whortleberries (*Vaccinium mytilus*). The latter are of primary importance in Sweden in the late summer (Skoog 1970). Elderberries (*Sambucus nigra*) are also very acceptable as soon as they drop to the ground, and if birds have been at the haws, badgers will eat the fallen ones with relish. Yew (*Taxus baccata*) berries are eaten greedily, the succulent outer parts being digested while the poisonous seeds are either vomited, or pass through the gut unchanged and so appear in the droppings. If badgers have access to orchards or gardens they will eat what fruit is available. Windfall apples (*Pyrus malus*), pears (*Pyrus communis*), plums (*Prunus domestica*), cherries (*Prunus avium*) and peaches (*Prunus persica*) have all been recorded, apples being particularly important in late autumn.

Badgers have been known to climb wall-trained plum trees to eat the fruit. Being clumsy climbers they may damage the trees by breaking off smaller boughs in their efforts to reach the fruits. They may also visit vineyards in France, Spain and Italy to feed on the grapes and have even been known to do so in Britain. Olives are a seasonal favourite in some areas.

Cultivated soft fruit are a badger's delight. One lady living near Bristol was particularly unfortunate as badgers not only ravaged her strawberries on a large scale but also broke down the raspberry canes to reach the fruit, stripped the red currants and sampled the gooseberries! I hasten to add that her garden was near a wood where badgers were plentiful and that the damage occurred during the summer drought of 1975. Preventative measures can be taken to avoid this kind of damage (p. 212). To put the eating of fruit into perspective, it should be stressed that under normal circumstances badgers seldom have access to soft fruit, and in orchards, their takings consist largely of windfalls.

Of the non-succulent fruits, acorns are the most important. Acorn crops are notoriously fickle, but in a good year they provide large quantities of food for badgers from late October. As acorns lie on the surface of the ground, they may be found as late as January and are even discovered under snow cover. One November Ernest watched a group of seven badgers foraging under the oak trees for hours on end. Each acorn was given individual treatment and thoroughly masticated before another was taken. In a badger's stomach semi-digested acorns look like very coarse porridge. Beechmast and sweet chestnut are less favoured but are eaten in times of scarcity; hazelnuts and walnuts have been recorded (Ognev 1935). Parts of the shell appear in the droppings when hazelnuts are eaten, so the kernels are not extracted before swallowing (M. Budd, pers. comm.).

Underground storage organs of plants are eaten seasonally. As early as late December, if mild, you can frequently see the pits where badgers have dug out and eaten the corms of the wild arum (*Arum maculatum*). The shoots, which contain toxic oxalic acid, are bitten off and discarded. Badgers also dig up the globular tubers of pig-nut (*Conopodium majus*). Ernest has watched recently weaned cubs digging for them at dusk within a few feet of where he was standing. In some areas they are an important food. In Scotland, they constituted as much as 14% of the diet in Speyside in summer; the badgers dug as deep as 40 mm but ignored those deeper than this (Kruuk 1989). It is significant that they eat them when the plant is in bloom; in winter they may not be able to locate the tubers. Bluebell bulbs (*Scilla non-scripta*) are eaten occasionally; likewise, the related vernal squill (*Scilla verna*) are dug out from the cliff turf in Cornwall (D. Frost, pers. comm.). Wild tulip bulbs are eaten in Armenia (Roper & Mikevicius, in press).

Onions, carrots, beetroots, swedes and parsnips are eaten occasionally, and of these, those with the highest sugar content are preferred. Sometimes badgers enter gardens and eat some of the bulbs.

In the very early months of the year when the sap is rising, badgers occasionally strip off the bark of beech and sycamore trees near the sett and lick up the sweet exudations. The eating of the bark (confirmed by stomach analysis) is correlated with this behaviour. It is not a common practice and where it does occur, very few trees are affected (Neal 1948).

Green food

The green parts of plants are of minor importance and although the leaves of many plants have been found in the dung it would seem probable that most had been taken accidentally. However, in winter and in very dry weather in summer, grass is sometimes eaten in large

FIG 6.14 *Occasionally badgers will feed on root crops, particularly if they contain sugar; in this case, beetroot.*

quantities, occasionally almost exclusively, but little is digested. During the drought of 1975, Ernest watched adult badgers deliberately eating grass; this suggests that in summer at least it may be a means of taking in moisture. During severe weather in winter, it might serve the same purpose.

Bradbury (1974) also found clover leaves in the dung, sometimes in the absence of earthworms and grass. On several occasions his samples contained virtually nothing but clover. There have also been reports of badgers eating kale and cabbage.

Fungi

The larger fungi are eaten occasionally but do not appear to be important items in the diet. Bradbury (1974) mentions traces of bracket fungi in winter and possibly remains of a

FIG 6.15   *Badger drinking from a hollow in a sycamore tree. Photo M. Chesworth.*

species of *Morella*. Others have recorded mushrooms (*Agaricus* sp.), puffballs (*Lycoperdon* sp.) and various toadstools including species of *Boletus* and *Lactarius*.

Drinking

In the wild, badgers drink from streams, rain puddles and cattle troughs. In regions where standing water is scarce owing to the porous nature of the rock, they will drink from the hollows between branching tree trunks; mud marks on the tree bark often show where they have clambered up. In captivity, they drink regularly, lapping like a dog. It does not seem to be essential for badger setts to be near a permanent supply of water, so it is probable that they derive most of their water requirements from their food.

Miscellaneous Items

Badgers do not confine themselves to the edible; they will chew at a variety of hard substances. Cubs will often gnaw at sticks at the sett entrance and badgers near golf courses even make a habit of chewing golf balls which they have retrieved from the rough! Even a cricket ball was taken by a badger and left in its dung pit area covered in tooth marks. When a sett was excavated near a housing estate, three footballs and two tennis balls were found which had apparently been taken into the sett by the badgers (Roper *et al.* 1992). However, a most extraordinary case was related by Croome Leach (pers. comm.). He regularly watched a sett near Bristol and on one occasion, he and his companion heard a badger making a scrunching sound near the sett — something like a dog cracking a large bone. It was too dark to see what it was eating. On shining the torch, the badger was seen to eject something from its mouth before going back to its sett. On picking the object up, it was found to be a large piece of bottle glass. There was no doubt at all that the badger had previously been scrunching up glass. Later, a piece of broken-off top of an old-fashioned ginger-beer bottle was found down the entrance of the sett. It would be nice to know why it was indulging in such a dangerous pastime!

SUMMARY

The badger is a forager, not a hunter. It is extremely catholic in its diet and remarkably adaptable, exploiting any available source of food in a great variety of habitats within its wide geographical range. These include such extremes as urban situations and semi-arid or mountainous regions. The badger is above all, opportunistic, making the most of any source of food readily available wherever it is living. In Britain and many Western European countries where earthworms are easily obtained, these are its preferred food, but as we have seen, in other parts, where they are scarce or unavailable, it is sufficiently adaptable to concentrate on other major sources of food such as cereals, rabbits, fruits and insects according to abundance and season. This adaptability must be a major reason for its success as a species.

CHAPTER 7

Social Life

BADGERS are social animals which live together in groups in well-defined territories. All members of a social group know each other as individuals. They may inhabit the same sett, or at particular seasons occupy neighbouring ones within the territory of the group. The territories of neighbouring social groups are by definition exclusive and do not overlap.

This social organisation (which will be referred to in more detail later) is established by means of an elaborate signalling system involving visual, vocal and olfactory elements. Visual signals are only useful when the badgers are in close proximity, but vocal ones can be detected over much longer distances and are particularly helpful in darkness, or where undergrowth is thick. However, both visual and vocal signals do not persist beyond the very short periods when they are being used. By contrast, olfactory signals may last for many days or weeks and other badgers may react to them long after the one that has made them has gone elsewhere. This lasting effect is most important in the social life of badgers and compares with the human activity of putting up notices when the occupier cannot be around all the time.

THE SIGNALLING SYSTEM

Signals are primarily for communication between members of the same species, although some may be effective with other animals, and some olfactory signals may be of use to the badger that makes them, as when using its own scent marks to find its way back to more familiar country.

Visual signals

The badger's relatively poor eyesight probably precludes the wide use of visual signals, but they are used to a limited extent. In most carnivores, the animal's carriage reflects its mood and this is detected by others which take appropriate action. In badgers, one animal may stretch its neck forward and lower its head when another approaches. This may be a sub-missive gesture: for example, sows have been seen to do this when the dominant boar from a neighbouring sett pays a visit and the two come face to face. However, submissive gestures probably play little part in the community life of badgers since all the members of a social group are usually friendly and constantly make physical contact with one another. Hans Kruuk (1989) believes that the lowering of the head may also be a signal that the badger is about to attack. The tail may also be used as an indicator; when raised vertically by a boar it is associated with sexual excitement. This is usually accompanied by a general fluffing up of the fur. This often occurs when cubs are excited, and as a defensive action when attacked. It may also be used by adults when attacked by dogs.

The badger's facial stripes may serve the purpose of accentuating any aggressive signals towards conspecifics. Hans Kruuk (1989) found that adult boars would attack a model mimicking the badger's facial mask significantly more than models without the characteristic black and white pattern (see also p. 16).

Vocal signals

With such excellent hearing, it is not surprising that badgers make good use of vocal signals, although they can be silent over long periods. Vocalisation is much more common during the period February–June, as this includes both the main mating period when excitement among adults is at its height and the period when cubs indulge in boisterous play. At other times vocalisation is less noticeable.

Badgers make a variety of threat sounds. There is a deep-throated, muffled growl which is a clear warning that an attack may follow. Growling also suggests annoyance, as they have been heard to do this below ground when they are impatient to come out and know that an observer is there. This is not to be confused with the whickering of cubs as they play below ground before emergence.

Another threat noise is the bark. This is a gruff, staccato note which is used if another badger comes too near when it is feeding and may be preceded by a growl. The bark is often used when a badger is badly frightened, prior to headlong flight down the sett. It has been heard when a badger has approached very close to an observer and suddenly realised their presence — there is often a sudden snort as the badger takes in air through its nose, followed immediately by the bark as it runs away. Badgers will also spit like a cat when frightened. Ernest once witnessed a prolonged fight between two badgers at Camberley in Surrey, during which growling, snarling and spitting noises were greatly in evidence.

Many people have commented on the badger's scream or yell. Unfortunately, errors of identification are easy to make, as the scream of the vixen is extremely variable and in some respects very similar to that of the badger. However, many instances described are undoubtedly authentic. Frances Pitt (1941) vividly described it in this way: 'Badgers will make a most fiendish noise, uttering yell after yell of heartrending quality — scream after scream, long drawn and awful'. We can fully endorse this from personal experience; it is enough to make your hair stand on end!

The circumstances under which this screaming has been heard vary considerably and its meaning is still not fully understood. It may well be that with further recording and analysis the scream will be found to be a general term embracing several distinct vocalisations, each with a different significance. However, the scream has great penetrating power so that it can be assumed that its function is to carry some message over long distances.

On some occasions screaming is the result of severe fright. It has been reported in wild cubs of about 15 weeks being picked up when they have wandered near an observer and each time this has caused the cub to scream piercingly and repeatedly until put down.

FIG 7.1 *Frightened cub running back to sett, hair raised. Adults will also fluff up their coat as a threat and in defence.*

Kenneth Watkins (pers. comm.) used to let out his tame sow badger cub each night and on one occasion was awoken by persistent screaming. He found the cub (aged 8 months) face to face with a large wild boar badger and in the morning the cub returned quite dazed and battered. This screaming appeared to be due to fear, as it took place before any attack was made.

Aubrey Seymour (pers. comm.) was awakened at midnight by a badger screaming just beyond his garden fence. The screams continued for some minutes, the badger only pausing to take short breaths. He described it as the sound of a beast in mortal agony. Five minutes later he heard another bout of screaming about 400 m away where there was a big sett, and while this was going on, he heard a badger pass by his garden in a great hurry, going in the direction of the screaming. It was in a great state of agitation judging by the low grunts it was making. It is possible that this screaming was a cry of pain or distress which caused the second badger to return hurriedly. This explanation is supported by another account of screaming being heard during the night and when investigations were made a dead badger was found lying beside the road in the direction from which the scream had come.

In different circumstances the scream may be used as a challenge, being reported most frequently between February and April, the period when territorial aggression by boars is at its highest. Screaming also occurs mainly where badger population density is high. But it is not confined to the early months and has been heard throughout the year to November. Ernest's view is that it is caused by extreme fear, but also serves as a long-distance call, which may be a cry of pain or distress, or a territorial challenge.

Finally we should mention that Hans Kruuk in his book *The Social Badger* casts doubt on the existence of the badger scream, pointing out that no one has ever reported *seeing* the phenomenon. He suggests that another animal, maybe the fox, is responsible.

A much more familiar sound is the whicker. This is characteristic of excitement and is most in evidence during cub play. It is a very variable high pitched chatter, interspersed with stronger staccato notes — often when a cub is bitten rather harder than usual. Lower-pitched little growling noises may be incorporated among the more typical higher notes. Play between adults is often accompanied by similar whickering, but the sounds are not so high-pitched.

Very young cubs make a very querulous trilling chatter, which probably changes into the whicker when they become older. They make this when they greet the sow when she returns to suckle; it seems to signify an excited welcome.

Adults, especially sows, also make single high-pitched staccato sounds which have been likened to the note of a moorhen (*Gallinula chloropus*). Cubs have been seen to react to this call by quickly returning to the sow. It may also serve as a contact call when badgers are travelling. John Whall (pers. comm.) has heard this particularly in January when the note was sometimes repeated two or three times. He has observed a badger making this call: 'it rears up on its hind legs, its front paws right off the ground and the head and neck stretched forward, runs, and then repeats the process a few moments later'. This is very reminiscent of the smaller carnivores, such as stoats and weasels. When cubs are foraging over an area, they have also been heard to make these staccato notes on finding some insect or other prey.

Finally, there is a series of vocalisations of varying intensity which may be likened, somewhat inadequately, to purring. The sound really has more of the qualities of a whinny, or a cross between that and a purr. A sow uses a very quiet form of this vocalisation when with young cubs and possibly when nursing them. It seems to express affection and at times reassurance, as when cubs are above ground for the first time. Captive animals will make the same noises when about to be fed and when they want attention. It becomes louder the greater the anticipation and excitement and may be made by both boars and sows.

Then there is a much deeper and more vibrant whinnying purr which is made by the boar and is very evident in the mating season. In February, when the sow is below, a boar may excitedly patrol the whole area making this sound almost continuously. It also accompanies mating (see p. 172).

Scent signals

'To stink like a badger' is a phrase not usually interpreted as a compliment, but to the badgers themselves scent is an essential part of life. A badger's sense of smell is, to us, incredibly good. A badger's world is a world of smells, and scent signals play a very signifi-cant part in their social life. In many instances their function is informative, in others they arouse emotions, but usually they do both.

There are various possible sources of scent which may be significant.

The sub-caudal gland (Fig. 7.2). This is a large pouch, opening by a horizontal slit formed as an invagination of skin just under the tail. Its walls secrete a copious supply of a pale yel-low fatty substance which is stored in the pouch. It has a rather faint (to humans) musky scent. A badger sets scent or 'marks' with this gland.

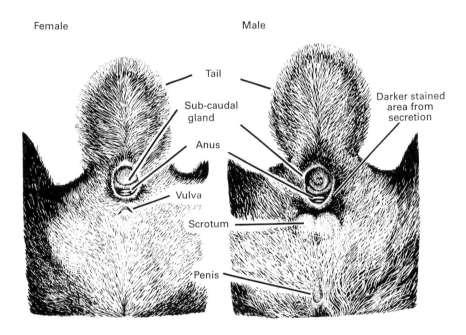

FIG 7.2 *Sub-caudal region of adult badgers, seen from below.*

The anal glands: these are two glands situated under the skin either side of the tail region, which open by short ducts just internal to the anus. They secrete a darker yellowish-brown fluid with a very powerful rank musky odour, which is unpleasant when concentrated.

The faeces: these have a very characteristic smell which is probably largely derived from anal gland secretion. So the faeces act as the vehicles for passing scent to the outside world.

Sweat and sebaceous glands: these give off a typical badger smell. It is often quite noticeable to the watcher just prior to emergence and may be the first indication that a badger is about to come out. This scent is particularly noticeable when badgers have been playing vigor-ously together and are hot — like dogs after exercise!

Urine: in some mammals this is the main scent marker, the leg-cocking action of the dog being a familiar example. Graham Madge was watching badgers grooming each other when the boar sprayed urine on several of them; this led to attempted mating. It is probably important in establishing the oestrus condition of the sow, as some sex hormones are excreted in urine. There is a growing body of evidence of the importance of urine as a scent marker in badgers. Studies by Brown *et al.* (1993), using fluorescent dyes as biomarkers to facilitate the detection of urine deposited by badgers, have revealed that the pattern of urine deposition is very complex, with seasonal, age and sex differences. Indeed these authors have suggested that urine may be a more important scent marker than faeces.

Inter-digital glands: these are again important in some mammals for leaving scent, but at present no work has been done to demonstrate their function or even their presence in badgers. However, claw scraping on trees near the main sett may be associated with the use of such glands and the scuffing action of the hind feet of a badger after defecation may be another example. However, the feet may only be the means of distributing the scent.

Evidence is accumulating regarding the function of the sub-caudal and anal glands as described below.

A characteristic action of badgers is the setting of scent from the sub-caudal gland on other badgers. This 'marking' or 'musking' takes place between all members of the same social group, but most frequently by the dominant boar and particularly in the mating season. The tail is raised and the animal backs onto the other or even straddles it leaving a trace of secretion on the fur. Martyn Gorman *et al.* (1984) showed by chemical analysis that this scent contains a number of fatty compounds (each with a characteristic smell) which are present in varying proportions in different individuals. Thus each badger has a personal scent. They also showed that trained animals could distinguish between the scents of different badgers. So because musking takes place between all members of the group, the group acquires a characteristic scent composite, which differs from those of neighbouring groups. Hence a friend or stranger may be distinguished by smell.

An individual's personal scent may change slowly in composition with time. This is no problem to the members of the group as they repeatedly set scent on each other and so 'keep up' with any change. As Gorman *et al.* (1984) pointed out, this change could also be an advantage if a badger moved to another social group. Kruuk *et al.* (1984) also suggest that the quantity of secretion produced is related to a badger's social status with dominant males producing the most.

Musking of a sow by a boar is common during the mating season, and is also a means of familiarising a badger with its surroundings. H.R. Frank (1940) was one of the first to discover the implications of this action. Carrying his tame badger to country which was unfamiliar to it, he set it down and watched its behaviour, and very soon it was rooting about for food, oblivious of his presence. As it foraged, he noted how it periodically squatted and set scent on various objects in its path, such as pieces of vegetation, stones or even the bare ground. Frank marked these places with small sticks. On taking the badger to the same area on subsequent occasions he found that it marked exactly the same objects with its musk. This repeated musking when travelling from a sett builds up a series of scent trails which act as highways to badgers living there. They lead to places of particular importance such as feeding grounds. On reaching its destination the badger leaves the main scent path and forages more widely. Later it searches around until it picks up the home path once more. Some of these main paths become so impregnated with scent from generations of badgers that even if the field across which the path runs is ploughed up they will still be able to detect the scent and a new path will soon develop in the same place.

In some cases where badgers have been rehabilitated following injury, their release back into their home territory has been helped by rubbing them with soil taken from the spoil heap outside their home sett. This has been done only when the badger's home is known for certain, and it should be stressed that there is no proof that this action is beneficial. Long experience of rehabilitating injured badgers has convinced those concerned that the technique has merits. Prolonged absence from its territory may mean that a reintroduced badger could have difficulty in being accepted and settling in again. The familiar smell of soil impregnated with scent of other group members seems to aid the reintroduction process.

When badgers bring fresh bedding to the sett they do so backwards, and it is at first surprising that they unerringly find their way back to the sett without looking where they are going. One explanation is that they are keeping to a scent path. Similarly, a badger on its travels keeps its snout near the ground to pick up the scent more easily.

John Sankey (pers. comm.) reported that cubs bought up in captivity usually start to musk when about 9 weeks old, young males showing the habit less strongly. This corresponds to about the time when cubs come above ground for the first time in the wild. A captive cub will musk on all sorts of objects, such as the shoes of its owner or an object in its pen such as a feeding trough. Living in an area permeated by its own smell seems to bring assurance and relaxation to the individual concerned.

When H.R. Frank's tame cub came across a place where a wild one had entered her territory through the fence, she at once set scent and did so on each of the snuffle holes the wild one had made in the course of foraging. This seems to be an instance of making a personal mark which would inform other badgers that this was her territory. Similarly, a sow in early spring with small cubs below will often musk near the sett before going out to forage.

Throughout the year, but from January to May in particular, latrines are established at strategic places over the home range, predominantly at the perimeter and near main paths. These act as territorial markers, and anal gland secretion, when added to the dung, gives it a powerful aroma. In addition, badgers often set scent from the sub-caudal glands nearby, so that information is supplied by both glands. Badgers will react to foreign dung by defecating themselves as well as setting scent. In this behaviour, defecation seems to be an emotional response to the intrusion of another badger while the musking is like signing the protest. Boars visit these perimeter dung pits more than other members of the group.

Anal gland secretion is more volatile and may also be released directly. This is a less subtle process and corresponds to the defence action of the skunk which squirts the fluid at the aggressor by violently contracting the muscular walls of the sacs. In the badger, this action is far less intense and only happens when an animal is suddenly frightened. John Sankey mentions how some of his tame animals have done this and the smell has lasted on textiles for weeks after. Ernest has also experienced this when a badger has suddenly discovered him and fled in fright. Incidently, the teledu (*Mydaus javensis*) is called the stink badger because of the potency of its anal gland secretion.

THE SOCIAL SYSTEM

Anyone who has watched badgers in most parts of Britain will be aware of the fact that they are social animals. In contrast to most Mustelids, where individuals lead a solitary existence for much of their lives, badgers share their sett and a territory with other members of their social group. The excavation and maintenance of the sett and the marking and defence of the territory are responsibilities shared by all individuals within the group. Beyond this it is difficult to understand the reasons for sociality in badgers, and indeed a fascinating debate has developed in recent years among students of badger behaviour to try to unravel this mystery.

What are the advantages to badgers of living together in a social group? The trouble is that the ideas put forward to explain the badger's social system are not easy to test, and a theory which appears to explain the circumstances which prevail in one particular part of the country will not necessarily explain those which prevail elsewhere. To begin with there is considerable variation in the extent of sociality seen in badgers. In the high-density populations of Britain and Ireland, for example, well-defined and stable social groups are the norm, whereas in the Doñana National Park in Spain adults typically live in pairs, and in the Maremma Natural Park on the dry Mediterranean coast of Italy, badgers conform to the usual solitary Mustelid habit with individual animals occupying their own territories.

This variation in social behaviour is undoubtedly an adaptive response to the variety of habitats which badgers are able to exploit, but just why there should be an advantage to living in groups in the more productive areas is a question which concentrates the minds of biologists. Perhaps the most plausible theory is that first put forward by Hans Kruuk (1989) who claims that as a group, badgers can defend the resources necessary to sustain them throughout the year more efficiently than they could as single animals. The theory rests on the notion that badgers' food resources are dispersed in discrete patches, and a number of these patches are required for the badgers to be able to find food under the different seasonal and climatic conditions prevailing. For one badger to hold a territory large enough to encompass a sufficient number of food patches, it would have to defend a proportionately long boundary, whereas a group of animals can share this responsibility more economically. This idea relies heavily on the presumption that earthworms are the main food source for badgers, and on the climatic and seasonal factors which determine their availability. In order to test this idea, the 'food patches' in which earthworms occur must be discrete, easily defined and measured, something which is not easy to show in practice. So the theory might hold in those parts of the badger's distribution where earthworms are the main food source, but is less tenable in places where other foods feature more prominently in the diet.

David Macdonald & Hans Kruuk (1985) have described the badger as a 'contractionist' species. They attempt to categorise animals with social and territorial tendencies into those which occupy the smallest economically defensible area ('enclaves'), and those which attempt to hold the largest area they can defend ('empires'). Coyotes (*Canis latrans*) and wolves (*Canis lupus*) are examples of the latter, but the fact that badgers do not attempt to expand their territories, even when there is vacant habitat adjoining their patch, is evidence that they clearly fit the former description.

Ultimately the density of badger populations will be determined by the food supply, provided that other habitat requirements are available, such as terrain suitable for digging setts. The most clearly defined and stable badger social systems appear to occur in the areas of highest density. However, whilst some aspects of social behaviour may be explained simply by variations in population density, the pattern is too complicated to be explained by this variable alone. For example, in a study of badgers living in a moderately high-density population at Wytham Woods, Oxfordshire (Woodroffe *et al.* 1995) a greater degree of dispersal was detected in both males and females than was found in a very high-density area at

Woodchester Park. One important aspect of social life is the movement of individuals between social groups. This is highly variable between localities and is discussed in detail in Chapter 8.

In addition to the defence of food and other resources, it is possible that territoriality in badgers has something to do with their reproductive strategy. Tim Roper *et al.* (1986) suggested that latrine use (obviously an important activity in the maintenance of territory) by badgers was related to the defence of oestrous females by resident males. This hypothesis was based on the finding that peaks in the frequency of latrine use coincided with peaks in mating activity. However, W.J. Cresswell *et al.* (1992) argued that the absence of mate guarding, the frequency of cuckoldry and of mixed-paternity litters suggested that mating is not the sole, or even the major, prerogative of resident boars. Their study pointed to a food-based explanation for territoriality rather than one based on reproduction. Current opinion among biologists is that the food-based and the reproduction-based hypotheses are not mutually exclusive. The truth is that we are still a long way from a full understanding of the badger's social life.

COMPOSITION OF THE SOCIAL GROUP

The only reliable method of estimating the numbers present in a social group is to count the individual badgers (techniques using radio isotopes are fraught with problems, and anyway are beyond the scope of amateurs). This is not difficult if the badgers occupy a single sett which is watched regularly throughout the year. But social groups often use several setts on the territory and the badgers often shift from one to another. The difficulty of counting individuals was overcome in Ernest's early work (Neal 1948) at Rencomb, Gloucestershire by posting watchers near each sett on certain nights and correlating observations. In this way, they were able to show over a period of 3 years that the social group occupying the four setts in Conigre Wood fluctuated between nine and 11 at the peak season when cubs were present above ground. However, another social group about 2 km away at Eycott used only one sett, but the numbers fluctuated more widely from year to year (7–12).

During bovine tuberculosis investigations the Ministry of Agriculture completely removed a number of social groups in the Cotswolds, Avon and Cornwall. These gave precise figures of group size (Cheeseman *et al.* 1981). Twenty-four groups were removed during the period June–October, average group size including cubs being 5.6 (range 4.8–7.6), adults only, 4.2 (range 3.3–5.8). In four parts of Scotland it was estimated that for seven groups the average number of adults was 5.4 (2–11) (Kruuk & Parish 1982). So as a rule of thumb, five badgers per social group during the winter may be the average in undisturbed situations. However, it must be stressed that this is an average figure and fluctuations are wide, both from year to year and from one group to another. Some groups are consistently smaller than their neighbours and Kruuk & Parish (1982) thought that this is related to the quality of worming areas on the range, modified by conditions which affect worm availability. A summary of the available data on group sizes is given in Table 7.1 which contains samples taken from different areas around Britain. It is worth noting that these data were collected mainly from medium to high-density areas and there are reports of smaller than average groups occurring in areas where badger populations are sparse.

The proportion of the sexes within a group varies considerably. In 24 groups, Chris

FIG 7.3   *Badgers in socialising area near sett entrance.*

(Cheeseman 1981) found the number of adult males ranged from zero to five and adult females zero to seven with a combination of two males plus two females being the most common. Hans Kruuk (1978) found that one group in Wytham Woods contained males only: two very old, three young adults and one middle-aged whose nose was missing, perhaps bitten off. This bachelor group may have been excluded from neighbouring ones. Chris has not found bachelor groups in Gloucestershire, but did record an all-female group which did not breed over two seasons and which was christened 'the nunnery'! In most demographic studies of badgers, a slight preponderance of females has been found in the adult population.

The largest number of badgers recorded in a single social group, which was not artificially sustained in any way, is 35, of which 30 were adult or yearling badgers. This exceptional record occurred at Woodchester Park in 1989. The social group concerned occupies a territory of 35 ha, which is only slightly above the average for this area. Other social groups in this study area are consistently larger than average. One particular example over the 10-year period from 1985 to 1994 inclusive had an annual average of 15.7 badgers (range 11–25).

TABLE 7.1　*Mean number of adult badgers per social group recorded by various studies*

Area	Source	Sample size	Mean number of adult badgers per social group
Avon	Cheeseman *et al.* (1981)	7	3.6
Cornwall	Cheeseman *et al.* (1981)	6	3.3
Gloucestershire	Cheeseman *et al.* (1981)	6	4.3
Gloucestershire	Cheeseman *et al.* (1981)	5	5.8
Ardnish	Kruuk & Parish (1982)	2	3.5
New Deer	Kruuk & Parish (1982)	2	9.5
Speyside	Kruuk & Parish (1982)	3	4.0
Wytham, Oxford	Krunk & Parish (1982)	13	7.0
Staffordshire	Cheeseman *et al* (1985)	5	6.4
Gloucestershire	Cheeseman *et al* (1987)	14[a]	5.7
Bristol	Harris & Cresswell (1987)	10[a]	3.3
Mean			5.1

[a]Based on data averaged over 6 years; only those social groups that were active throughout the study period were included in the average presented here.
Source: Modified from Cresswell *et al.* (1990).

The territory of this group was a mere 24 ha, smaller than the average of 30 ha. The reason for this area supporting such a large number of individuals was not immediately apparent as the habitat within the territory was not unusually productive. If cubs are excluded from the total, the annual average number of adults plus yearlings was 11.1 (range 7–17). When used to derive measures of density, these averages give a staggering overall average (adults and yearlings only) of 46 badgers km² for the animals living in this one territory! Whilst this example may be exceptional (the average for Woodchester Park is about 25–30 adults plus yearlings km²), the figures do serve to illustrate the optimal quality of the habitat in the Cotswolds. In semi-urban situations some setts become partially closed communities and this may give rise to abnormal numbers. Don Hunford (pers. comm.) in Essex found 22 in one sett in 1979, including at least three lactating sows and their seven cubs.

It is therefore possible in the spring to have in one main sett up to three or more breeding sows with their cubs, several mature boars and perhaps a few remaining yearlings. More often, when the group is large, it is broken up into smaller units which live in separate setts within the same territory, or if the sett is large and straggling, in different parts of the same one. Indeed, a correlation has been found between the number of females producing litters per group and the density of annexe setts (Cresswell *et al.* 1992), the inference being that the presence of annexe setts provided the opportunity for pregnant subordinate females to bear their litters successfully.

It seems likely that in an expanding population, social groups may gradually separate off as more setts are dug. This happened in a large sett in the Brendon Hills in Somerset, which Ernest kept under observation for 18 years. The sett is situated in a long, narrow copse 500 m long, which stretches between arable fields. When first observed in 1966, the badgers

FIG 7.4 *Badger emerging.*

occupied the western end only. The copse is on a slope and the soil, formed from red sand-stone, is ideal for digging. During the following 10 years, badgers spread along the whole of the copse digging seven distinct setts. Two of these were seldom used for long, and foxes bred in one of them most years. Since 1971, badger activity has been concentrated around setts near each end of the copse where cubs were born most years. Towards the middle of the copse two setts have been used sporadically, mainly by yearlings. Foraging patterns from the two end setts are now quite separate and the boundary between these two newly formed social groups is well marked by latrines.

Plate 1. Sow (at back) with two well-grown cubs, still suckling after summer drought, July.

Plate 2. Part of a very large social group. Essex. Photo Don Hunford.

Plate 3. Albino. Note pink eyes and lack of melanin in hair and claws. Photo Gordon Burness.

Plate 4. An erythristic and normally-coloured cub from the same litter. Photo Michael Morgan.

Plate 5. Adult boar setting scent on sow.

Plate 6. A sow, gripping cub by neck prior to dragging it down the entrance. Photo Jill Hutchinson.

Plate 7. Badgers at entrance leading to a coal mine. Northumberland. Photo Jill Hutchinson.

Plate 8. Foraging in a bluebell wood. Photo Ted and Glen Coleman.

Plate 9. Climbing wire netting. Photo Ted and Glen Coleman.

Plate 10. Yawning. Note dentition. Photo Jill Hutchinson.

Plate 11. Sow bringing back a bundle of green grass as bedding.

Plate 12. Grooming session. Photo Don Hunford.

Plate 13. Badger asleep in couch. Photo C. Cheeseman.

Plate 14. (Above) Sow suckling well-grown cubs. Photo Eric Ashby.

Plate 15. (Left) A litter of five cubs, estimated 3–4 days old, discovered in a large heap of hay in a barn. Somerset. 30 January.

Plate 16. Cub aged about 8 weeks by sett entrance.

Plate 17. (Top left) Woodland sett showing the ground outside hard and smooth, caused by cub play. Mud marks may be seen on the scratching tree.

Plate 18. (Top right) Badger nest in hollow tree with bedding overflowing. Sweden, August.

Plate 19. (Left) An 'up-and-over' made by badgers when crossing a hedgebank bordering a Somerset lane; March.

Plate 20. (Above) Remains of a wasps' nest dug out the previous night. September. Photo Frank Hawtin.

Plate 21. American badger, *Taxidea taxus*; North America. Photo Pat Morris.

Plate 22. Hog badger, *Arctonyx collaris*; S.E. Asia. Photo Ardea Photographics.

Plate 23. Honey badger, *Mellivora capensis*; north Kenya.

ORGANISATION OF LIVING SPACE

How far do badgers travel? The actual distance travelled will obviously depend on the time spent above ground and the type of activity the badger is engaged in. Very precise information on this aspect of badger behaviour has been obtained by the combined techniques of spool-and-line and radio-tracking. Brown (1993) found a clear relationship between the total time a badger was above ground each night and the distance travelled. Individuals were rarely active above ground for less than 1 h and during this time they would typically cover about 600 m. After 4 h of activity the distance increased to about 2400 m; so badgers seem to travel at an average of about 600 m h^{-1}. A boar systematically marking the territorial boundary might cover much greater distances, whereas an individual gleaning cereal grains in a field of stubble would obviously travel less. Wijngaarden & Peppel (1964) in Holland tracked badgers for as much as 6 km during a night, but the point of greatest distance from the sett was only 1.6 km.

It is clear from the mapping of badger setts in any area where the population density is high, that if outliers are ignored then the main breeding setts are spaced out at remarkably constant intervals. This is particularly noticeable in places where some geographical feature, such as an escarpment, causes the setts to be located in a linear manner. The higher the population density the nearer the main setts are to each other, a factor that is presumably influenced by the availability of suitable food in the area.

Looking at badger spatial organisation from a rather different perspective, it has been found that the locations of the main setts themselves probably influence the positions of territorial boundaries. When badger social group territories are mapped, it is noticeable that the main setts are often centred within the territorial boundaries, and that the boundaries themselves are usually mid-way between the main setts. A mathematical technique (Dirichlet tessellations) has been used to predict where the territorial boundaries should lie, given the locations of main setts (Doncaster & Woodroffe 1993). This technique can be likened to throwing a handful of pebbles simultaneously into a pool of water. The ripples spread out and eventually meet. It was found that the real boundaries were very close to the mathematically predicted ones, demonstrating that the distribution of main setts does indeed have a significant bearing on the position of territorial boundaries.

Kruuk (1982) found at Wytham Woods that the average distance between main setts was about 500 m. A similar spacing has been found in the Brendons, Somerset, but here the entire region is so suitable for badgers that a saturation point for territories appears to have been reached. In small favourable localities much shorter distances between main setts have been recorded and in the Cotswolds for example the distance between main setts is a mere 325 m. In regions less suitable for badgers the setts tend to be spaced out according to the distribution of more favourable habitats and the availability of sett sites themselves.

In order to estimate range size, Skoog (1970) put down herrings as bait near main setts, incorporating tiny coloured glass beads. By examining the dung for traces of the beads he estimated the distance the badgers travelled.

Hans Kruuk (1978) made further studies at Wytham. He regularly placed food near each main sett, incorporating coloured plastic pellets in his mixture of peanuts and syrup. A different colour was used in the bait for each sett. By examining the various latrines for the coloured pellets he was able to map out the area covered by each social group. This enabled him to calculate that at Wytham, on average, each social group used an area of about 50 ha (Fig. 7.5).

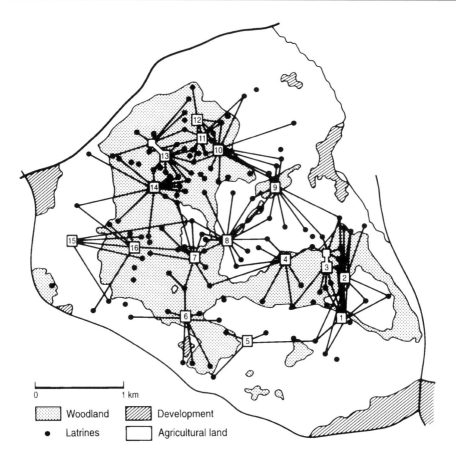

FIG 7.5   *Territory of badgers of Wytham, as shown by recoveries in latrines of coloured food markers presented on the setts (1–16), Hans Kruuk 1978.*

Since then Chris, working along similar lines in Woodchester Park, where badger density was unusually high, found that for the 32 territories each social group used on average 30 ha, range 15–90 ha (Cheeseman 1979). This contrasts with regions of Avon and Cornwall where the average size was about 74 ha, and in four parts of Scotland (Kruuk & Parish 1982) 183 ha (range 120–309).

By combining radio-tracking with bait-marking experiments, Chris showed that territories were not exclusive as badgers sometimes trespassed. This was particularly evident in the breeding season when males made sorties into neighbouring territories, probably for mating. It was also discovered that not all badgers in a group used the whole of the territory for foraging. Females in particular had smaller home ranges. Over a period of 3 months in the spring some individuals were using areas as small as 12 ha, each having preferred areas.

During several years of bait-marking experiments in Gloucestershire Chris also found that territories varied little from year to year. Even when some groups were completely removed during disease-control operations the boundaries of the surrounding territories did not encroach on the cleared ones. A few badgers took up residence in the cleared area within a short period of time but their movements were more haphazard than normal. It seems that it will take up to 9 or 10 years before the population builds up and a stable pattern of territories is seen once more (Cheeseman *et al.* 1993).

Kruuk (1989) found that badgers not only mark the perimeter of their ranges with latrines, but the paths which often run between territories are also impregnated with scent. Marking was often done on hummocks on which virtually every passing badger deposited a secretion from its sub-caudal gland. Badgers were also seen to rub their sub-caudal region 30–40 cm up a tree or post on the boundary while making a 'handstand'.

Areas delineated by territorial latrines and perimeter paths may be looked upon as defended areas, at any rate during the first 4 or 5 months of the year. At this time aggression between badgers is not unusual and fighting can be very severe particularly in high-density regions.

Kruuk (1989) described five fights, four of which occurred on range boundaries. There was a lot of biting, and each ended with the intruder returning to its territory. But more often badgers would avoid each other. Walking up to a boundary they either turned back or followed the perimeter path. Twice Kruuk saw badgers converging on a boundary and avoid contact by walking into their own territories. Don Bradman (pers. comm.) cites one instance of territorial fighting between two boars where one later died of its wounds.

The occurrence of bite wounding in boars seems to follow a roughly bimodal pattern, with one distinct peak in February–March and a less well-defined increase around September (Cresswell *et al.* 1992). The pattern in sows is different, with a lower overall incidence and less clearly defined peaks occurring in April and November–December. Of the 10 fights on which Ernest has exact data, eight of these occurred during the period February–April, the other two being in the autumn. Fights occur more commonly in regions of high density. Don Hunford (pers. comm.) commented on this in Essex, where urban spread has restricted the living space for badgers. Here a high proportion shows signs of battle including torn ears and scars, particularly on the back above the tail.

When filming badgers at Camberley in Surrey, Ernest lightly blocked up certain holes to increase the likelihood of badgers using the part he had illuminated for filming. He had not realised that in doing so he had forced another badger towards a part of the sett which was clearly the sow's territory. The intruder was seen to sniff at the entrance, but would not enter and as it turned, the resident sow shot out and attacked it. There was a tremendous fight as they twisted and turned and attempted to come to grips, growling, snarling and spitting as they fought. Eventually, the sow chased the other right through the wood. The noise went on for a full 3 minutes. This, and other rather similar evidence, strongly suggests that for this short period of the year a sow with small cubs defends what has been described as a monopolised zone within a sett.

There are many records of yearlings brought up in captivity being attacked by resident wild badgers. On some occasions they have actually been killed, but more often have returned severely battered, with nasty wounds. Again, a captive badger kept in a rural district will often attract the attention of the dominant boar of the local social group who will attempt to break into the pen in which it is kept. From these accounts it is clear that a resident boar will fight any intruder which does not have the correct communal scent of his social group.

There are some signs of a hierarchy within social groups, but its extent is uncertain. It is probable that in large groups there is a dominant boar; usually an older and larger animal. During the mating season in particular he may visit neighbouring groups and assert his dominance there too. It is also probable that there is a sow which is dominant to other females in the group; she has first choice of breeding sites and is usually the older animal.

So to summarise, it appears that in high-density areas, each social group occupies a territory which is actively defended particularly during the first 4 months of the year. Notices to that effect are posted on the perimeter in the form of latrines and scent marks and the members of the group, particularly the boars, regularly visit these 'frontier posts' adding more dung, reinforcing the scent signals implying ownership. Later in the year territorial behaviour is far less evident, perimeter latrines are used less and there is much more evidence of peaceful foraging. In summer and times of food shortage members of a group may go beyond the territorial limits without necessarily being molested. On one occasion, Chris saw members of three separate social groups foraging in a small field of oat stubble. Within the defended territory lie one or more setts and if a sow has young cubs she may mark with her scent a small monopolised zone, often no more than a small part of the main sett. This she will defend against intruders.

FIG 7.6   *Latine area at territorial boundary in high density area. Gloucestershire.*

Although this summary describes the general picture, exceptions are bound to occur and we would here once more remind the reader of the enormous variation seen in badger social systems. Where conditions are less favourable the tight system of territories is less evident. Badgers have to roam more widely to find sufficient food, so ranges become large. Boundary marking and patrolling along the whole perimeter then become physically impossible and latrines become restricted to such places as good worming patches or where a seasonal abundance of food is found. The latrines then appear to serve as marks of possession. Similarly in urban situations, Stephen Harris (1982), working in Bristol, found that territorial boundaries were poorly defined as home ranges overlapped more.

One speculates whether territoriality is mainly a high-density phenomenon essential for conserving sufficient food throughout the year when competition is fierce. When setts are few and far between this becomes less necessary and only vital food areas are marked. It should also be borne in mind that latrines may also serve to provide other information concerning such questions as 'who is around' and his or her sexual state.

So the badgers' social system has many advantages. By having relatively large social groups containing more than one adult of each sex, an area can be defended more effectively. This is of great value during the breeding season and in times of food shortage. It is then that small ranges are particularly advantageous as the residents know the area so well that they can predict where food is likely to be found according to weather conditions. They can thus exploit a food source without unnecessary loss of foraging time and energy in random searching. If the sett is near the centre of the territory, access to all parts of the perimeter for defence and to different feeding areas is facilitated.

ASPECTS OF SOCIAL LIFE

Play

Badgers, in common with most carnivores, are very playful animals. Play is by no means confined to the cubs as adults frequently join in, and also play on their own. Cub play during the fortnight following their first emergence above ground is very tentative and mainly occurs just around the sett entrance. They keep in close contact most of the time, pushing with their snouts and toppling each other over more by accident than design. Sometimes the sow is with them and may often be seen lying across the sett entrance while her cubs scramble over her body and play with her. As co-ordination develops and they become stronger, they venture further from each other and from the sett entrance, but it is not until they are about 12 weeks old that play becomes really boisterous.

Play varies greatly in type and intensity according to circumstances. In secluded places where cubs are at ease it may be vigorous, wide-ranging and uninhibited, but where disturbance is frequent it is less spontaneous, especially in the vicinity of the sett.

Several varieties of cub play may be recognised. 'King-of-the-castle' is the usual type, where one cub will take up position on top of the heap outside the sett or on the bank above and the others will try to dislodge it and then take up a similar position. When bigger, the game may take place on a favourite tree trunk, but the idea of dislodgement is still there. Beatrice Gillam described how she watched three well-grown cubs in July playing on a horizontal tree trunk with a 2.5 m drop below. There was not a lot of room and falls were frequent, but the badgers appeared to come to no harm.

A variation is for one cub to emerge and then turn round and prevent the second from coming out. The first has the advantage of position and will playfully bite the one below each time it pops its head out. Eventually, the second comes out with a rush and there is a chase. Chasing is a characteristic form of play. It often occurs round and round a playing tree near the sett, so that after a week or two no vegetation remains. When one cub catches up with the leader, it will bite it on the rump or tail and then flee as the other rounds on it and takes its turn of chasing.

Objects may also be used as playthings. Golfballs retrieved from the rough come into this category and sometimes old tins may be used. Occasionally, when two cubs play with the same object, a tug-of-war ensues as each fights for possession.

Specifically aggressive play can also occur. This often starts quietly but develops dramatically as excitement rises. One August, Ernest witnessed this from such close quarters that two of the well-grown cubs he was watching collided headlong with his legs, nearly knocking him over. He felt he was a partner in the game as they played at his feet. One cub got hold of the ear of the other, then the tail and tried from below to tip it on to its back. They spun together in tight circles, trying to bite each other's tail and then both rushed up the bank. More scrapping took place and one lost its balance and went head over heels down the slope like a furry ball. Quickly recovering, it climbed the bank once more and immediately they were at it again. Occasionally, one would leap-frog over the other and if knocked over would roll on its back and bite upwards at its opponent. All the time there was a constant whickering of excitement, with intermittent louder yelps.

Sometimes, cubs will grip each other in a mutual bite, when the lower jaw of one is gripped by the jaws of the other. As Eric Ashby remarked, a twist by one badger will put the other on its back as a result of this grip.

Incidentally, rolling down the slope like a ball was a popular pastime of Mark Fisher's tame badger (pers. comm.). He writes, 'I have been amused to notice that when rolling down a steep slope she can stop however fast she is going to save herself from crashing into a wall or beck'. He also told of how a wild badger was seen to escape from dogs in the fells by rolling down a scree. Stories of badgers rolling on gin traps were also quite frequent and some appear to be authentic.

Analysis of such boisterous play suggests that the main components are typically the following:

(1) chasing;
(2) attempts to bite and hold the side of the neck, ears and tail;
(3) attempts to turn the other upside down by using a low approach and then giving an upwards or sideways movement of the head;
(4) rolling over on to the back in defence;
(5) flight.

Sometimes during bouts of play, cubs will momentarily show displacement activity and 'attack' vegetation. J.F. Chapman (pers. comm.) watched them pulling up bracken and shaking young trees in their excitement. He also described how there was a large sloping stone outside the sett's main entrance which the cubs used to slide down over and over again.

Play between adults has many ingredients of cub play. Early one May, Ernest watched an adult boar and sow playing together quite aggressively near the sett. They started to play head on and mouth to mouth with their jaws half-open, twisting and turning in mock

FIG 7.7 *Play amongst adults can be boisterous.*

fighting without closing their jaws. This led to aggressive attempts to get a grip on ears and neck and as the excitement grew they turned in tight circles as they went for each other's rump and tail. It seemed significant that whenever play stopped temporarily the sow always had her back to the sett entrance. It was found out a week later that she had cubs below.

Play clearly has a number of different functions. It obviously promotes physical development and co-ordination and many of its features train the animal for more serious fighting later without causing harm in the process of learning. It may also help to get rid of surplus energy. However, badgers are very social animals and it is possible that an important function of their playing together is to strengthen the bond between members of the same social group by constant physical contact. Play between adults probably also has sexual significance, although mating may often take place without preliminary play.

Grooming

It is a familiar sight to see badgers grooming after emergence. This they do with great thoroughness, contorting themselves in various ways to get at every part of their anatomy. Typical positions are shown in Fig. 7.8.

FIG 7.8   *Grooming attitudes.* (Michael Clark)

One of the more amusing postures often shown by an adult boar is when he sits fairly upright on his haunches, possibly leaning slightly backwards and scratches his belly with slow deliberate actions of both front paws. He will sometimes do this while sitting in the shallow bowl-like depression often found near a sett entrance.

Katharine Tottenham (pers. comm.) told a rather intriguing story of a badger she brought up in captivity. It was given straw for bedding, but on one occasion this contained a dried thistle. It sorted it out, appeared to comb it upwards from the root with its front claws and then rolling on to its back proceeded to scrub its chest with the prickles, holding the plant between its front paws. This appeared to be a deliberate action, because following this incident Mrs Tottenham regularly used to cut large green thistles for it and as soon as they were put into the pen it went through the same drill exactly!

Although scratching may be a natural response to parasites, and possibly to midges, it also appears to bring satisfaction to the scratcher. Sometimes it persists for half an hour or more! Mutual grooming also takes place and has a social function. The badgers nibble at each other's coats, and when several are in a tight huddle it doesn't seem to matter who does it to whom. A sow will also carefully groom her cubs and may hold one down with her front paws while she goes over its fur methodically.

Phil Drabble (1971) described how mutual grooming regularly took place between an adult boar and sow in his artificial sett before emergence. His tape recordings showed that quite often the grooming lasted for at least half an hour and was accompanied by low whinnying purrs of affection. He suggested that mutual grooming might help to distribute scent from one animal to another.

John Sankey (pers. comm.) reported that if the skin on a tame badger's back is rubbed with the fingers, or vigorously combed, the animal at once starts to groom itself, a piece of cloth or a human hand, whichever happens to be easiest to reach. The teeth are run over the surface and hair is drawn through them, but there is no attempt to bite.

Badgers will also lick their fur like a cat, although they will not use a paw in order to clean their face. Licking often takes place when they come back from foraging. Mutual licking also occurs occasionally. David Mitchell (pers. comm.) described how two adult badgers (boar and sow) faced each other and then proceeded to lick each other's face, neck and back.

What happens when badgers die

It is strongly believed by some countryfolk that badgers bury their dead. Good evidence is hard to come by, but several instances of badger funerals have been published. Unfortunately, the most detailed and dramatic accounts have been related at second hand (Versey-Fitzgerald 1942, Hampton 1947) and it is difficult to know to what extent they are accurate. The common factors in both these accounts were that a hole was dug, the body was dragged to it by more than one badger and earth was heaped on top.

It is certainly established that badgers will drag the body of a dead one for some distance. Bronwen Doncaster related how she saw a badger laboriously drag another across a road one February night. In spite of interruptions by passing cars, the badger persisted and eventually dragged the body up the far bank, where it was found the next morning. There is also an account by Joseph O'Kelly (1969) of a badger, killed by a car, being covered in leaves on two successive nights, presumably by badgers. The leaves had to be dragged some distance from a copse in order to do this.

Ernest once found a dead cub aged about 10 weeks outside a badger sett. He did not touch it, but watched that night to see what the other badgers would do with it when they emerged. In the event, it was an anticlimax; several adults came out and passed within 1 m of the body but they took no notice of it and went off!

All that can be said at present about badger funerals is that if they do occur, they are very rare events. But badgers are remarkable creatures and it is well to keep an open mind about the possibility. In a review of the evidence relating to badgers burying their dead, Roper (1994) concluded that the most likely explanation for their occasional habit of carrying badger carcasses into setts, or burying them elsewhere, is that they do so because they are treating them as carrion and caching them against future need.

One thing is quite certain; the majority of badgers that die naturally die in their setts. On several occasions in the past when setts have been excavated diggers have found the remains of dead badgers in side tunnels which had been walled in with earth, presumably by other badgers. No doubt when this happens and the body has decomposed, others will re-excavate that part of the sett and the bones will be pushed out with the soil — perhaps years later. This is the logical explanation of why badger skulls are often found on the spoil heaps outside well-established setts.

CHAPTER 8

Reproduction and Development

FOR many years the details of the breeding cycle of the badger were the subject of much speculation and controversy, largely because observations on a nocturnal animal were difficult and partly because the cycle was by no means typical. It was not until field observations were correlated with anatomical and physiological investigations that some of the complexities were unravelled (Neal & Harrison 1958). Since then, a number of important studies have been carried out which have extended our understanding considerably.

One of the remarkable features of the reproductive cycle of the badger is that mating and fertilisation can take place during any month of the year but the cubs are born at one season only. This is brought about by delayed implantation, a phenomenon first shown to occur in badgers by Fischer (1931). In this process, the fertilised eggs start cell division as they travel down a tube leading from the ovary and enter the uterus as tiny blastocysts (hollow spheres of cells). Here, instead of implanting in the walls of the uterus in the usual mammalian manner, they remain free within the cavity of the uterus for 2–10 months — the time varying according to the time of mating. During this free state, the blastocysts keep alive using a minimum of oxygen and food that diffuse through their surfaces from the surrounding uterine fluid, growing steadily but very slowly.

For the sake of clarity, we will describe the reproductive cycle starting with the birth of the cubs, since other events in the breeding cycle are to some extent governed by this happening.

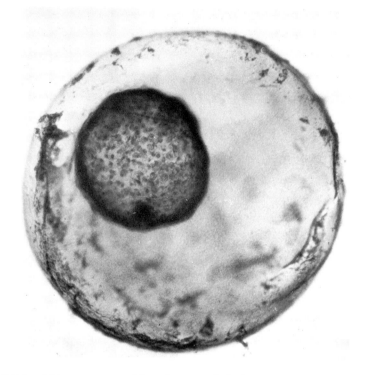

FIG 8.1   *A blastocyst recovered from the uterus of a badger in June; diameter 1.5 mm.*
Photo Professor R. Harrison.

BIRTH

It is not possible to be certain of the exact dates when badgers are born in the wild because birth normally takes place in an underground chamber. However, there are a number of records of birth dates in captivity and a significant number of accounts of litters of cubs only a few days old, some discovered as a result of digging before this was made illegal. Another method of calculating likely birth dates is to judge from the size of foetuses found during post-mortems. A far less reliable means of estimation is for regular watchers at a main sett to take the first time when cubs are seen above ground and work backwards, assuming that they first emerge when about 8 weeks old. This provides useful corroboration but is only accurate to within about 2 weeks.

Taking data from all these sources for 97 litters in southern and south-west England, the great majority of births (76%) occurred between mid-January and mid-March (Fig. 8.2). The peak period is during the first fortnight in February, but late January and early March dates are frequent and December births certainly occur; for example, on 1 January 1960 a terrier brought out from a sett a small cub estimated to be a few days old (N. Barker, pers. comm.). Since cubs are not seen above ground before around 8 weeks old, the following

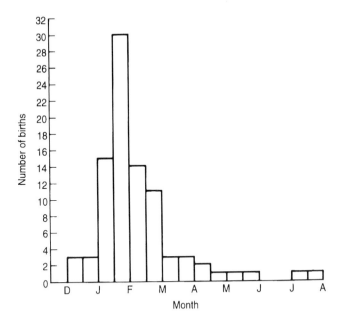

FIG 8.2   *Birth dates of badgers from south-west England (in half months).*

sightings also suggest December births: cubs were seen above ground on 18 February in Devon by N.R. Sultanian (pers. comm.) and on 25 February by David Humphries (pers. comm.) in Gloucestershire. Humphries adds that the two cubs had obviously been up for some time as they were quite confident and chased each other down a bank. However, any births in December and after April can be looked upon as exceptional. The latest records are from Devon, where two families, each of three cubs, were dug out on 29 July and 5 August, their age estimated by R. Murray at 3–4 weeks. A cub with eyes still shut was also recorded in Germany in June by Frank (1940). A particularly interesting late birth was described by Don Hunford (pers. comm.) who has regularly watched a large sett for many years. On 12 June 1993 a very tiny cub, 'even smaller than those usually seen for the first time above ground', emerged at 22.20. He estimated its birth date as early May or late April. It came in for a lot of rough treatment and lost much of its fur. However, it survived, but was still relatively small in late autumn.

   There is a correlation between average birth times and latitude. For south-west France, the average, calculated from embryo size in Canivenc's material (Canivenc and Bonnin-Laffargue 1966) is 31 January, for south-west England, 7 February (Page *et al.* 1994), for Yorkshire, towards the end of February (Paget & Middleton 1974b), in Scotland, probably early March, in Germany (Frank 1940) and Sweden (Ahnlund 1980), early March and in Russia, late March with April for the Caucasus (Ognev 1935). The time of birth also varies more locally according to altitude.

The number of cubs in a litter varies from one to five. To find the average number born, good evidence is obtained by counting the number of healthy foetuses during the last few weeks of pregnancy and the placental scars left by previous pregnancies which are easily seen as dark patches on the inner surface of the uterine wall, and through direct evidence from litters born in captivity or from those occasionally discovered in the wild. From a combination of these data from south and south-west England (Neal 1977, up-dated), of 39 litters, 8% were singles, 18% twins, 51% triplets, 18% quads and 5% quins, averaging 2.94 per litter. Anderson & Trewhella (1985) estimated from much larger samples mainly from England (Neal 1986, Page *et al.* 1994), Central Sweden (Ahnlund 1980) and Switzerland (Wandeler & Graf 1982) that the average number per litter for Europe was 2.7. However, they also used data derived from the number of blastocysts in the uterine horns during the delayed implantation period (p. 175) in addition to counts of foetuses present and placental scars left from the previous pregnancy. It is now well established that losses occur at all stages of the cycle — some blastocysts do not implant (p. 177) and some early foetuses may be resorbed or aborted, so this figure must be treated with caution.

Many badger watchers have recorded the number of cubs per litter seen above ground 8–10 weeks after birth. In a sample of 110 litters (Neal 1977), 11% were singles, 52% twins, 29% triplets, 6% quads and 2% quins with an average of 2.36. Compared with the average at birth from the same area quoted above of 2.94 this represents a drop since birth of 19.7% during the period below ground. Wandeler & Graf (1982) have shown

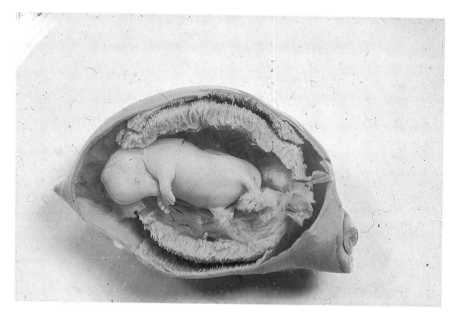

FIG 8.3 *Uterine wall partially removed to show three-week-old foetus (about 15 mm long). Note umbilical cord and surrounding placenta.*

that in Switzerland a number of sows in spring had fresh placental scars but no sign of suckling offspring, suggesting that a number of whole litters did not survive. In Woodchester Park, a very high-density area, 35% of sows that produced cubs ceased lactation early and this loss of entire litters was thought to be due to infanticide by dominant sows (Cresswell *et al.* 1992). This conclusion was based on strong circumstantial evidence; for example, there was an increase in aggression between breeding sows at this time and the main peak in bite wounds in sows occurred in April — a time when cubs are more mobile but have not yet appeared above ground. It is also significant that a much higher proportion of bite wounds occurred in breeding than non-breeding sows, suggesting that it is lactating sows that are mainly responsible for infanticide. In addition, known cases of infanticide also occurred during this period (Lups & Roper 1990, S. Harris, unpubl. data). However, it is important to stress that this is not the only time that death occurs between birth and emergence above ground, as on a number of occasions we have seen very young cubs dead on the spoil heap outside a breeding sett in February and March and deaths caused by mature boars cannot be ruled out. Deaths below ground at this time are difficult to monitor. (See also p. 187).

THE NEST CHAMBER

The nest chamber is an enlargement of one of the tunnels, often a side one and larger than average; it may have a second tunnel leading from it. It is filled with bedding prior to the birth of the cubs and is often situated not far from an entrance. This has the advantage of better ventilation and also enables the sow to isolate a small part of the sett system from the rest of the residents and have the exclusive use of an entrance for coming and going.

When preparing to film at Camberley, Ernest saw condensed water vapour rising like steam from one entrance on a frosty morning in February caused by the heat of the badgers' bodies not far down the tunnel; bedding was taken down the same hole and later the cubs were heard being suckled approximately 4–5 m from the entrance. This is no isolated case, as it is often possible to predict the entrance the cubs will use when they eventually come above ground by noting the one into which bedding is taken during February and March.

When brought up in captivity, cubs up to 3 or 4 weeks old need much warmth to survive, so you would expect the temperature of the nest chamber to be quite high (see also p. 41). It seems probable that the temperature inside the nest itself may be as high as 18–20°C since small cubs brought up in captivity need a similar temperature to survive.

For the first few weeks the cubs are buried in a mass of dry bedding which is an excellent insulator, so the heat from their bodies is retained. Observations carried out on a breeding badger in a large artificial sett with three chambers showed that when her two cubs were young she always curled up with them (Kidner, 1993, pers. comm.). This would reinforce the heat generated. However, there have been several records of dogs entering setts during the day and bringing out small cubs without being molested by the mother, suggesting that she was sleeping in another chamber. However, Kidner believes this happens because the sow is so sound asleep she is not aware of the dog's presence. She cites as evidence an instance when an older badger entered the breeding chamber and was not noticed by the mother for 10 minutes. We can certainly vouch for the soundness of sleep of wild badgers (p. 54), but more evidence is needed of the sow's behaviour at this time under natural circumstances before firm conclusions can be reached.

BREEDING ABOVE GROUND

Very occasionally, breeding has been recorded above ground in Britain. On one occasion a farmer, Sam Musgrave (pers. comm.), heard whickering from a large heap of grass and reeds in a hawthorn hedge on a peat moor in Somerset. When he poked it with a stick, a sow badger burst through the roof and stood grunting at him before slowly retreating. Inside the heap, he found several small cubs. A few days later, the sow had taken her cubs away, the roof had gone, but the heap was still 0.5 m high and more than 0.7 m in diameter. The grasses and reeds seemed to be roughly woven together giving strength to the walls, probably a result of the sow rotating her body when inside. Clearly the sow could not dig into the peat since the water-table was nearly level with the surface (Neal 1969).

Another Somerset farmer, Jack Richards, discovered a nest in a large lean-to shed butting on to his barn. It was used to store rough timber planking. It was dark inside, and as Ernest and the farmer stood together listening, they heard the unmistakable whickering of small cubs coming from the far side. On climbing over the timber, the noises stopped, and on switching on a torch and peering down between the planks, they saw a sow lying at full length on a large heap of hay. The light made her eyes sparkle but she did not move; she was on her side and suckling a cub! After some time, she slowly stood up, shook herself and without undue hurry made her way between the planks into the open barn next door. As they watched, the cub moved round and round, burying itself in the heap of hay. Moving the top covering gently with a stick, they found two cubs huddled together which were about 4–5 weeks old. On being exposed, they started to pull the hay around them and were soon buried again (Neal 1969).

Another nest was discovered by a farmer's wife in a large barn near Curry Rivel, Somerset on 30 January 1986 (Neal 1987). Squeaking noises were heard coming from a mound of loose hay in one corner; Ernest visited the barn the following afternoon. The mound was approximately 2 m × 1.5 m × 0.75 m and whickering could be heard coming from it. The farmer carefully removed some hay, a little at a time, and the sow's head could just be seen. She quickly disappeared through a tunnel in the hay and out of the barn into an adjoining wood. When the farmer removed more hay, a litter of five small cubs 3–4 days old could be seen huddled together (Plate 15). Outside the barn, the sow's entrance hole under the corrugated iron barn wall could be seen with much hay lying around. Heavy rain had caused the wood to be waterlogged. But about 30 m from the barn, near the edge of the wood, there was a trail of straw leading from an area where pheasants had been fed to a more elevated part of the wood where a sett was found. The fresh trail of straw suggested that the sett was occupied by other badgers. Incidentally, this event proved that all five cubs came from the same litter. So often when five cubs are seen playing around a sett they are the progeny of more than one sow.

In all these cases of breeding above ground, the surrounding area was waterlogged and the sows appeared to be young animals. It is likely that they had looked for a dry area away from the main sett to have their cubs where they were safe from the attentions of the dominant sow.

THE NEW-BORN CUB AND EARLY DEVELOPMENT

On average, new-born cubs are about 120 mm long from the tip of the snout to the root of the tail, which is usually another 30–40 mm long. Weights are much more variable, ranging from 75 to 132 g in Britain. In a litter of four, the two males weighed 90 g and 80 g and the females both 75 g (G. Dangerfield, pers. comm.). However, twin foetuses weighed by A. Killingley were 132 g for the male and 130 g for the female. Other weights from southern England were 84 g and 100 g for males and 89 g for a female.

At birth the cubs have a pink skin which is covered with greyish-white silky fur, more sparse on the ventral side. Darker hairs can usually be made out in the position of the eye stripe and on the lower part of the limbs. Occasionally, the eye stripe is just visible on full-term foetuses, but in some cubs it becomes visible only a few days after birth. The eyelids are fused, a state which lasts several weeks. Dangerfield has bred many badgers in captivity and has found that the eyes open consistently around 5 weeks. However, it does not follow that when the eyes are open the cub can use them for seeing since at this stage the cubs are normally living in complete darkness underground and will continue to do so for several more weeks. Observations on cubs brought up in captivity suggest that where light permits they are only able to focus on near objects some weeks after their eyes have opened.

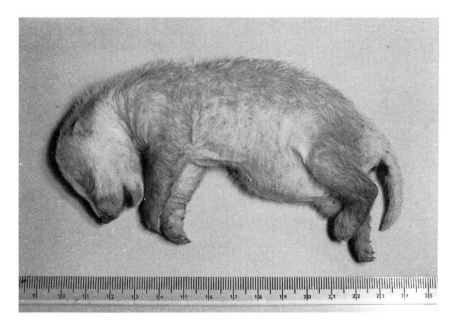

FIG 8.4   *New-born cub.*

However, by the time they would normally be above ground they appear to notice objects within a radius of a metre or so (p. 30). When 6–7 weeks old cubs start exploring the underground tunnels but seldom come above ground before 8 weeks of age.

Working on a social group whose members were all individually known, Rosie Woodroffe (1993) made the important discovery that badgers, like a number of other mammals such as jackals and mongooses, show alloparental behaviour, i.e. related individuals co-operate with the mother in raising her young. Using ultra-sound scans, she determined that three females within the group were pregnant in January, but by April only one had cubs, the others having lost their litters. To her surprise, one of the latter, along with a yearling sow, spent much time caring for the cubs. Care took the form of babysitting while the mother was away feeding. On one occasion the babysitter chased the 9–10-week-old cubs below ground when she detected Woodroffe's presence. On another, she chased a fox away from the sett area, and another time chased off a visiting male that had bitten one of the cubs. A babysitter was present on 11 out of the 14 nights she watched. On three occasions before the mother left to forage, the mother and a babysitter were seen to carry the cubs from the breeding burrow to where the non-breeder slept. Grooming of the cubs by a babysitter was also seen. Woodroffe was also able to prove that the mother had been a non-breeding female the previous year and that one of the cubs she helped raise became her babysitter the following year. This caring behaviour is of potential benefit in so far as it allows the mother to get more food during the time she is suckling, improves the chances of the cubs surviving and no doubt enables the yearling babysitter to gain experience which may help when she has cubs of her own. It is highly probable, but not yet proved, that this alloparental behaviour also occurs during the period between birth and the cub's first emergence above ground.

On several occasions, and in successive years, Jill Hutchinson (pers. comm.) saw a sow 'take young cubs by the scruff, tail, bottom or other part' and drag them back to the sett when one had strayed too near her watching position (Plate 6). Strangely, the sow allowed them to come out again almost straight away. A second sow was also resident in that sett. With hindsight, this could have been another instance of babysitting behaviour.

Small cubs have also been seen being moved from one sett to another. Graham Madge (1982) described how in early April he was watching a sett with about 27 entrances. Most of the holes were on an open hill site, but three were on the flat near the river. A sow emerged from one hole about 30 minutes before dusk and disappeared down another, 10 m from it. She soon emerged carrying a cub in her jaws by the scruff of the neck; it was hanging quite limp. She carried it at speed down the slope and almost threw it into one of the lower holes. In a minute or so she repeated the performance with three cubs in succession. The whole removal took 14 minutes and was carried out in an urgent and purposeful manner. Madge estimated that the cubs were 4–6 weeks old. Why the cubs were moved is a matter for conjecture, but another litter of cubs was seen later at the same sett, so the removal may have been another example of a sow protecting her cubs from a more dominant breeding sow, or from a boar, but it could also have been an instance of alloparental behaviour.

The badger watcher is fortunate to see cubs younger than 9–10 weeks old since they usually emerge for the first time well after dark. Continuous all-night vigils for 10 consecutive nights between 18 and 28 April 1953 gave a good picture of early behaviour (Hewer & Neal 1954):

Cubs were first seen on 25 April, although previously their shufflings and whickerings were heard down the tunnel. The cubs first appeared at the entrance at 22.50, keeping in close contact. They were constantly on the move, investigating each stick or lump of earth within reach and testing out their sense of balance on the sloping sides of the entrance. They were visible for about 10 minutes on the first occasion. They appeared again at 01.35 and were out for longer. The next evening they were seen at 20.40 for a short time and again at 01.00 for 25 minutes. On each of these occasions the sow was below ground, but near the entrance, and at times, her low whinnying purrs could be heard.

When only one cub is present, the first emergence is somewhat different as the sow brings up the cub herself. On 28 April at a sett on the Quantock Hills, Ernest saw a sow lying just inside the sett entrance. A cub appeared from below and nosed about close to her body but would not venture further. However, when she got up and walked a few paces away it followed her and then crept under her body where it remained half hidden as she slowly walked away. Not long after, it left the sow and scampered back to the sett. On another occasion, a tiny cub was seen poking out from below the sow at a sett entrance on the Mendips. This time she kept nosing it down the hole, presumably to keep it in (D.B. McGreggor, pers. comm.).

The date when cubs first appear above ground is related to the time of birth. April is the usual month in south and south-west England but much earlier appearances have been recorded (p. 158).

At 9–10 weeks of age, cub appearances above ground become more regular. They may emerge before dark, their activities become more energetic, and as their powers of co-ordination develop, their play becomes more variable and purposeful. At this stage, they learn very quickly, many associations being built up, especially in relation to scent, touch and hearing. Early on, any sudden noise results in a scamper for home but they soon learn to discriminate between sounds and no longer react adversely to familiar noises. Cubs become more venturesome when 10–12 weeks old and constant assurance is of less importance. They explore the new environs of the sett and play becomes boisterous and prolonged. This causes the ground outside the main entrance to be beaten flat and appear almost polished.

A number of adult activities are foreshadowed. Setting scent on objects near the sett may be seen occasionally, although it is difficult to observe in the wild, owing to the low position of the body. Tame cubs do this constantly. They also start making snuffle holes (shallow pits made by the snout when feeding) with snout and claws. Shuffling backwards with leaves and sticks is often observed from 9 weeks onwards; at first it is only momentary, but later it becomes more sustained and develops into the habit of bringing back bedding to the sett. E. Nettleton (pers. comm.) found that if cubs were separated from adult badgers when about 10 days old, they nevertheless carried out all these actions later in a similar way. This suggests that setting scent, forming snuffle holes, digging and bringing back bedding are inherited patterns of behaviour.

GROWTH RATE

Cubs born in the wild in February appear to be nearly as big as small adult sows by the late autumn, but the growth rate varies with the available food and this in turn is affected by the weather conditions. During dry summers in Britain, such as 1955 and 1975, growth was much slower and the cubs could be distinguished from adults by their much smaller size well into the next year. Slow growth during dry seasons is likely to be due to lack of available earthworms.

FIG 8.5   *Cubs aged 5 weeks, raised in captivity. In the wild, they would remain underground at this age.*

Chris measured average growth rate over 16 years in a high-density area (unpubl. data). He found that weights increased sharply from July to November in both the first and second years of life, with little change between December and June. Males put on more weight than females and by the end of the second year the difference was about 1 kg (Fig. 8.6).

Records for captive badgers show a similar pattern but the growth rate is often considerably higher. For example, Frank (1940) showed that for two cubs, the male weighed 16.8 kg by the end of the first year and the female 12.2 kg: clearly the result of plenty of food and comparatively little exercise!

Occasionally in the wild, one cub from a litter may be abnormally small. Such runts

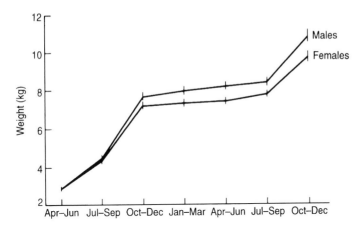

FIG 8.6   *Mean growth rate of badgers over the first two years at Woodchester Park,*
Gloucestershire. Data from bi-monthly weighings over 16 years where numbers weighed
ranged between 87–313 for males and 101–384 for females. Source: C. Cheeseman
(unpubl. data).

seldom live long, but there are records of them surviving for several weeks after their emergence above ground.

LACTATION

Lactation, during a year of normal weather, lasts for a minimum of 12 weeks, often several weeks longer. This is followed by a period of weaning when supplementary suckling takes place. In a sample of 308 sows from south-west England, Bob Page *et al.* (1994) recorded 69 lactating sows, mainly in the period February to June, but with five in July and none thereafter.

During the prolonged summer drought of 1975 which started in May, a sow which had given birth to two cubs, probably in February, was still suckling them in July. This was almost certainly an adaptation to conditions when food was extremely difficult to find. It is probable that the sow was able to keep up her milk supply by ranging further and feeding on different food. Up to the autumn of that year Ernest examined dead sows which had large nipples and mammary tissue still secreting. This ability to continue suckling during adverse conditions is clearly of great survival value. However, if the sow has weaned her cubs, and a drought follows, many cubs die of starvation.

The sow nurses her cubs underground, lying on her side or back. When several weeks old the cubs will knead her mammary glands as they suckle, so towards the end of lactation her abdomen may be almost devoid of hair.

When the cubs are 6–8 weeks old, the sow returns to the sett three or four times during the night between bouts of feeding. It is certain that she nurses them on some of these occasions, but some visits are only for a minute or so, presumably to see that all is well with the cubs.

During all-night watches at Camberley (Hewer & Neal 1954) the sow's movements were noted as follows (the missing data being due to the sow using another entrance out of view):

Date	Emergence	Return
21–22 April	19.56	20.52 GMT
	21.10	21.36
	23.03	?
	02.08	03.15
	03.22	03.40
27–28 April	20.00	21.01
	21.02	22.45
	23.51	?
	02.23	03.20

WEANING

On average, in south-west England, weaning starts in the first half of May. During this period, the cubs are still dependent on their mother's milk but they supplement their diet at first by foraging near the sett and later by following their mother further afield and feeding near her. A typical sight is of a foraging sow with small cubs bustling along at her shoulders, taking a keen interest in anything the sow stops to investigate. Cubs are usually independent by 15 weeks when they forage independently. By this time their permanent dentition is fully functional and the majority of milk teeth have been replaced (Fig. 2.15).

During weaning there is some evidence that sows regurgitate food for the cubs. Howard & Bradbury (1979) found the gizzards of earthworms and fibrous material in the gut contents of a 1.1 kg cub. Regurgitated food seems the most likely explanation. On 1 June 1982, Chris Ferris (pers. comm.) witnessed regurgitation in the wild at close quarters and we will paraphrase the account from her diary:

> The mother left the field edge and came over to her two cubs. I saw something drop from her mouth — a piece of worm which a cub gobbled up. In its desire to get more, it jumped up excitedly at its mother's face and began, puppy like, to lick around her mouth. She turned slightly away, but her boisterous cub persisted with the licking. She then began to heave, coughed and brought up a great heap of worms which the cub proceeded to eat. I saw her regurgitate again six nights later, this time without being stimulated by the licking of the cub.

Eric Ashby (pers. comm.) has filmed rather similar behaviour, but circumstances suggested food carrying rather than regurgitation. He writes of a sow feeding in a ditch a few metres from a sett where cubs were playing near the entrance:

> Now and again she noisily ate something, perhaps a snail. Suddenly she left the ditch and visited the cubs. Again she went to the ditch, finding something to eat now and again. Once more she came back to the cubs, and this time I noticed that her mouth was slightly open, and on reaching the cubs she appeared to drop something which was immediately taken by a cub.

A few weeks after weaning, a sow and her cubs may move from a sett where she has bred. Over a period of 6 years at one small sett, in the 3 years when cubs were bred there, it was abandoned for several weeks in late May or June, but in years when cubs were absent this did not happen until August or September. After each move the sett was thoroughly cleaned out before being occupied once more (M. Clark, pers. comm.). Although large main setts are normally occupied continuously throughout the year, there is often a corresponding shift from one part of it to another soon after weaning has taken place.

TIME OF SEXUAL MATURITY

Females

In south-west England, most sows ovulate for the first time when 13–14 months old (March and April with some in early May); others have their first oestrus later, particularly between mid-July and October (Neal & Harrison 1958, Cresswell *et al.* 1992). In Sweden the picture is very similar although a small number may not become mature until 2 years old (Ahnlund 1980).

Diet plays an important part in determining the time of maturity, since when food is abundant, the first oestrus may be earlier. Cubs brought up in captivity and fed well have had their first oestrus in the late autumn and this is now known to occur in the wild when the cubs are 9 months old (Fargher & Morris 1975, Ahnlund 1980, Page *et al.* 1994).

Chris Ferris (pers. comm.) has provided evidence from field observations. A badger family where she knew the individuals intimately had become habituated to her presence. One sow had her litter on 7/8 February 1983. Her female cub injured her paw and became unwell, and she allowed Chris to examine the wound. This was treated with hydrogen peroxide and she was given antibiotics in food. By mid-June the cub was fully recovered, was completely trusting and would greet Ferris whenever she appeared. In December she was seen to mate three nights in succession on 3/4/5 of the month. She was then seen regularly, but on 24 January only briefly. The next night she did not appear at all, but on the 26th she came to greet Ferris and it was clear that she was lactating. Thus it is possible that this sow had achieved puberty by the age of 10 months, was mated and bore her cubs when just under a year, after a gestation period of about 7 weeks, presumably without delayed implantation (p. 157). This interpretation must be treated with some caution, however, because there is some evidence that sows may lactate without having given birth to cubs (W. Cresswell, pers. comm.)

Males

Anatomical research in Sweden showed that the majority of males became mature in the spring and summer of their second year (12–15 months) although some took longer, and very exceptionally not until the end of the year (Ahnlund 1980). The same picture was found in Switzerland (Wandeler & Graf 1982). In south-west England a similar pattern was found, but in addition, some males became mature as early as January when 11 months old (Page *et al.* 1994).

DISPERSAL AND MOVEMENTS BETWEEN SETTS

Movements of badgers between social groups may be classified as either true dispersal (permanent) or visiting (temporary). In most studies the majority of males and females have remained in their natal groups all their lives, a fact that has led to the suggestion that there must be a degree of inbreeding. However, recent genetic studies (Evans *et al.* 1989, da Silva *et al.* in press, Woodroffe & Macdonald, in press) showed that badgers in Woodchester Park and Wytham showed no sign of this. It was found that most cubs were fathered by a minority of males which were immigrants from other social groups. These were the only males in the group unrelated to the females present, they had higher levels of male hormone and remained fertile well into the autumn.

Telemetry studies in Woodchester Park (a high-density area) showed remarkably little evidence of yearlings emigrating (Cheeseman *et al.* 1988a). In these studies 629 badgers were marked and released and of those recaptured in subsequent years only seven males and one female had changed social groups. In Wytham (a moderately high-density area), Woodroffe & Macdonald (in press) found that annual dispersal was higher (6.6% in males and 9.6% in females). In the low-density area of Speyside (Kruuk & Parish 1987) only male cubs dispersed (26.1%) and in the urban badger population of Bristol (Harris & Cresswell 1987), dispersal was quite usual, 27.7% in males and 11.3% in females. So male immigration appears to be more common in low-density populations.

Males disperse singly. However, female dispersal in Wytham took the form of coalitions of two or three individuals, often sisters, although one case involved sows of different ages thought to be a mother and her two daughters. These coalitions appeared to choose territories where there was only one female in the social group. In these cases Woodroffe & Macdonald (in press) were unable to determine the fate of the displaced females which were never seen again.

At Woodchester bait marking showed that visiting by males took place mainly at the peak of the mating season in the early months of the year (Cheeseman *et al.* 1987). Later it was shown that visiting did lead to matings in some cases (Evans *et al.* 1989). In Wytham, Woodroffe & Macdonald (in press) found that visiting was more common when females were in oestrus. They found that visits occurred between May and October with a peak in September; however they were unable to cover the early breeding season for welfare reasons when more instances would have been expected. They go on to say that 'these visits may represent attempts to obtain extra-group matings, since genetic evidence suggests that some cubs are sired by males from other groups (Evans *et al.* 1989, da Silva *et al.* in press)'. As younger males in a social group are closely related to the resident females and young females are related to the dominant male, this visiting by both sexes may represent their only chance of mating without dispersal.

THE BREEDING PATTERN

The general picture is emerging that breeding within a social group mainly concerns the older sows one of which normally breeds each year. There is no doubt that individual sows can breed regularly. G. Dangerfield (pers. comm.) kept one sow which had litters 4 years out of 5 and observations in the field on easily identifiable animals confirm this (R. W. Howard *et al.* pers. comm.). In Scotland, Kruuk (1978) found that typically only one litter was produced each year per social group. However, this is certainly not the case in south and southwest England where more than one litter commonly occurs when conditions are good. At Rendcomb, Gloucestershire, two litters occurred in successive years, one in a main sett and the other in an annexe (Neal 1948). At another sett near Taunton, during 4 consecutive years, litters were born in the main sett and in three of these, second litters were born in annexe setts (Neal & Avery 1956). The phenomenon was also widespread at a sett watched regularly for 20 years in Somerset (Neal 1986) and much other evidence is also available from badger watchers in many parts of the country. Of these, the most spectacular was recorded by Don Hunford (pers. comm.). In one very large social group in Essex where extra food had been provided, 13 cubs were born in 1983. However, the best statistical evidence gathered over many years comes from the high-density area of Woodchester Park (Cresswell *et al.* 1992). Here, 34% of social groups failed to breed each year, 45% had one litter, 14% had two, 4.5% had three and 0.6% had four litters. The presence of annexe setts or of very large main setts appears to be the important factor in allowing this to happen.

The body condition of adult females is another factor which plays a part in determining how many adult sows in a group breed successfully. Females which were relatively heavy in autumn were found to be more likely to produce cubs the following spring (Woodroffe & Macdonald, in press), and in another study, 22% of those sows that failed to develop blastocysts had a lower body mass, less body fat, larger adrenal glands, poorer health and larger numbers of bite wounds than sows with blastocysts (Cresswell *et al.* 1992). It should be noted that this was in a high-density area and that these findings on fecundity may vary markedly at different densities (see also p. 179).

MATING AND MATING BEHAVIOUR

The duration of copulation is very variable. Many instances reported in the field lasted less than 2 minutes, but usually ranged from 10 to 90 minutes. Some of the records of short matings were probably only rutting behaviour where penetration was not achieved; these can be ignored, but others seemed to be genuine copulations. Long-duration matings are characteristic of other members of the Mustelidae such as the mink, *Mustela vison* (30–40 min), the sable, *Martes zibelina* (50 min) and the polecat, *Mustela putorius* (up to 3 h). There is no doubt that long-duration mating in the badger takes place when sows are in full oestrus. At this time there is great excitement among the males and some rivalry may be apparent if several are present.

With some pairings, no preliminary play of any kind is seen but in others there is considerable excitement with violent scuffles and much emission of scent. Usually the sow receives the boar quite passively and does little apart from occasional musking to initiate the mating.

The first sign of interest shown by the boar is often the raising of the tail into a vertical position and the emission of a loud and often continuous deep whinnying purr. He may then approach with a shuffling motion taking short steps with the legs kept rather rigid. On mounting, he grasps the sow with his front legs in front of her flanks, keeping his position by gripping her neck or ear with his teeth, sometimes weaving his head from side to side before getting a grip. The sow may give a yelp if the bite is too vigorous.

Over the main mating period, February–May, the dominant boar in particular, is constantly on the alert for any sow on heat. At this time, the boar (or boars) is kept away from that part of the sett where a sow has her cubs, and lives elsewhere, sometimes in another part of the main sett complex. Usually he emerges first and on certain nights may trot excitedly from hole to hole making deep, vibrant whinnying purrs almost continuously. He will sometimes half disappear down a hole but will not enter, presumably because any breeding sow would be aggressive. His whinnying suggests that he is trying to call up the sow, but the wider patrolling of the surroundings may be to keep the area free from potential rivals. On such nights, if a sow is in oestrus, she is likely to emerge and mating will follow; if not, guarding her cubs will be a priority and she will probably wait until the boar has left the area before leaving to forage herself. However, alloparental behaviour in some social groups may make this less necessary.

On nights when sexual excitement is considerable, violent play or attempts at mating may suddenly be interrupted by a bout of frantic digging or the bringing back of a bundle of bedding to the sett entrance, only to be abandoned. This appears to be a displacement activity.

A number of accounts of mating have been recorded in detail. Paget & Middleton (1974b) describe how in early June, the sow emerged 20 minutes before sunset, followed almost immediately by the boar. There was a period of scratching, mutual grooming and musking and the boar started to vocalise loudly. He then began to paw the ground before mounting the sow. After mating for about 25 minutes, the sow ran off, but the boar spent further minutes both sniffing the ground where the mating had taken place and then scratching soil over it before leaving hurriedly after the sow.

Badgers can certainly be promiscuous. Howard (1951) observed two boars copulating with the same sow during the evenings of 4 and 5 April 1951. It started when two boars, which were calling loudly, literally dragged a sow out of an entrance. Both tried to mount her but one eventually gained control and remained in the mating position for some time while the second stood by 'purring' loudly. A sudden noise caused all three to rush back into the sett, but after about 20 minutes they re-emerged and one boar immediately mounted the sow and spent the next hour in the mating position. Meanwhile, the second boar wandered about the sett digging little holes here, there and everywhere, and occasionally approaching the copulating boar, but would retreat on receiving a threatening reaction. Sometimes the attack succeeded and the mating boar would dismount and chase the other away. When this happened, it was clear that the sow wanted attention as she would run to the struggling boars, and given the slightest chance, would raise her tail and back on to the nearest boar's flank. The boar would then raise its tail and mount. The next night one of the boars mated with the sow for 40 minutes but dismounted when he went to investigate a strange badger which came near the sett. Meanwhile, the second resident boar took the opportunity of mounting the sow and remained in undisputed possession for a further 40 minutes. The first boar on returning no longer took any interest in his rival and allowed mating to continue. At times when neither boar was mounted, one would guard her, and if the other approached would go to the sow, smell her rump, turn round, raise his tail and set scent on her. As Howard remarked 'the affair was not one of billing and cooing, but of tailing and purring'. Another example of promiscuity was witnessed in Yorkshire in June 1972 (Paget & Middleton 1974b).

Duration of oestrus

The length of oestrus is probably 4–6 days. R.W. Howard (pers. comm.) recorded that over the period 1–6 April at one sett, he saw rutting behaviour on 1 April, on the 4th and 5th copulation occurred on and off for several hours, but on the 6th all signs of sexual activity had abated. Paget & Middleton (1974a) saw a very similar sequence of events in Yorkshire. In captive badgers John Sankey (pers. comm.) saw prolonged mating on 5 consecutive days and nights (4–8 May) and in another year there were 3 days of long-duration matings (22–24 May) preceded by nights when shorter pairings occurred. Eunice Overend (pers. comm.) described how her tame sow, when on heat, became extremely restless for about 10 days. It was possible to see her swollen vulva which was pink when in full oestrus, as in bitches.

So when a sow is in oestrus she will be mated for long periods, on and off for several days and nights, and as ovulation is induced by the stimulation of copulation this pattern of events is likely to be important in bringing about fertilisation.

Time of mating

After years of controversy, it is now well established that mating can take place during every month of the year in Britain. However, the main peak is undoubtedly in the spring. Having said that, there are many factors which influence this event, such as age of maturity, time of birth, failure to conceive after a mating, loss of blastocysts during the period of delayed implantation and the occurrence of a secondary oestrus in some sows during that period. These will be referred to later.

Evidence for times of mating can be derived from field observations and from anatomical investigations. Together they give a good picture of events.

Field observations

Field records of mating are not statistically sound as more watching has taken place during some months, mainly in the spring when cubs are about and watching is more interesting; the more unpleasant winter months have tended to be avoided except by the dedicated few. Also, most observers watch in the vicinity of setts and are unable to follow activities once the animals have left, and although it seems very probable that most mating takes place near setts, some instances have been observed in other parts of the territory including open fields and woods (C. Ferris, pers. comm.), but how frequently this occurs is unknown. Neither is it certain whether mating takes place below ground in the wild, although this seems likely as some tunnels and chambers in well-established setts are large enough for this to be possible and mating has certainly taken place in artificial setts (Drabble 1970) and under captive conditions in prepared chambers (G. Dangerfield, pers. comm.; J. Sankey, pers. comm.). So some bias is inevitable.

Nevertheless, a large number of people have now carried out regular watches throughout the year, and some, such as Keith Neal with Roger Avery (1954–6) and Paget & Middleton (1974a), have paid particular attention to the early months. Others have followed the activity of badgers at night away from the sett on a regular basis. An excellent example of this is the work of Chris Ferris who observed mating on 35 occasions during 5 years of intensive observations in all weathers throughout the year between 1979 and 1983. Because the badgers had become habituated to her presence she could also watch them from close quarters away from the sett area. Her eight observed December long-duration matings provide a unique record, as previously no work of such an intensive nature had been carried out during that month in such a manner. What is more, these December matings were all estimated to have involved sows under a year old. This may be very exceptional in the wild as all her records are from an area of Kent where market gardening is carried out and food is plentiful, particularly as regular irrigation allowed greater availability of earthworms during dry periods. This is comparable to cubs in captivity having access to large quantities of food and becoming mature early.

So although the results do not give a completely accurate picture they show general trends and are the best available at the present time. They provide useful corroboration of evidence obtained from anatomical investigations. Figure 8.7 gives the timing of 116 well-documented long-duration matings. When these occurred at the same sett on several nights in succession they were counted as one as almost certainly they involved the same sow during a single oestrus.

Anatomical evidence
One of the best indications of maturity and the time of oestrus of mature sows, and hence of mating period, is obtained by sectioning the ovaries of a large sample from each month

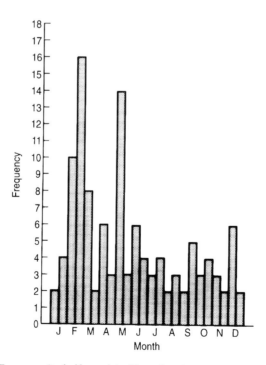

FIG 8.7 *Frequency (in half months) of long-duration matings witnessed in the field, plus several in captivity.*

of the year and noting the presence of large follicles (over 1 mm in diameter). Such follicles indicate that ovulation is imminent. In addition, the histology of the vagina and uterus changes in response to the hormone oestrogen which is secreted in larger amounts at this time (Neal & Harrison 1958). Occasionally, specimens are found where ovulation has just taken place indicating almost exactly when mating had occurred.

From such investigations it was shown that for sows aged 3 or more years, there was a seasonal pattern of ovulations with the main peak in January–February and a smaller one in the period July–October. Yearling sows on the other hand had their first oestrus later with a peak in March–April and another which coincided with that of some older sows later in the year (Cresswell *et al.* 1992) (Fig. 8.8). The two peaks in the spring for the two age groups probably explain those for mating seen in field observations (mid-January–early March and April–May).

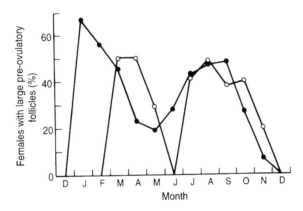

FIG 8.8   *Seasonal occurrence of large (> 1.0 mm) pre-ovulatory follicles in female badgers. Females > 3 years old (filled symbols), yearling sows (open symbols). From Cresswell et al. 1992.*

Further evidence is available from the presence and size of blastocysts (Ahnlund 1980, Cresswell *et al.* 1992, Page *et al.* 1994). Small blastocysts are first seen in February and they grow steadily but very slowly until the time of implantation (usually late December). The number of sows with blastocysts rises steeply to a peak of about 90% by April for 3 year olds or older, while that for yearlings reaches a maximum of about 70% 2 months later. This confirms that most older animals are mated during a post-parturient oestrus and younger animals when first mature at 14–15 months. Some blastocysts are lost during the summer in both age groups but by October the great majority of older sows contain blastocysts, in some populations up to 100% but fewer in yearlings (see Fig. 8.9).

A strange phenomenon associated with delayed implantation in badgers is that sows may sometimes have one or more further oestrus periods during this time, even though healthy blastocysts are present, and that matings at this time bring about further ovulations and the formation of more corpora lutea — the glands which develop in the follicle after ovulation and produce the hormone progesterone (Neal & Harrison 1958). Later studies have shown

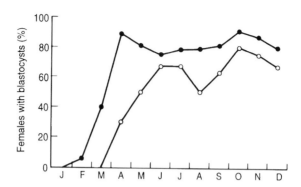

FIG 8.9   *Seasonal occurrence of blastocysts in female badgers. Sows of 3 years or older (filled symbols), yearling sows (open symbols). From Cresswell et al. 1992.*

that this phenomenon occurs in all age classes, but more often in younger females (Ahnlund 1980, Wandeler & Graf 1982). Some of these matings lead to fertilisation and new blastocysts are added to the existing ones, a phenomenon known as superfetation. In one study ova and blastocysts were found together in six sows, and on 11 occasions healthy blastocysts of two sizes were found in the same sow (Page *et al.* 1994). This phenomenon was also demonstrated in the study by Cresswell *et al.* (1992). In addition, genetic studies show that litters of mixed paternity are not uncommon (Evans *et al.* 1989); however, this could also be explained by matings carried out by more than one boar during a single oestrus. Superfetation also explains why in all studies the mean number of corpora lutea increased during the delayed implantation period, sometimes greatly in excess of the number of blastocysts present.

This increase in the number of blastocysts in late summer and autumn reflects a further mating period around that time probably due to later maturity of some yearlings and older animals having a further oestrus. The importance of this autumn mating period is emphasised by the data obtained in Wytham (Woodroffe & Macdonald, in press).

Turning now to the male side of the picture it has been shown that the weights of testes in animals of 3 years and over are greatest in the period mid-January–May with a gradual decrease in the later months. Similarly, the proportion of adult males capable of mating in terms of sperm viability was 100% in the early months compared with a minimum of 79% in November, younger animals having a rather shorter season (Page *et al.* 1994). Thus some males are capable of mating during any month although it appears probable that it is the older and stronger animals that sire most of the cubs.

It is also significant that the seasonal occurrence of severe bite wounding in adult males follows a similar pattern with a peak in the early months, three times greater than in August–October (Cresswell *et al.* 1992). It is also greater in immigrant males with high testosterone titres in October (Woodroffe & Macdonald, in press).

Thus one can conclude from all this evidence that the main mating period is between January and May with older females probably accounting for the main peak in February and yearlings of 12–14 months for the second in April–May. In addition there is a lesser mating period between July and October when some sows have a second oestrus either during the delayed implantation period, or because they have lost their blastocysts, and when some late developing yearlings have their first oestrus. Very late matings, such as in December, appear to involve sows in their first year which have matured early. The relatively small number of matings observed in other months probably involves yearlings coming into oestrus at different times or sows having a secondary oestrus during the delayed implantation period.

It follows from this wide range of mating times that the period of delayed implantation will vary considerably in different animals from about 10 months for a February mating to 2 in an October one, and probably none at all if a young sow is mated in December. Three examples involving different times of mating with consequent variations in the period of delayed implantation are shown in Fig. 8.10.

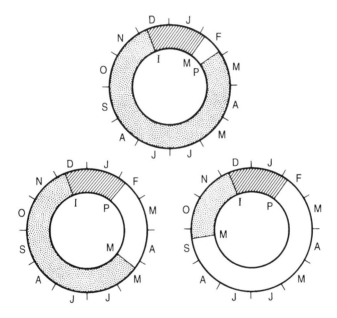

FIG 8.10 *Examples of variation in the period of delayed implantation in badgers, caused by February, May and September matings. I = implantation, P = parturition (birth), M = mating, against the month of the year.*

IMPLANTATION

Not all blastocysts implant, the lowest proportion being in high-density areas such as south-west England — 32% (Page *et al.* 1994) and 44% (Cresswell *et al.* 1992), compared with 77% in Sweden (Ahnlund 1980). It would be interesting to know what happens in regions where badgers are rare and social groups restricted, perhaps to a single pair. An even higher success rate would appear to be probable.

The average date of implantation over different parts of the badger's range may be roughly calculated from the dates of birth recorded since the period between implantation and birth is between 6 and 7 weeks. Thus available data suggest that for south-west France the mean date is mid-December, in south-west England, late December, in the north of England, early January, in Scotland, Sweden and Germany, mid-January and in Russia, late January or early February. However, the range of birth dates in all regions is wide, so implantation dates must be correspondingly variable. In Britain implantation time ranges from late October to February but the extremes are very unusual, the great majority occurring during the last week in December and the first fortnight in January.

A more accurate method of assessing implantation time is to measure the size of foetuses by ultrasound scanning and calculating the date using a standard growth/time formula. Woodroffe (in press) used this method for the badgers of Wytham Wood over a period of 3 years. The average date for 18 badgers was 25 December, ranging from 8 December to 14 January. However, most of the data was from 2 years, one during which food was scarce due to drought, the other when food was plentiful. In the former, body condition was significantly poorer than in the latter. Interestingly, for the poor year the mean implantation date was 2 January and for the good one, 18 December. This suggested that good body condition resulted in earlier implantation.

What factors trigger implantation?

One of the intriguing problems of the reproductive cycle is what factors cause implantation to take place at the appropriate time. One factor is undoubtedly the influence of the hormones, oestrogen and progesterone on the lining of the uterus, making it spongy and receptive to the blastocyst. But what causes these hormones to be secreted in adequate amounts at the appropriate time?

It is known that variation in daylength influences the time of implantation in some mustelids (Pearson & Enders 1944) and although badgers are strictly nocturnal in winter and consequently are unlikely to be affected by this factor, it has been suggested that increase in night length correlated with greater activity may be factors (Canivenc & Bonnin-Laffargue 1966). But if activity is a factor it should apply equally to badgers in all regions. This is not so, as in Russia badgers are semi-dormant during the winter, bedding up completely by the end of November and living on stored fat. A short warm spell in cold winters does not bring them out, but in mild ones some may emerge briefly in January and February (Novikov 1956). By contrast in south-west England some activity occurs throughout the winter, except during periods of severe frost. However, regular counts at main setts during the winter months have shown that fewer animals come above ground regularly between mid-November and the end of December. It is probable that breeding sows are less active than younger and non-breeding adults at this time, but more data are needed before this can be substantiated.

This drop in numbers during the period prior to implantation suggests that some animals become semi-dormant at this time, an observation supported by those who have kept badgers in captivity and found that after feeding heavily during the autumn, they go off their food, sleep a lot and do not become active again until after Christmas. This semi-dormant period has been confirmed by Fowler & Racey (1988) who showed that there was a 90% drop in activity above ground under semi-natural conditions near Aberdeen (57°N) from November to January and that body temperature dropped by up to 8.9°C during this period.

Increase in night length seems to be an improbable trigger for implantation, but Canivenc, after a number of years of research, succeeded in 1971 in inducing early implantation (Canivenc 1979). Using six captive sows which had been mated soon after the birth of their cubs, he placed them in an experimental chamber in May where they were subjected artificially to a gradual increase in night length and a reduction in temperature of 10°C. Implantation occurred in July. Since then, further experiments were carried out in a similar manner but with no drop in temperature which also resulted in autumn births (Canivenc *et al.* 1981).

These experiments proved conclusively that under artificial conditions increase in night length brought about earlier implantation and birth. But is it possible for these factors to operate in the wild? There are potent reasons for believing they do not. First, badgers are strictly nocturnal after the end of October, and thereafter their times of emergence are well after dark and in no way related to sunset times (see Fig. 5.1). Second, as night length increases more dramatically in northern latitudes and temperature drop is more severe, you would expect that implantation would be earlier in northern regions. The opposite is the case (p. 178). Third, the range of dates of implantation in any one region may be very wide, some being well before the longest day and others very much later. Lastly, there is the phenomenon of two sows living in the same social group under the same conditions of night length and temperature, but having their cubs as much as 5 weeks apart. Such discrepancies are not unusual.

When looking for a factor which triggers implantation, it is logical to seek one which applies equally to badgers in the sub-arctic as in southern France. This factor must also be variable, as it has to account not only for the variation due to latitude, but also the wide variation in any one locality. This suggests that a factor other than a climatic one is at work — one that relates to each individual badger.

Relative inactivity may well be the key to the problem since it is during the semi-dormant condition that implantation occurs, just as it does in bears after a period of delayed implantation (Neal 1977). It is well established that the putting on of much fat is a requisite for hibernation or semi-dormancy in many species and badgers certainly do this to a considerable extent, particularly in the autumn months. But the ability to put on fat varies with the availability of food and the length of time when foraging is possible; these factors could influence implantation time. There is much anecdotal evidence by badger watchers that after dry summers and autumns when feeding is difficult due to lack of earthworms, either a poor year for cubs follows or the litters are later than usual (Neal 1986). Later work at Woodchester showed that sows which were relatively heavier in autumn were more likely to produce cubs in the spring (Cheeseman *et al.* 1987). Similarly, Woodroffe & Macdonald (in press) confirmed that only sows in relatively good condition bred successfully following dry summers and concluded that this was correlated with loss of foetuses. It was also shown at Woodchester that social groups of large size in this high-density area had poorer reproductive success than in smaller ones. It is possible that this could reflect greater competition for food, especially in dry seasons, within the restrictions of territory and hence the putting on of less fat. Thus the presence of sufficient fat appears to be an important factor in breeding success.

So let us return to the question why semi-dormancy could bring about implantation. A possible hypothesis (Neal 1977) is as follows. It is certain that one factor causing implantation is the secretion of steroid hormones which cause the uterine lining to become

receptive. In most mammals this occurs soon after fertilisation when oestrogen and progesterone are secreted from ovarian tissues. In badgers this normally occurs after a long period
of delayed implantation, during which only very small amounts of these hormones appear
to be secreted as the corpora lutea are largely inactive and show poor vascularisation (Neal
& Harrison 1958, Page *et al.* 1994). Thus insufficient steroids are secreted to bring about
implantation. However, steroids are soluble in fat and during this period they may gradually be absorbed in the fat which is increasingly being stored, in the same way as insecticides
such as DDT are known to be. This continues until the sow goes into a state of semi-dormancy. It is then that she starts to live off her fat supplies and as this is diminished, the
steroids are released into the blood stream in sufficient quantities to bring about implantation. Much more research is needed before this hypothesis can be accepted or refuted, but
it does supply a possible explanation of the variability in implantation times both among
individuals in the same locality and according to latitude, which an external factor such as
daylength fails to do.

Indirect evidence for this hypothesis comes from recent work on humans which confirms
that fat does store steroids and influences the amount of oestrogen circulating in the blood.
It was also shown that some of the male hormone present in *women* is converted by fat into
oestrogen, significantly adding to that secreted by the ovaries (Frisch 1988).

The lowering of body temperature associated with a drop in ambient temperature and
semi-dormancy may also influence implantation. Fowler & Racey (1988) found that the
body temperature of one sow fell to 28°C immediately prior to implantation.

One further factor that should be discussed is the effect of stress. This is known to retard
implantation in rats. Badgers captured as adults and subsequently kept in isolation have on
occasions produced cubs up to 15 months afterwards (Cocks 1903), so it is likely that stress
caused by captivity delayed implantation beyond the usual time.

Delayed implantation is a remarkable adaptation to ensure that cubs are born at the most
appropriate time for survival. This, according to the restrictions of climate, is as early in the
year as possible. In spite of wintry conditions, the new-born cubs in January and February
are well provided for. They are kept warm thanks to the central heating system provided by
the mother and the cubs themselves, and the insulating properties of all the bedding in
which they lie. Because of the long lactation period, the cubs are already large by the time
they are weaned and then the season is sufficiently advanced to provide plenty of food in a
normal year. This gives them the whole of the summer and autumn to put on enough fat
for survival during the severe winters which are characteristic over much of the badger's
range. It would also appear that delayed implantation has enabled southern species to disperse into colder regions.

How the period of delayed implantation has evolved is a matter of speculation. However,
it would seem to be significant that within the Mustelidae, those species which have more
than one litter a year never show it, but the majority of those with only one litter do.

It is possible that the badger's ancestors were smaller animals which had more than one
litter a year and that during evolution as they grew in size a second litter became disadvan-
tageous. If this were so it could be one reason for the further oestrous periods which occur
in many present-day sows even though healthy blastocysts are present. Perhaps too, the
retention of these further oestrous periods is a safety device to ensure eventual fertilisation
even if earlier matings have been unsuccessful?

Macdonald (1993) suggests a second oestrus allows the sow to adapt to changes in the male situation within the group as when a dominant boar dies and/or another takes over after the first mating. This might lead to litters of mixed paternity, diminishing the dangers of infanticide and inbreeding. Alternatively, as Ahnlund (1980) suggests, matings throughout the year, including the period of delayed implantation, may serve to strengthen the bond between the sexes, thus helping to maintain the male's defence of the social group's territory over a longer period.

CHAPTER 9

Numbers

HISTORICAL

IT is very difficult to obtain reliable information on the past status of badgers in Britain. Hence it is not possible to assess changes in the country's badger population with any accuracy. However, from Parish Council registers in the 17th and 18th centuries, there are many records of head money being paid for badgers. They come from many parts of the country and suggest that the badger had a wide distribution in those days. Payment ranged from 4d to 2 shillings per head.

There was considerable persecution of the badger in the 19th century and it is probable that numbers dropped considerably. By the end of the century, badgers were considered rather rare. Indeed, various reports (summarised in Cresswell *et al.* 1990) concluded that not only was the badger rare, but it was also endangered. However, this may have been due to paucity of records as most estimates were based only on local experience. The consensus of the reports published at around the turn of the century was that badgers were rare or uncommon in many parts of England, and that they were sparsely distributed in Scotland. The reason for this situation was almost certainly the pressure exerted by gamekeepers, who saw badgers as legitimate quarry on their list of game predators.

Lack of keeping during the period of World War I, and for some years after, gave some respite to the badger and numbers steadily increased, so that by the early 1930s they were fairly common in suitable areas all over England and Wales, but this increase was less noticeable in Scotland.

Pitt (1935) reckoned for the Wheatland district of Shropshire that the number of setts had increased from 10 to 37 in an area of 220 km² in the 34 years from 1900. This would seem to be typical of the general rate of increase in the country as a whole.

During and after World War II, the population continued to increase steadily up to about 1960. No doubt this was helped by the increasing tolerance towards the badger by landowners, farmers and those concerned with hunting and shooting, the helpful policy adopted by the Forestry Commission who welcomed badgers on their land, and a more favourable public opinion generally. During this time, too, there was a significant increase in the number of nature reserves on which badgers were protected.

However, between 1960 and 1972 a number of adverse factors were increasingly taking their toll and in some areas numbers started to decline. These were the ever-growing numbers of badgers killed on the roads and railways, the possible reduction in fertility due to much greater use of pesticides of the chlorinated hydrocarbon type, a great increase in some parts of the country of badger digging and the use of cyanide gassing on farms and shooting estates. The latter was illegal, but was nevertheless practised as a routine measure in many places. The effect of these adverse factors was very much greater in some districts than others, so although badger numbers continued to rise in some regions they fell quite dramatically in others.

The passing of the Badgers Act in 1973 resulted in a reduction in badger digging for sport and this allowed another increase in the population in areas particularly affected by persecution. By 1974, there is little doubt that in the southern half of Britain population density was higher than at any previous time. However, since then numbers have been significantly reduced particularly in parts of the Midlands, South Wales, Yorkshire and some northern counties owing to a considerable increase in illegal digging. There may also have been a fall in numbers in those parts of south-west England where culling took place because of the bovine tuberculosis problem. This programme of culling has continued since badger control began in 1975, with one short interruption in 1982. While the impact on badger populations is likely to be restricted to those localities where control has been targeted, the overall effect on the population of the south-west has probably been minimal. Indeed, in the survey by Cresswell *et al.* (1990), it was not possible to detect any significant reduction in badger activity even in the 1-km squares where control had taken place. The introduction of a new strategy incorporating the use of a live test for TB in 1994 will actually lead to *more* badgers being killed on an annual basis than before, so it remains to be seen what effect this will have on badger populations.

DISTRIBUTION OF SETTS

In recent years there have been two major surveys of the distribution of badger setts in Britain. The first of these summarised the results of the National Badger Survey instituted by the Mammal Society in 1963 (Clements *et al.* 1988). The survey itself was conducted by a co-ordinated team of county surveyors, and the intention was to map as many of the badger setts occurring across Britain as possible. Inevitably this type of survey tends to reflect

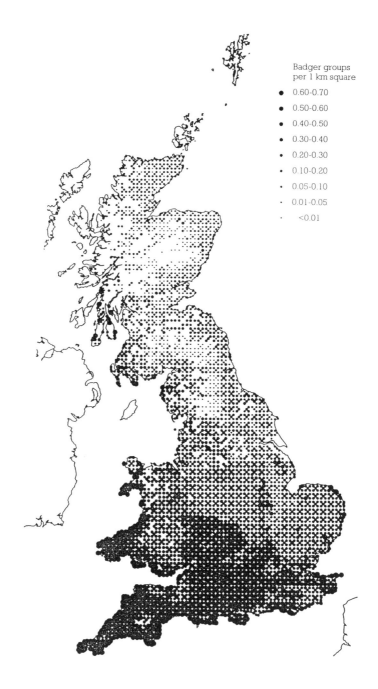

FIG 9.1 *Estimated mean sett densities in the various land classes in Britain (from Cresswell et al. 1990. See also Table 4.2, p. 76)*

the distribution of surveyors rather than the subject of study. Also, when carried out over a long period of time, the situation can change and information collected at the beginning can become out of date. Nevertheless, this survey resulted in an estimate of 36 000 main setts in Britain, giving an estimated total adult badger population of 216 000, which is fairly close to the estimate arrived at in the second of the recent sett surveys (Cresswell *et al.* 1990). (Fig 9.1).

This survey was carried out on a different basis. It was decided to survey a sample of the different habitat types in which badger setts are known to occur using 1-km squares as the unit of measurement. Eventually a team of people, many belonging to the various badger groups around the country, surveyed nearly 2500 1-km squares. Main setts were distinguished from others and a figure of 42 891 main setts was calculated for the whole of Britain, giving an estimated population of 250 000 adult badgers with an annual production of about 105 000 cubs.

Both these surveys make a number of assumptions. First, it is assumed that badgers are organised into social groups throughout their range in Britain, and that each group has a territory in which there is one main sett. Thus if main setts alone are identified and counted, it is possible to arrive at an estimate of the total number of social groups. Then it is assumed that there are on average six adult badgers to each social group to arrive at the population estimate. There are of course inherent weaknesses in these assumptions. For instance it is known that badgers are not necessarily social, and thus organised into group territories, throughout their European range (see Chapter 7), and it is also apparent that some areas of good habitat sustain much larger than average group sizes. Nevertheless, short of actually counting the total number of badgers present in Britain at any one time, which of course is impossible, these types of survey probably give us the best estimate we are likely to get of badger numbers. The great advantage of a rigorous type of survey such as that conducted by Cresswell *et al.* is that for the first time it gives us a baseline against which future population trends can be measured. It is the intention to repeat the survey at approximately 10-year intervals, and at the time of writing the second was underway.

The results of the survey by Cresswell *et al.* (1990) give average density estimates for badgers in the various land classes in Britain. In exceptionally favourable districts for badgers, the survey showed social group densities of 0.6–0.7 per 1-km square. In more typical areas which may be described as good badger country, 0.3–0.4 badger groups per 1-km square are often found.

Extraordinarily high numbers of setts have been found in a few regions. For example, in 1971 officials of the Ministry of Agriculture mapped 443 setts in an area of just of 10 km² (40 square miles) near Thornbury in Gloucestershire and in a much smaller region in Dorset, 247 setts were found in 1217 ha. It is obvious that a high proportion of these setts were not occupied at any one time and many were small, but clearly the population was very high indeed. In the exceptionally high-density population at Woodchester Park, there were 3.0 badger groups per 1-km square.

In two studies social group size varied according to local conditions but the population density was not correlated with group size; it was the size of the territories that was significant (Cheeseman & Mallinson 1981, Kruuk & Parish 1982). In very favourable country, territory size was small and density high and vice versa. The two variables of group size and territory size are in fact quite independent of each other (Kruuk 1989), and it therefore does not follow that a large territory will necessarily hold a large number of badgers. Group size, according to Kruuk, is correlated with the biomass of the badger's main food, i.e. earthworms, whereas territory size is determined by the dispersion of suitable feeding areas for this same food source.

FACTORS INFLUENCING POPULATION DENSITY

There is good evidence that in many high-density areas in Britain the number of main setts occupied has remained fairly constant over several decades if human interference has been minimal. So it can be assumed that apart from periodic fluctuations in numbers the population too has remained steady.

When population density is steady, it follows that recruitment into the population through births and immigration must equal the loss through deaths and dispersal. So any change in density which occurs will be the result of factors influencing any of the four items in the equation. Figure 9.2 shows the changes that have occurred in the average number of adults per social group at Woodchester Park over a 16-year period (21 undisturbed groups, annual average number of adults present). The graph shows that numbers gradually built up over the years to 1986, and remained relatively stable thereafter. In the latter years it would appear that the population density has hovered around the maximum which the area can sustain, but the reason for the increase during the initial years is less clear. One possible explanation is that prior to the commencement of this study badger numbers were suppressed by persecution. It was only in 1973 that effective protective legislation for badgers was introduced, and it is now known that depleted badger populations take a long time to recover (Cheeseman *et al.* 1993). If the trend in the population density at Woodchester Park reflects what has happened over the same period in other undisturbed badger populations, there does seem to have been a general increase which has resulted in an approximate doubling of the population density.

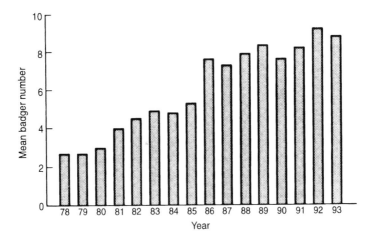

FIG 9.2   *The average social group size at Woodchester Park over time.*

In order to find out the average recruitment of cubs into a population per year we must take into account the sex ratio, age of maturity, proportion of breeding females, average litter size and life expectancy.

The sex ratio at birth is 1:1. Figures from road casualties obtained from the Ministry of Agriculture, Fisheries and Food for south-west England, combined with Ernest's own data, showed that out of 571 casualties, 278 were males and 283 females. However, Chris (unpubl. data) found that the numbers of adults at breeding age showed a marked preponderance of females with a ratio of 1:1.4 (males:females). The discrepancy between the data may be due to the greater likelihood of males becoming road casualties, since they are more widely ranging.

Sows and boars usually become mature when 12–15 months old (range 9–24). However, although most sows mate, not all bear litters. So although the average litter at birth is 2.7 the average productivity per female per year is only 1.67 and the figure for birth rate per head of population is 0.6 (Anderson & Trewhella 1985).

Life expectancy can be calculated where long term capture/recapture studies have been carried out. Figure 9.3 shows survivorship curves for male and female badgers from the population at Woodchester Park (C. Cheeseman, unpubl. data). Males have a higher mortality rate so that the proportion of females goes up with age.

It is not known precisely how long a badger can live in the wild, but Chris Ferris reported a boar, known well since a cub from a large mark on its flank — an old traffic injury — which was killed by diggers at 11½ years. She described it as 'big and rather ponderous, but hale and well; it had sired 3 cubs the year it died'. Ernest once saw a badger of great age, it was round as a barrel and very stiff in the joints, and there are several records of other very ancient animals being dug out, some of these being virtually blind. The oldest known badger in the population at Woodchester Park was a female which was an adult when first captured, and remained alive for a further 12 years, thus making it at least 14 when it died. There are a few records of other individuals in this same population, out of over 1500 individuals captured, which lived to at least 12. However, it appears to be unusual for badgers to exceed 10 years; very few may reach 15 or even more. One captive badger kept by Ruth Murray reached 19½ years and this would appear to be a record.

The mortality rate is difficult to assess accurately, but the most reliable method is based on age distribution in the population. However, the accuracy of this method is dependent upon each age class being sampled equally and this is difficult to achieve. The regular trapping, marking and releasing of a significant proportion of a population has given good results (C. Cheeseman, unpubl. data). It is clear that greatest mortality occurs in the first year after which the mortality rate is relatively constant at about 25–30% per annum (Fig. 9.3). In the first year mortality may be as high as 50–70%. Attempts have been made to estimate losses during the 8 weeks following birth, but as this period is spent underground accurate information is difficult to obtain. Comparing the size of litters seen above ground with those of birth rates, Ernest estimated an 18% loss. Other data based on the proportion of females with fresh placental scars found not to be rearing cubs suggest up to 25% (Wandeler & Graf 1982; H. Ahnlund unpubl. data). Data from Woodchester Park show an average annual postnatal to pre-weaning loss of 29%, although it must be pointed out that this figure may not be representative of populations living at lower density. It is also probable that when yearlings are dispersing and attempting to join a new social group, rather more losses than usual may occur.

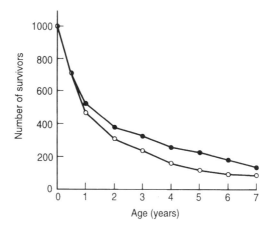

FIG 9.3   *Survivorship curves for male and female badgers at Woodchester Park.*
(● = males, ○ = females)

Anderson & Trewhella (1985) calculated from data on fecundity and maturity that the average intrinsic growth rate of the population is 0.2 per year. This slow potential increase is of course regulated by various constraints such as disease or adverse feeding conditions such as droughts. These adverse factors may cause a population to decline by 30% or more, but recovery is usually achieved in 2–4 years. If, however, a number of social groups are removed, as in disease control operations, recolonisation may be very slow. Two removals in the high-density population at Woodchester Park revealed that the population took 9–10 years to recover to pre-removal levels (Cheeseman *et al.* 1993). Obviously the time of recovery will vary with the status of the surrounding badger population and the extent of the area where eradication occurred.

It appears likely that in the earlier stages of recolonisation the individuals present do not provide the stability needed within a social group to allow successful breeding. In one such area cubs were not produced for 3 years although adults of both sexes were present (Cheeseman *et al.* 1993). A possible explanation of this could be that because social groups are such closely bound entities, when a vacuum is produced, recolonisation does not necessarily take place from contiguous groups but builds up in a haphazard manner from wandering individuals seeking either new territories or acceptance by another social group. If this is so the speed of recolonisation would be governed by the reproductive success of the various social groups in the region and the extent of the area where eradication occurred.

Dispersal of young badgers (p 170) is extremely restricted in high-density regions (Cheeseman *et al.* 1988a). In other areas it would appear that there is a tendency for female yearlings to remain and males to disperse. But what effect dispersal has on the genetic relatedness of populations is unknown. Various studies are in progress to try to resolve this by using DNA fingerprinting to reveal genetic relatedness between individuals.

INTRINSIC FACTORS CAUSING POPULATION CONTROL

It is well known that some years are better for cubs than others and it seems likely that any intrinsic constraints on breeding mainly occur at implantation.

If it is true that putting on fat is a requisite before implantation takes place then a summer and autumn when food is very scarce might lead to conditions when implantation becomes less likely, so fewer litters would be born the following spring. In 1975, badgers in many parts of Britain were in very poor condition owing to the severe drought that lasted from June into the late autumn. This also coincided with a poor acorn and blackberry year. So it was most unlikely that much fat was stored. The spring that followed was certainly a very poor season for cubs in many parts. But whether this was due to failure to put on enough fat is an open question. Obviously, much more evidence is needed before this hypothesis can be proved or refuted.

Failure to implant may also be due to stress. Badgers in captivity, captured as adults, could be considered to be living under conditions of mild stress and it is in such animals that record periods of delayed implantation have been noted. It is also true that although mating has occurred many times in badgers kept in captivity, only a small proportion have had litters. So stress may interfere with implantation.

It may be that under conditions of very high density badgers are subjected to increasing stress and in some seasons, difficulty in obtaining sufficient food. These two factors together could play a part in population control when numbers become too high. However, this must only be looked upon as a speculation.

CAUSES OF DEATH

Natural enemies

In Britain it would appear that badger numbers are not much affected by natural enemies apart from humans. Adult badgers in particular are seldom killed by other animals, although there are isolated examples involving foxes (p. 65), and occasionally badgers may be killed by hounds if found above ground. They may also die of bite wounds received during territorial disputes (p. 149).

Cubs are rather more vulnerable. During the first few weeks of life they are left on their own for long periods and a few may be killed by dogs entering the sett during the day. Occasionally, a vixen or a boar badger may kill them. It is also possible that if a sow is disturbed soon after the birth of the cubs she may kill and eat them. This has occurred in captivity and Chris has circumstantial evidence that it has occurred in the wild (unpubl. data).

In February, it is not unusual to find a dead cub, less then a week old, on the spoil heap outside a main sett. There is seldom any sign of injury, although several have been seen with small punctures in the skin, probably made by the sow's teeth when the cub was carried out. It is possible that these cubs had died through being lain on. R.S. Elliott (pers. comm.) reported a case of a cub, about the size of a small rabbit, which he found dead outside the sett; there was a mass of bedding around the entrance and it appeared to him that the cub had been cleared out with the bedding.

Cubs may be taken by wolves (*Canis lupus*), lynxes (*Felix lynx*) and wolverines (*Gulo gulo*) in regions where they occur, and eagle owls (*Bubo bubo*) are said to take cubs occasionally. Golden eagles (*Aquila chrysaetos*) may also take them, but these are likely to be as carrion. However, it cannot be ruled out that diurnal raptors such as eagles and buzzards (*Buteo buteo*) may very occasionally kill cubs in the late evening.

Starvation

Starvation is an important cause of cub death. It occurs mainly in the period following weaning, particularly in extremely dry summers such as 1975 and 1984 when mortality was marked. We suspect that starvation is a much more common cause of death than is generally realised. Eric Ashby considers it quite usual in the New Forest area, especially in parts well away from farmland where there is a relative lack of earthworms in the acid soils.

Chris (unpubl. data) found that in Gloucestershire in August 1984, following the severe drought, that most of the 70 badgers caught for sampling and release were in poor condition with low average weights. He also found animals which had died of starvation. In contrast, by November 1984, following a wet autumn with food in abundance, most were in good condition with higher average weights than normal for the time of year. This illustrates how rapidly badgers' fortunes may fluctuate with the vagaries of the climate.

Disease

There are no records of major disease epidemics wiping out large numbers of the population; indeed it seems unlikely that disease plays an important part in population control.

In Britain, the most important disease afflicting badgers is tuberculosis due to the bovine strain of tubercle bacillus, *Mycobacterium bovis*. However, the mortality due to tuberculosis in badgers is very low (Cheeseman *et al.* 1989). The implications of this disease are discussed in more detail in Chapter 10. In Europe, badgers are known to contract rabies. Over the five years 1989–1993 a total of 1099 cases were recorded in badgers across the whole of Europe. However, the fox is the main reservoir and vector of rabies in Europe, and badgers as well as many other wild and domestic species contract rabies through being bitten by a rabid fox. Badgers are also susceptible to anthrax.

In an analysis of causes of death of badgers from Gloucestershire and North Avon, Gallagher & Nelson (1979) found that the great majority were due to road accidents; others had died of tuberculosis, non-tuberculosis bite wounds, starvation and arteriosclerosis. However, any sample including just those badgers which are *found* dead is bound to be subject to bias. It is extremely difficult to obtain a true picture of the relative importance of the various causes of death, but one thing which seems certain is that road traffic accidents are by far the greatest single factor. In Woodchester Park for the years 1978–1993, Chris found 258 marked badgers dead. Fifty-one of these were too decomposed to allow the cause of death to be determined reliably, but of the remaining 207, 134 (65%) had died of road accidents, 18 (9%) from tuberculosis, 15 (7%) from starvation, 18 (9%) had been killed and 22 (11%) died from rare or unknown causes (unpubl. data). The proportion of deaths due to road accidents must be regarded as a minimum because it is known that some individuals struck by cars die later either in their sett or somewhere away from the road where the carcass is less likely to be discovered.

Pitt (1941) has recorded cases of pharyngitis/tonsillitis, and an acute respiratory condition of unknown origin was observed by D.A. Humphries (pers. comm.) in a colony of seven badgers near Cheltenham. To quote from his account:

> On the 18 April shortly after the arrival of a strange badger all the badgers appeared healthy, but the next night coughing and wheezing was heard before they emerged. On the 20th a sow emerged very late, wheezing loudly and attempted to reach the dung-pit which was on the bank above the hole. She was unable to climb far up the bank and slipped back, rolling over. After a short rest she dragged herself slowly down the hole. Several other badgers were suffering less severely on this date. By the 22nd all the badgers except the stranger had the disease, but the sow had almost recovered and was able to emerge as usual. No trace of the illness remained on the 25th.

Osteomyelitis could also be a cause of death, especially in old animals. Ernest has examined several skulls where there was gross malformation of bone associated with the socket of a broken canine which appeared to have been the primary locus of infection.

Parasites

Parasitic lung worm infestation has been reported from Germany (Schlegel 1933) and the disease proved fatal in a number of cases. No such condition has been recognised in this country. A number of species of gut parasites have been recorded, in particular, nematodes and tapeworms (Hancox 1980). In otherwise healthy individuals these are unlikely to cause trouble. It is not surprising that one of the tapeworms has the earthworm as its secondary host and another is believed to be acquired through eating dor-beetles.

Ectoparasites can be a problem and might account for the scratching behaviour so commonly observed in badgers. Bedding harbours many of these parasites and its periodic removal and replacement with fresh material probably assists in keeping down the population of ectoparasites.

Fleas, lice, ticks and mites have all been found on badgers, the commonest being the biting louse *Trichodectes melis* which is specific to the badger. In emaciated or debilitated animals, the louse burden and indeed the general ectoparasite infestation is often quite enormous. The skin may sometimes appear to be seething with the small white lice, and vast numbers of eggs, which are attached to the hairs, may be seen.

The flea most commonly found is *Paraceras melis*, but mole and hedgehog fleas (*Histrichopsylla talpae* and *Archaeopsylla erinacei*) also occur which appear to be accidental vagrants transmitted on to the badger when feeding on the more typical hosts of these species. Two other species of flea occur, but only rarely: *Chaetopsylla trichosa* (a single record from Scotland, but more from Continental badgers) and the human flea, *Pulex irritans*, which occurs on the fox. Perhaps the few records of this flea on the badger may be accounted for through badgers cohabiting with foxes.

Ticks are less commonly found on badgers, although prevalence varies with district. Hancox (1973) found ticks on 40% of the corpses he examined near Oxford, but from experience of Somerset badgers, Ernest considers this an unusually high incidence. Ticks are most often found on the ears, above the tail and on the inside of the thighs. Three species occur fairly regularly, the dog tick, *Ixodes canisuga*, the hedgehog tick, *I. hexagonus* and the sheep tick, *I. ricinus*. There are also records for *I. reduvius* and *I. melicola*. Ernest was told by Gordon Thompson that *I. canisuga* was originally assumed to be a parasite of sheep dogs

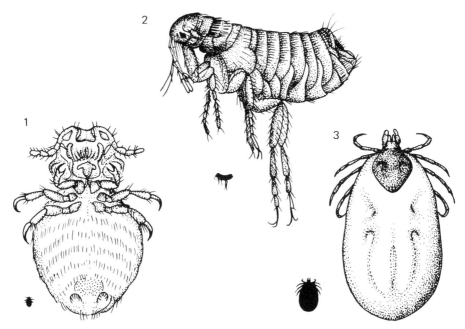

FIG 9.4 *Three common badger parasites. 1. Louse,* Trichodectes melis *female (ventral). 2. Flea,* Paraceras meles. *3. Tick.* Hexodes hexagonus *female (dorsal). Actual sizes are indicated alongside.*

in the north of England and in Scotland, but he considers the true hosts are foxes and badgers and that the parasitising of dogs was an adaptation, the kennel being comparable with the sett or earth.

Mark Fisher (pers. comm.), reporting on the badgers near Coniston in Cumbria, said that in his opinion one of the reasons why badgers did so well there was the absence of sheep ticks which were rife in other localities in the county. He cited the case of two cubs found in the open in Nab Scar, Grasmere, wrapped in sheep's wool and covered in ticks. The cubs were so weak that there was no hope of their survival. Another instance was described by F.S. Port in a letter to *The Field.* He found a dead full-grown sow with 'the whole of the face, neck, head and shoulders covered in sheep ticks — up to 1000 of them'. It is not possible to say whether they were the cause of death, but if not they were surely a contributory factor.

Mites occasionally infest badgers. John Sankey (pers. comm.) observed how one of his badgers after being at liberty for 5 weeks, returned with a local infection of mites. He was unable to remove them and a bald patch developed in the middle of the back, but two applications of benzine hexachloride dispersed the infestation and the hair grew again in 2 months. Ernest has also known of a mite infection of the ear. This causes intense irritation and may give rise to torn ears as a result of much scratching.

There have also been several reports of badgers suffering from mange, although this is not nearly so usual in badgers as in foxes. A. MacFarlane, who was head keeper of an estate in the north of Scotland, wrote about a badger which was lying in a fox's den and had no hair except a small tuft on its tail. A fox had used the den 3 years before and had also had mange. Chris has seen a badger killed on the road in Gloucestershire which was similarly devoid of hair, and other instances have been reported from the Netherlands.

Direct action by humans

All the factors mentioned so far are possible causes of death in badgers although some obviously play a much greater part than others in keeping numbers down, but by far the most potent factors in population control are those concerned with human activities.

For at least the past 200 years numbers have been kept down by direct human action. This has taken such forms as badger digging, hunting, trapping, snaring, shooting and gassing. During the 1960s and the early 1970s badger digging increased and in some areas became a popular pastime for city dwellers who went out at weekends into the countryside for the purpose. This development coincided with an increase in popularity of such breeds of terrier as the Jack Russell (Murray 1968). In consequence many setts were destroyed and the badgers killed.

Since the abolition of the gin trap, the passing of the Badgers Act (1973) and its amendment in the Wildlife and Countryside Act (1981) some of these direct pressures have been reduced. Badgers are now fully protected by law (see Appendix 1). However, enforcement is difficult and much persecution still takes place. Although badger digging is illegal it is still widely practised in spite of a number of convictions resulting in heavy fines. Badger protection groups have been set up in some areas to combat this menace. Cresswell *et al.* (1990) attempted to estimate the possible impact of digging on the British badger population. They calculated that about 9000 badger setts are dug each year, and assuming an average of one badger killed per dig, this gives an annual loss of 9000 badgers to diggers. The authors recognised that this was a crude estimate as no firm evidence exists on the number of badgers taken in digging operations, and it is sometimes difficult to distinguish between fresh digging and old, thus making it hard to estimate the proportion of setts dug each year. Nevertheless, there is no doubt that this is still a serious problem, and in some localised parts of the country, badger populations have been decimated by the activity of diggers.

Badger hunting with dogs, above ground after the badgers have left their setts to forage, has largely ceased, but 'lamping' late at night using spotlights from vehicles is another growing menace. The lights locate and dazzle the animals and guns, nets and dogs are used to kill or capture them.

Gassing with cyanide preparations such as 'cymag' has been widely used in spite of its being illegal to kill badgers in this way. It was used as a routine measure on certain farms and by some shooting syndicates for killing foxes and badgers. The Control of Pesticides Regulations (1986), made under the Food and Environment Protection Act (1985), made it illegal to gas foxes with hydrogen cyanide.

It is ironical that with the abolition of the gin trap, the practice of snaring badgers has greatly increased. Badgers are caught very easily by this method and Ernest knows of one wood in the Quantock Hills where a thriving colony of badgers was totally snared out by a farmer who, through ignorance or prejudice, considered they were a potential danger to his lambs. The action was entirely unnecessary. There are many reports of badgers being seen eating the carcasses of dead lambs, but not reliable eye witness account of a badger actually catching and killing one. In most cases the original culprit was almost certainly a fox or dog.

Snaring often results in much cruelty, as badgers are very strong and may go off with the snare round them to die a lingering death. We have many times seen badgers which have died in this way with the snare deeply buried in their flesh. Many badgers, of course, are caught in snares set for foxes, but some snares are deliberately set for badgers and large numbers are killed: this again is illegal, but is practised commonly.

So although legislation and public opinion have done much to reduce pressure on badgers, direct action against them still remains a very significant cause of death and a threat to their survival in some areas.

Traffic

A very large number of deaths occur on the roads in Britain each year. It is estimated that of the 25–30% of adult badgers which die annually at Woodchester Park, at least half of these are killed on the road (Cheeseman *et al.* 1987). If these figures are representative of the whole of mainland Britain, a staggering number of at least 37 500 badgers are killed annually on the roads. During the years when the Ministry of Agriculture, Fisheries and Food (MAFF) carried out a survey of the prevalence of TB in road casualty badgers, around 1000 a year were collected over a 16-year period (Cheeseman *et al.* 1989). Clearly this was only a small proportion of the total number killed. Although mortality due to the motor car is extremely high relative to other causes of death, it is unlikely that it has a major impact on badger populations, as in most areas badgers still breed below their full potential. The age structure of the population may be affected, as a high proportion of individuals are killed on the road before they achieve a natural life span. Mortality is often high following the opening of a major new road, but it is surprising how well badgers sometimes adapt to the new conditions, with many large badger setts having been established along road embankments. This is not to say that we should be complacent about the effects of roads on badgers. Some badly planned road schemes have undoubtedly had a detrimental effect on local populations, with perhaps the most serious factor being the bisection of established territories. Road building authorities are now taking a more enlightened approach to the problem, but it remains an issue where more research is needed.

The sample of road-killed badgers which was collected by MAFF has revealed some important details on the pattern of mortality. Davies *et al.* (1987) examined the seasonal distribution of 984 road-killed badgers recovered in the south of England during 1984 (Fig. 9.5). The data show a bimodal distribution in mortality for both sexes, with peaks occurring in spring and late summer. Interestingly, and contrary to the general finding that there is a preponderance of females in the adult population, there was no evidence of a statistical difference between the total number of males and females killed, nor any difference in the seasonal distribution of deaths between the two sexes. In addition, by examining the proportion of small carcasses in the sample the authors found no evidence that dispersal of young animals contributes to either of the seasonal peaks in mortality.

Data from another sample of road-killed badgers (Neal 1977) demonstrated that fluctuations in food availability may affect the precise timing of the second peak in mortality. In 3 of the 4 years of this study, the second peak in mortality occurred in September–October, but in the fourth year it occurred during July–August. This particular year (1975) was

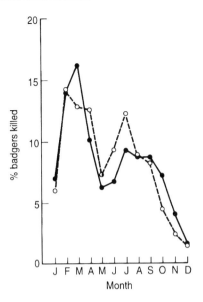

FIG 9.5 *Seasonal distribution of road-killed badgers.* (● = males, ○ = females).
Source: Davis *et al.* 1987.

exceptionally dry and it was proposed that the consequent difficulty in finding food had brought forward the second peak in mortality. This is consistent with the findings of Davies *et al.* (1987) where the data showed a second peak in July and August for the year 1984, which was also an unusually dry one.

Many badgers are killed on the railways where the track separates one sett from another and ancestral paths connect them. Charles Eyre (pers. comm.)w, a signalman who worked near Bath in Avon, reported that an average of four badgers were killed on the line every year less than 50 m from the signal box where he worked. There was also another crossing place in Somerset, near Taunton, where badgers were killed regularly by trains. These instances are typical of many parts of the country and in total must account for a large number of badgers. But the most serious threat is ground-level electrification. During the few months following the electrification of the line between Ashford and Deal in Kent, Michael Alcock (pers. comm.) recorded that 68 badgers were electrocuted, and over a longer period of time as many as 200 died in this way. Similarly, in Hampshire, Arthur Jollands (pers. comm.) picked up 11 badgers on a 5 km stretch of line near Alton in a single year and six more in the first 3 months of the next. Also, when the line was electrified in the New Forest area, 30 badgers were killed during the subsequent year over a 14.5 km stretch.

The number of deaths caused in this way does fall after a few years, but whether this is due to learning or reduction in numbers in the neighbourhood is difficult to know. Learning can only come through experience of the death of another badger, as contact with the rail is always fatal. A most intriguing aspect of the problem came to light through G.P. Knowles (pers. comm.) who knew a retired army officer who lived by the railway at Camberley in Surrey. Before electrification came to that line, foxes had an earth in the embankment and there was a badger sett just inside the wood nearby. Both species used to wander across the line regularly and when electrification came, there were many casualties. However, some time after this event, his informant saw a badger crossing the line in a zig-zag manner without getting harmed. Later he saw a fox do likewise, and subsequently many of both species crossed in this way. On inspection of the line he found that they passed between the gaps in the live rails! One wonders if these animals are capable of detecting the magnetic field surrounding the rail? Unlikely perhaps, but not impossible, as some animals can orientate their movements in relation to magnetic fields.

Poisons

Badgers are occasionally found which have died as a result of consuming poisoned bait. Some of these may be the victims of deliberate targeting of badgers, while others may be incidental, having eaten bait probably intended for other species. The Ministry of Agriculture, Fisheries and Food runs a scheme to investigate suspected incidents of poisoning of animals, known as the Wildlife Incident Investigation Scheme. Over the 3 years from 1991 to 1993 inclusive, there were 102 reported incidents in Britain involving badger deaths (Fletcher *at al.* 1994). Pesticide poisoning was confirmed in a small proportion of these (17) and the substances identified included paraquat, metaldehyde, mevinphos, and certain anti-coagulant rodenticides. In addition there were several incidents involving the suspected illegal gassing of badger setts. Although this problem is probably not significant in terms of the number of badgers killed, it is nevertheless a dangerous and unnecessary practice, particularly as the methods employed are often indiscriminate. For this reason the Agricultural Departments of England, Scotland, Wales and Northern Ireland maintain their joint Campaign Against the Illegal Poisoning of Animals (CAIPA), and all suspected cases of illegal poisoning are vigorously investigated in conjunction with the police, and prosecutions brought where possible.

In the past, the effect of various pesticides on badgers has been extremely difficult to assess, and no firm conclusions may be drawn except in a few well-documented instances. Great anxiety was expressed among badger watchers because there appeared to be a considerable drop in the number of cubs produced in some parts of Britain during the period 1962–1969. This was a time when the persistent organo-chlorine pesticides were being used in considerable quantities.

Where such pesticides as DDT and dieldrin were used regularly, large residues of these substances were accumulated in the tissues of earthworms, although they themselves appeared to be unharmed by them. So, it was argued that as badgers ate such large quantities of earthworms, the effect would be passed on. To investigate this hypothesis, a number of badger livers and fat samples were analysed, but the majority of them showed only trace residues, certainly not enough to cause death.

However, D.J. Jefferies (1968) found that between 1964 and 1968, of the 17 badger carcasses that he received for analysis at Monks Wood Experimental Station, at least six had certainly died from dieldrin poisoning and circumstantial evidence suggested that another six had died from the same cause. This, of course, was not a random sample of badgers found dead, but it does indicate the dangers of such pesticides. It was concluded that the probable chain of events was that seed dressed with dieldrin had been eaten by pigeons which had died as a result and been eaten in their turn by badgers.

The symptoms of dieldrin poisoning in the badger are apparent blindness, lack of appetite and convulsions, especially of the jaws. Badgers suffering in this way were seen above ground in daylight; they took little notice of people and sometimes wandered in circles, bumping into objects. Incidentally, foxes were affected by dieldrin poisoning much more than badgers, 1300 dying in the winter of 1959–1960 in the eastern counties of England alone.

Whether such pesticides absorbed in sub-lethal quantities interfered with the reproductive process in badgers (as it is known to have done in such birds as herons and buzzards) is now impossible to prove, but this could have been the cause for a decline in cub numbers in the late 1960s.

Fortunately, the total ban on this type of persistent pesticide in Great Britain has removed this particular hazard.

CHAPTER 10

Badgers and Bovine Tuberculosis

WHAT IS TUBERCULOSIS?

TUBERCULOSIS in cattle is caused by the bacterium *Mycobacterium bovis (M. bovis)*. When tubercle bacilli invade the body they typically cause a chronic form of disease characterised by the formation of 'tubercles' in the infected tissue. In cattle these lesions of approximately 1–20 mm in diameter are usually found in the lungs. In advanced cases lesions may appear in the udder, uterus and skin, but such cases are now very rare because infected animals are identified by routine testing before this stage is reached.

The particular type of tuberculosis which infects cattle acquired its specific name (*M. bovis*) because of its frequency of occurrence in cattle, but the bacterium can infect a variety of other mammals, including of course badgers and humans. Historically, when lesions of the udder were common, the disease could be spread from cattle to humans via infected milk and the drinking of untreated milk undoubtedly led to a large number of cases of tuberculosis in people.

PATHOLOGY IN BADGERS

The respiratory and urinary systems, together with their associated lymph nodes, are the principal sites of *M. bovis* infection in badgers, although tuberculosis lesions have been noted in all the major organ systems. It is considered that most renal (kidney) cases are probably secondary to pulmonary (lung) infection, although some may result from infected bite wounds. Skin lesions are not uncommon and probably also result from bites inflicted by an infectious badger. Lesions associated with the digestive system are rare, although intestinal ulcers and hepatic (liver) nodules are occasionally reported. The tubercles themselves when they occur in lung tissue, for example, are small (1–4 mm diameter), well defined, spherical and usually pale grey or ivory coloured. In badgers these lesions may very rarely become calcified (hardened due to deposition of calcium salts). In advanced cases the lesions may be found throughout the lung tissue and when these rupture, large numbers of bacilli are expelled and may be excreted in the sputum. An animal in this condition will be highly infectious and capable of passing on the disease through coughing and sneezing. Bacilli may also be swallowed in the sputum and pass out in the faeces. Similarly if an animal has open lesions in its kidneys, bacilli may be excreted in the urine.

HISTORY OF ATTESTATION

In order to understand the badger's current role in the occurrence of bovine tuberculosis, we need to go right back to the early part of the 20th century and look at the history of the disease in cattle. At this time there was some debate as to whether tuberculous cows posed a threat to human health. A Royal Commission which reported in 1912 concluded that this was the case and provided evidence to justify concerted action against the disease in cattle. However, it was not until 1934 that a Committee on Cattle Diseases recommended the introduction of a voluntary testing scheme. This was adopted the following year at a time when at least 40% of cows in dairy herds were infected with TB. The war years retarded progress, but in 1950 the programme was given renewed vigour with the introduction of compulsory testing on an area by area basis. By 1960 the whole of Great Britain was declared 'attested' and the incidence of TB in cattle had declined to a low level with the incidence of reactor herds down to about 1 in 50.

For a while it appeared that TB might be eradicated from the national herd, but pockets of infection persisted, particularly in south-west England. In some areas the incidence of TB in cattle was up to 15 times the national average, and even more worrying for the authorities, there was often no apparent source of infection.

ACTION AGAINST BADGERS

In 1971 a badger was found dead on a farm in Gloucestershire, having died from advanced tuberculosis due to *M. bovis*. Infection in cattle had recently been confirmed on the farm, and the farmer himself had been suspicious that badgers were the source of disease in his cattle. Following this the Ministry of Agriculture, Fisheries and Food (MAFF) initiated a survey of badger carcasses recovered throughout the south-west region and it soon became apparent that tuberculosis was well established in badgers; in the region of 20% of animals were infected. In 1973 the Ministry concluded that action was required against badgers where it was clear that they posed a threat to cattle. The nature of the disease in badgers, together with the knowledge that badgers regularly forage in fields grazed by cattle, suggested that badgers were probably responsible for the previously unexplained outbreaks of tuberculosis in cattle.

Initially, official action was to advise herd owners on methods of killing badgers in areas where badgers were implicated in outbreaks of tuberculosis in cattle. This was followed by legislative action to permit the use of hydrogen cyanide gas to kill badgers in their setts, but licences for gassing would only be issued to Ministry staff or persons under Ministry control. Gassing operations commenced in the autumn of 1975 and this was the principal means of control until 1982 when it was suspended because of doubts over the humaneness of the technique. In addition, the indiscriminate nature of gassing and the impossibility of post mortem assessment brought considerable criticism from scientists. Gassing was replaced by the use of cage traps and shooting the badgers captured, a regime which had the advantage of yielding carcasses for post mortem examination.

Right from the beginning this issue attracted fierce public debate. On one side of the coin were farmers who saw the badger as a threat to their livelihood, and on the other were people to whom the idea of killing one of our most popular native mammal species was an anathema. The analogy of a two sided coin is perhaps inappropriate as this particular issue has many facets. The view taken by individuals depends to a large degree on their background; farmers, zoologists, ecologists, veterinarians, epidemiologists, economists, administrators, mathematicians, conservationists, and so on, all stand at different points on the spectrum of attitudes, according to their own biases and inclinations.

One of MAFF's first actions was to set up a Consultative Panel on which all interests could be represented. The Panel was first convened in 1975 and has met approximately twice yearly ever since, with the only major change being the appointment of an independent Chairman in 1987. Its terms of reference are to keep under review the role of the badger as a reservoir of bovine tuberculosis, and the operational work on badger control carried out by MAFF.

Valuable though the work of the Consultative Panel has been, the contentious nature of the issue has led to two independent reviews being commissioned by MAFF. The first of these was conducted by Lord Zuckerman in 1980. Having considered all the evidence he concluded that badgers constituted a significant reservoir of bovine tuberculosis in parts of south-west England, and that MAFF's strategy of killing badgers in areas where they were believed to be responsible for outbreaks of disease in cattle was then the best means of containing the problem and should continue. It was also recommended that research should focus on the behaviour of badgers and on understanding the distribution of tuberculosis in badger populations, and that experts from the Government's Chemical Defence Establishment be called in to devise improvements in the technique of gassing setts. It was this last recommendation that led to the suspension of gassing as a control technique. Finally, Lord Zuckerman made perhaps his most significant recommendation, which was that the whole policy should be independently reviewed again in 3 years time.

In September 1984 the Minister of Agriculture appointed a three man team under the chairmanship of Professor George Dunnet, and their report was published in March 1986. Once again the review team were convinced that the badger was implicated in the relatively high incidence of tuberculosis in cattle in south-west England. However, they recognised that it was undesirable that a large number of healthy badgers were killed in the course of control operations. One of their recommendations was that a diagnostic test should be developed to detect the presence of tuberculosis infection in living badgers, and that the procedures for badger control should eventually be changed to discriminate between infected and healthy individuals. They also recommended continuation of field studies on the epidemiology of tuberculosis in wild badgers. While the diagnostic test was being developed the Dunnet team recommended the operation of an 'interim strategy' where badger control would be confined just to the farm, or part of the farm, where cattle infection occurred.

Of course the notion that badger control would eventually be selective, with only infected individuals being killed, received widespread support from farming and conservation interests alike. Alas this is not the way events transpired. By 1993 it was clear that the goal of developing a field test with a high degree of sensitivity (i.e. a test where the proportion of 'false' negatives would be low) was beyond the available technology. In December that year the Minister of Agriculture announced that a test had been developed with a high degree of specificity (i.e. the number of 'false' *positives* was low) but a rather limited degree of sensitivity — around 37% — such that it could not be used as an individual animal test in the badger control strategy as had been originally intended. This was disappointing, to say the least.

In 1994 a new strategy was adopted where the 'interim strategy' introduced by Dunnet would continue, but a trial would be conducted where the effects of a pre-emptive strategy would be scientifically evaluated. This pre-emptive strategy would employ the diagnostic test, and all the badgers in a sett containing at least one positive badger would be removed. For the first time in the history of the badger control programme, the proposed strategy would incorporate experimental controls so that the results could be analysed statistically and valid conclusions drawn. Another major departure was the adoption of the preventative approach, where the intention was to prevent tuberculosis being spread from badgers to cattle, rather than waiting for cattle to become infected and then to act as sentinels for the presence of disease in badgers which were only then subjected to control measures — a classic example of shutting the stable door after the horse has bolted. As well as the trial of a new control strategy based on the diagnostic test, together with continued research into relevant aspects of badger ecology and behaviour, there was to be research to develop effective vaccines for tuberculosis in badgers.

Previously the Ministry had been unconvinced that vaccines could be produced and delivered successfully. Perhaps the principal reason for the reassessment of this position has been the tremendous advances made in biotechnology recently, particularly in the field of genetically engineered vaccines. It now seems that there is a real prospect of developing a safe, effective vaccine for tuberculosis in badgers. For practical reasons such a vaccine will have to be orally delivered, and a long term research initiative has started towards this end. At last a solution is in sight which might satisfy all parties. To put this bold objective in perspective it must be said that the time scale between the announcement of the new programme and the implementation in the field of a vaccine is likely to be long, possibly in the order of two decades. This is why research into other aspects, such as ways of avoiding the transmission of disease from badgers to cattle, investigating the effects of removal on badger populations, and testing the effect of pre-emptive control, remains important in the interim.

POSSIBLE ROUTES OF BADGER INFECTION

It is simply not known how long TB has been present in badgers. The development of the pastoral system in Britain and the practice of keeping domestic cattle have taken place over hundreds of years. At some stage it is likely, given the past prevalence of disease in the national herd, that cattle may have passed *M. bovis* infection to badgers, possibly by excreting live bacilli in their dung which badgers subsequently rooted through when searching for dung beetles and their larvae. It is equally possible that badgers may have picked up infection from cattle sputum coughed on to pasture as they grazed. Badgers are susceptible to TB so the disease became established in some populations, producing a wildlife reservoir.

The available evidence suggests that the badger is an ideal alternative host, the disease persisting in badger populations in the absence of re-infection from any other species. TB may be transmitted from one animal to another by an aerosol, i.e. tiny droplets of moisture exhaled from the respiratory tract which may contain live bacilli. If such a contaminated aerosol is inhaled by another susceptible animal, infection may be established. Whether or not the bacteria remain alive and multiply in their new host will depend on the immune response and general condition of that animal, and to some extent the 'weight' of infection — the greater the number of organisms in the ineffective dose, the greater the probability that the immune defences will be overcome. In the close confines of a badger sett, it is easy to appreciate how disease transmission via an aerosol could take place. Animals sharing the same nest chamber would breathe the same air for long periods of time, thus a 'consumptive' badger would be likely to infect other susceptible animals.

Another mechanism of disease transfer in badgers is through bite wounding. We have seen (Chapter 7) that badgers are territorial, and fighting, with the inevitable consequence of bite wounds, is not uncommon. A badger with open lesions of TB in its lungs will pass bacilli in its sputum. Live bacteria will therefore be present in the animal's mouth, and if such an individual bites another, it would be as effective a way of transmitting TB as injection with a hypodermic syringe. Infected bite wounds are seen in a small proportion of cases and transmission by this route is likely to lead to rapid spread of disease to other parts of the body.

Perhaps the most surprising aspect of TB in badgers, when one considers the badger's life style and the opportunities for disease spread, is why the prevalence of disease in some infected populations is not much higher than it is. In the first review of the badger TB issue, Lord Zuckerman concluded that TB was probably a very significant cause of natural death in badgers, and that the disease even threatened the future of the badger itself. Fortunately neither of these speculations proved to be true. TB is a relatively insignificant cause of natural mortality, and there is no evidence to suggest that the viability of badger populations is affected by the presence of TB. It is nevertheless puzzling as to why more individuals do not catch TB. Part of the answer is likely to be the presence of resistance to the disease, both at the individual level and the 'population' level — thus explaining why TB is more prevalent in some areas. This is obviously speculative and there are bound to be other factors involved in explaining differences in prevalence and susceptibility to TB in badgers, such as geography, climate and population pressure through factors such as food availability and persecution. It is clearly an area where more research is needed.

Before leaving the subject of transmission of TB to badgers we should finally consider whether it is still likely that infection is spread from cattle to badgers. It is of course possible for a cow with open TB lesions to infect not only other cattle, but also badgers. Infectious cases do occasionally turn up in the cattle testing programme, but because of the sustained and systematic nature of cattle testing their frequency is now rare. So it seems unlikely that the occasional transfer of disease from cattle to badgers, if indeed this still occurs, is a significant factor in the epidemiology of TB. The notion has been put forward that the disease is being maintained in cattle and that they are simply giving it to badgers, but if this was the case then the programme of attestation would have been even more successful than it has been, through the identification and slaughter of infected animals. Additionally, there are areas of the country where TB is present in badgers but no infection occurs in cattle, and finally, if cattle to badger transmission was common we would expect to see much larger average numbers of reactors per infected herd, because other cattle would be infected as well as badgers.

HOW MIGHT BADGERS INFECT CATTLE?

What proof is there that badgers infect cattle with TB? This is probably the most common question asked when this issue is under discussion between those concerned with the problem and interested members of the public. The simple answer has to be that there is no scientific proof of a link but that the circumstantial evidence is substantial.

The first and only experiments carried out to demonstrate that badgers can transmit TB to cattle were conducted by Little *et al.* (1982) where cattle were housed together with both naturally infected and artificially dosed badgers under laboratory conditions. The experiments demonstrated that TB transmission can take place from badgers to cattle, but of course it is difficult extrapolating these results to badgers in the wild and the experiment was not designed to reveal *how* infection is picked up by cattle. So the results only really added to the weight of circumstantial evidence.

Further circumstantial evidence was gained from two areas where badgers were totally eradicated. In both areas persistent cattle TB was thought to originate from infected badger populations. One of these areas was around the town of Thornbury in the county of Avon and the other was centred on Steeple Leaze in Dorset. In both cases the area was completely cleared of badgers and kept clear for a period of 3 years. Cattle in both areas remained clear of infection for several years after the badgers were eradicated, and of course it was tempting for the authorities to point to this result as proof of badger involvement and a demonstration of the effect of badger control. However, there are two important points to remember. First, badger control in the two areas was much more rigorous and sustained than has ever been the case in control areas elsewhere, so the results could hardly be expected to reflect what would happen under the normal control regime. Second, there was no control in the experimental sense (i.e. similar areas where no badger removal took place for statistical comparison). So the results were scientifically null and void; just more circumstantial evidence.

It would actually be very difficult and expensive to carry out field experiments to prove beyond doubt that badgers are the source of infection in cattle, so given the weight of circumstantial evidence the badger control programme has been based on the assumption that badgers are a wildlife reservoir for TB in cattle.

Much attention has been focused on how TB might be transmitted from badgers to cattle in the field. We have seen how TB can be present in any of the main body organs, and depending on the site of infection, the various ways in which live bacilli can be passed out into the environment: sputum from infected lungs (and contaminated faeces if sputum is swallowed), urine from infected kidneys, and pus from abscesses and skin lesions are the most likely routes. Which of these are more important is a matter for speculation but it is generally thought that sputum and urine are probably the most potent sources of infection, owing to the large numbers of organisms which are excreted in these products, and their relatively high frequency of deposition.

Cattle grazing areas where infected badgers have been present will obviously be exposed to the risk of infection. It is known that cattle generally become infected with TB via the respiratory route, and as there is no evidence of any direct contact between badgers and cattle, it is likely that cattle pick up infection by contact with contaminated badger faeces and urine. Badgers spend a large portion of their foraging time on pasture in search of earthworms and other invertebrates. It is possible to appreciate how live tubercle bacilli can be left behind in faeces and urine during this activity, possibly on the leaves and stems of plants on which cattle graze. In order for *M. bovis* bacilli to enter the respiratory tract of cattle, they would either have to be inhaled in an aerosol, or ingested and then subsequently inhaled with gases produced from the rumen while chewing the cud.

This speculative route of infection operates in the open field situation, where cattle may of course be able to detect grass contaminated by badgers and avoid the patch concerned. Another possibility lies in what are termed high risk situations, such as farm buildings, where contaminated badger faeces and urine may be deposited when badgers visit these places in search of an easy food supply in the form of food concentrates, like dairy nuts. A cow offered food concentrate in a feeding trough which has been visited and contaminated by a tuberculous badger does not have the same degree of choice as a cow in the open field; food concentrates are usually manufactured so as to be highly palatable and the animal is not likely to reject such food even if it is contaminated.

In order to investigate the notion that cattle may be able to detect badger faeces and urine and therefore choose whether or not to eat contaminated food, some fascinating work was done by Paul Benham (1985). He showed that cattle will avoid grass contaminated by badger urine and faeces for periods of up to 14 and 28 days respectively. Perhaps the most significant finding of this work was the fact that a few cattle were not selective, raising the question of whether this category of animals is responsible for the TB outbreaks that occur in cattle which are believed to be of badger origin. The obvious way to test this hypothesis would be to carry out behavioural experiments on a batch of TB reactor cattle to see whether a significant proportion of them show this failure to discriminate, but so far this has not been done.

Another matter which has not been satisfactorily addressed is the longevity of *M. bovis* under different environmental conditions. It is known that the TB bacillus is sensitive to extremes of temperature, ultra-violet light, desiccation and rapid contamination by other bacteria and fungi outside the host's body. So its survival will depend on the combination of these factors at the time and place of deposition. The survival time could vary between a matter of hours under the least favourable conditions to perhaps weeks at the other extreme. In soil, or the relatively constant temperature, high humidity and darkness of a badger sett, the period of survival could be much longer.

There are clearly great gaps in our knowledge as to how cattle become infected with TB and the length of time the TB organism persists in the environment. We do, however, have some information on the pattern of deposition of faeces and urine by badgers. The use of latrines by badgers in territorial marking is well documented and the presence of latrines in areas grazed by cattle would appear to present an obvious risk. An advisory leaflet given by MAFF to farmers in TB areas already recommends that cattle are denied access to badger setts and latrines by simply fencing them off. Recent work by Brown (1993) has demonstrated the potential significance of badger urinatory behaviour. In this study 52% of badger urinations occurred at latrines, with 28% occurring on pasture away from setts or latrines, and of this latter category the bulk of urinations (83%) were associated with places where badger runs converged to cross linear features such as fences and hedgerows, and especially those where the opportunities to cross were restricted. In addition, it was found that the number of these crossing point urinations increased with the number of linear features crossed. It was suggested (White *et al.* 1993) that these crossing point urinations are potentially a major source of bovine TB infection in cattle, and that areas of greater habitat heterogeneity, with a higher concentration of linear features, have greater levels of contamination of pasture with badger urine and so more opportunities for disease transmission.

The field work by Brown (1993) to establish patterns of badger excretory behaviour involved some novel technology. In addition to the fitting of a collar carrying a radio transmitter and 'Betalight' to aid nocturnal observation, a spool carrying fine nylon thread was attached to the collar to facilitate precise tracking of the badger on its nightly wanderings (see Chapter 12). Animals were also labelled with fluorescent dye to make their urine and faeces fluoresce under ultra-violet light. The human tracker, festooned with high-tech apparatus including radio receiver, image intensifier, UV lamp, pocket Dictaphone and even cellular telephone in case of accident in some remote spot, was hence able to detect exactly where badgers deposited their urine and faeces.

EFFECTS OF CONTROL MEASURES

While this book was being prepared, a badger control programme had been running in some shape or form for nearly two decades. Inevitably the question has been posed as to whether badger control results in any beneficial effect in terms of a reduced incidence of TB in cattle. Over the period 1975–1994 the incidence of TB in cattle fluctuated, with a marked increase in the latter years (Fig. 10.1). Some people argue that badger control has had a beneficial effect, and that without it the situation would have been worse. An extreme of this view is that constraints on badger control, e.g. trapping restricted to just the affected farm and the release of potentially infected lactating females, have prevented greater success in reducing cattle TB. At the other extreme there are those who contend that the whole strategy has been a waste of time and money (and badgers). Unfortunately the truth will never be known because the effects of badger control cannot be scientifically evaluated without 'experimental controls', where some areas are left without treatment for statistical comparison.

There has been the suggestion that badger control may exacerbate the spread of disease, by causing social disruption in badger populations leading to increased movements and dispersal. This was recognised as a potential disadvantage and in 1994 in a review of their

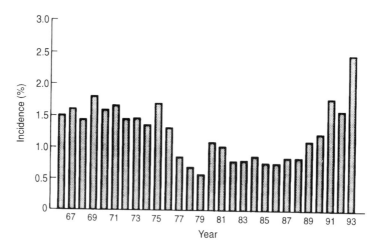

FIG 10.1   *Cattle TB incidence 1966–1993 in the south-west region of England.*

strategy MAFF listed an investigation of the effects of perturbation on badgers as one of their research objectives.

DISTRIBUTION OF TB IN BADGERS

Fortunately the association of TB in cattle and badgers appears to be confined principally to south-west England, and only there in certain 'hot spots' which amount to about 10% of the area of the region. However we know that TB is not exclusively confined to the badgers of south-western counties, with records of tuberculous badgers from as far afield as Lothian in Scotland, many parts of Wales and several other counties in England outside the south-west. In all 22 counties in mainland Britain have evidence of TB in badgers. The worst affected counties are Gloucestershire, Avon and Cornwall, all with accumulated prevalence of over 7%.

For epidemiological purposes, if one regards the badgers on mainland Britain as belonging to just one population, then TB can be said to be endemic in badgers in this country. This being so, badger control might only ever achieve a short to medium term benefit, as re-colonisation by badgers into cleared areas would only cause the problem to recur sooner or later.

EPIDEMIOLOGY

Studies carried out on temporal variations in herd infection (Wilesmith *et al.* 1982) have led to the suggestion that the cyclic patterns which occur are probably the result of temporal variations in the prevalence of infection in badgers, these in turn reflecting fluctuations in badger population density. It now seems that the situation is not as straightforward as this.

Long term research (Cheeseman *et al.* 1988b, 1989) on the natural progression of TB in a wild badger population has revealed that badgers do indeed exhibit a cyclic prevalence of

TB infection, but their population density does not show the expected mirror of this pattern, being remarkably stable through time. Thus while the disease may be density-dependent, in that there will be a threshold density below which TB would die out, the relationship between the population density of badgers and the prevalence of TB (if present) is clearly not a linear one.

One of the epidemiological conundrums is why TB is present in some badger populations in south-west England and not in others. This does not appear to be related to the density of badgers, for TB is apparently absent from some high-density areas, notably parts of Somerset, Devon and Dorset. Reasons put forward to explain these differences include possible genetic variation in different badger populations, that is badgers in some areas may be genetically more predisposed to TB infection than those in other areas; or simply a quirk of fate where badger populations in certain areas were never infected by cattle in the days when TB infection in cattle was rife.

OTHER SPECIES

There is no doubt that TB occurs in badgers, with a high prevalence occurring in some areas, and a weight of circumstantial evidence to implicate the involvement of badgers in many cattle TB outbreaks where there is no other possible source of infection. This does not mean that TB occurs exclusively in badgers, and the possible role of other species has been the subject of investigation.

Obviously obtaining a satisfactory sample size to determine the presence and possible distribution of disease even in some of the commoner species would be extremely difficult and expensive. MAFF therefore examined carcasses of animals submitted by the public rather than carry out systematic sampling, and the results are published in the series of reports on 'Bovine Tuberculosis in Badgers' (MAFF 1976-1994). Representatives of almost all mammal species occurring in Britain have been examined, although sample sizes range from just a few of the rarer species to hundreds of the commoner ones. *M. bovis* has been isolated in deer (*Cervus* sp., *Capreolus* sp. and *Dama* sp.), fox (*Vulpes vulpes*), bat (*Pipistrellus pipistrellus*), mink (*Mustela vison*), rat (*Rattus norvegicus*), ferret (*Mustela furo*), hedgehog (*Erinaceus europaeus*) and mole (*Talpa europaea*), but in none of these species has the prevalence been significant, and in all species except deer the disease has not been present in a progressive state. In parts of East Sussex a systematic survey was carried out to investigate the possible role of wild mammals, other than badgers, in the maintenance of *M. bovis* in an area on the South Downs. *M. bovis* was not isolated from any of the 15 species examined (Wilesmith *et al.* 1986).

It therefore appears that no other species apart from the badger is likely to constitute a significant reservoir of bovine tuberculosis in Britain.

OTHER COUNTRIES

Britain is not alone in having a wildlife reservoir of TB. Ireland has a similar problem with its badger population, although it is difficult to know what proportion of outbreaks in cattle in Ireland is due to badgers because there is still evidence of lateral spread amongst the cattle themselves.

In Wood Buffalo National Park in the Northwest Territories of Canada, controversy surrounds proposals to cull wood bison (*Bison bison athabascae*) which are a wildlife host for TB which occasionally spills over into domestic cattle. On the African continent buffalo (*Syncerus caffer*) populations are known to harbour TB and pose an obvious risk for the free ranging domestic cattle. A similar situation occurs with feral Asian water buffalo (*Bubalus bubalis*) which roam some parts of Australia's Northern Territory and concerted attempts have been made to cull this introduced species.

Perhaps the most fascinating example of a parallel to the British TB situation comes from New Zealand. The Australian brush tailed possum (*Trichosurus vulpecula*) was introduced to New Zealand during the last century primarily for the exploitation of its fur. With no natural predators and a habitat highly suited to the species, it thrived reaching densities of 25 ha^{-1} in the forest/pasture zones. The discovery of *M. bovis* in possums in the late 1960s, and the species' habit of defoliating native trees, has led to possums being regarded as one of the country's major pests. Drastic measures have been taken to control the animals, from 'blitzkrieg' operations in the 1970s and 80s involving dropping poison-laced carrots from aeroplanes over the affected areas, to current attempts to develop new means of pest population control using genetically modified viruses which sterilise the host against its own reproductive proteins. It is fortunate that in Britain TB only affects small areas of the southwest of England, and with the badger being a popular indigenous species control is aimed at management of the disease rather than elimination of the host.

THE FUTURE

In this chapter we have tried to give the reader an unbiased account of this very complicated issue. It is an extremely contentious subject, and one regrettably where politics, speculation and emotion still tend to outweigh hard scientific fact.

The two extreme options of doing nothing and eliminating badgers in the problem areas are clearly unacceptable. It is very difficult to strike a balance because any middle ground is bound to be a compromise which will inevitably attract criticism from one side or the other. Radical solutions, such as not keeping cattle at all in the problem areas, do not seem realistic at the present time.

As far as the vaccine option is concerned it is important to remember that a badger vaccine will not necessarily produce the panacea which everyone would wish for. A vaccine will have to be reasonably effective to be successful in suppressing TB in badger populations, but it is unlikely to be anywhere near 100% effective. There will also be a need to develop a delivery method that will ensure as many badgers as possible are vaccinated. A bait delivery system would obviously have major advantages and fortunately badgers are a relatively easy species to persuade to take bait. There may be a need to deliver the vaccine via an aerosol so that it is introduced into the respiratory tract. Achieving this with a bait which will have to be ingested by the animal will be difficult, though not impossible. It will be necessary to understand what type of immune mechanisms exist in badgers so that the right sort of vaccine can be developed which will enhance the badger's natural disease resistance. Candidate vaccines will have to be identified and thoroughly tested in laboratory and field trials. So this research is going to take many years to reach fruition. TB in cattle will still need to be managed in the interim, and even when a suitable badger vaccine is ready for implementation, it is unlikely to stand alone as the sole means of tackling the problem. Hence we must continue research on all the available options — it would be folly to put all our eggs in the vaccine basket.

In the 20 years this saga has been running it has always been an extremely contentious issue. It is probably safe to predict that the controversy will continue for as long as TB persists in badgers and cattle.

CHAPTER 11

Badgers and Humans

BADGERS, in common with most wildlife today, are greatly influenced by human pressures, either directly or indirectly, and their survival in many regions is no longer mainly dependent upon their ability to adapt to changing conditions, but is largely determined by our attitude towards them.

Inevitably, on a crowded island like Britain, any wild mammal species, especially one of fairly large size, conflicts in some ways with our interests. The badger is no exception. Attitudes vary as to what action should be taken when these conflicts arise, but today it is increasingly realised that wildlife is a priceless asset which should be conserved, even if this entails slight economic loss or inconvenience. The majority of farmers and land-owners take this view and are tolerant of the presence of badgers on their land and many welcome them and guard their interests jealously. This attitude is justified, as scientific evidence makes it clear that the activities of badgers are mainly neutral to human interests; in some districts they may do a little harm but they also do good by reducing the numbers of potential pests. It is all a matter of balance. Under normal conditions badgers need no control, but exceptionally, if the population density becomes unusually high, they may become a matter for concern and reduction in numbers may be justified. The Badgers Act 1992 (Appendix 1) clarifies the steps which may and may not be taken if badgers have to be controlled. However, we would stress that badgers are not the kind of species which undergo cyclic explosions in population density. Indeed, they seem to be remarkably adept at

210

holding their numbers at around the maximum any particular habitat can sustain, and it is not necessary to consider the long term management of badger populations. In recent years badger numbers in Britain have recovered in many areas where they were persecuted for decades. This increase in some populations has led to some remarkably ill-informed opinions and explanations, with much talk of badger 'population explosions'. Obviously there are some regions where badgers are still under pressure, despite the protective legislation. The second National Survey (see Chapter 9) will give a better idea of long term population trends, although of course this will only give an overall picture and will not provide accurate evidence of local population fluctuations.

Conservation of any species involves maintaining the right balance and this can only be achieved through an enlightened attitude of understanding and tolerance. Extreme sentimentality on the one hand, and entrenched prejudice on the other, do nothing to achieve a sensible balance of interests. In this chapter, we would like to face realistically the points of conflict which may occasionally arise between badgers and humans and emphasise the positive steps that may be taken for the benefit of both parties. But first let us look at the urban situation.

URBAN BADGERS

Badgers are remarkably adaptable animals. Not only have they succeeded in colonising a great variety of rural habitats, but they have also clung on with extraordinary tenacity to many urban situations and become well adapted to urban life.

In 1969, W.G. Teagle, in his admirable survey of badger distribution within a 32-km radius of London, recorded 164 setts he knew personally and at least another 110 which were reported on good authority. Some of these setts, which are still active today, are situated in commons and parks within a remarkably short distance of Central London. It is doubtful whether they still occur in the Hampstead area, although reports of sightings have been published from time to time, certainly up to 1967. The most memorable sighting on Hampstead Heath occurred during World War I when a pilot made a forced landing there in the early hours and came face to face with a badger!

There is one main road in Greater London which badgers often cross, once the stream of buses and cars has subsided, in order to get from their sett in the grounds of a teacher's training college to the gardens of a convent — where on one occasion they drew attention to themselves by attempting to undermine a statue!

Many other cities such as Bristol, Bath and Birmingham have their quota of setts and in the early morning badgers are commonly seen by police patrols and late-night travellers. Stephen Harris (1982, 1984a) made a splendidly comprehensive study of the Bristol badgers. He found 80 setts in a 5.5 km² arc of the north-western part of the city. Forty were in strips of woodland, scrub or bramble-covered banks, 29 in private or semi-public gardens and the remainder in places such as horse paddocks and under outbuildings. Compared with rural areas Harris found that home ranges overlapped more and territorial boundaries were not well defined; it was the area around a sett that was heavily marked by latrines rather than the perimeter.

Earthworms, although readily available on lawns, playing fields and open commons, were exploited far less in Bristol than in rural areas, the badgers relying on a greater range of foods. Certain categories predominated according to season. Thus from January to May this was scavenged food (24% over the year), June to July, invertebrates other than earthworms (20%), August to November, fruits and vegetables (35%) and December, earthworms (18%). Scavenged items included food taken from dustbins, compost heaps, bird tables and food specially put out by householders for the badgers.

Compared with rural areas emergence is characteristically later, usually well after dark; the badgers play very little, go straight off after emergence and restrict bedding collection mainly to the autumn and early spring when nights are longer. The major cause of death is from traffic.

Occasionally urban badgers have got into difficulties. One was found trying to get into the cellar of a girls' school and another was found in the crypt of one of the churches. Stephen Harris (pers. comm.) tells the story of a badger which lived under the floorboards of an occupied house, entering through a broken air brick. When several floorboards had been removed to lay new piping it would come into the rooms to eat the cat's food. One night the lady of the house was awoken 'to absolute bedlam: the badger was chasing the cat around her bed'!

Some years ago, patients in sanatoria in both Surrey and Hampshire had their lives greatly enriched by nightly visits from badgers which would come right up to the windows of their wards. One patient was able to coax a badger to within 1.5 m of his bed by laying a trail of scraps.

However, when badgers are in such close proximity to people they may sometimes cause annoyance by digging shallow pits in the lawns after earthworms and cockchafer grubs, digging up flower bulbs or carrots or eating soft fruit. If this happens there are one or two deterrents on the market which can be tried. A rope should be soaked in the deterrent substance and supported on short sticks about 125 mm high across the line of entry into the garden. It should be re-soaked every few days, especially after rain. This technique is more effective if it is used before entry becomes a regular habit, for example, before the fruit ripens. Before using any deterrent it is necessary to check whether the product is legal for use against badgers.

However, deterrents are usually only of limited success and if badger damage is serious there is only one really effective remedy, which is to erect an electric fence around the affected area. There are two basic types of electric fence which are used against badgers: a two-strand 'polytape' or 'polywire' construction, with the wires set at approximately 7.5 cm and 20 cm above ground level, and rabbit 'Flexinet'. There is a moderate financial outlay for this type of equipment, but this has to be weighed against the extent of the damage being caused by badgers. Most keen gardeners who spend a great deal of time and money on their gardens would not baulk at the cost of purchasing the kit for an electric fence to prevent badgers eating the fruits of their labours. Chris speaks from personal experience. After a particularly disastrous year when badgers ate the pick of his sweetcorn, carrot, strawberry, raspberry, beetroot and even potato crops, the installation of an electric fence during subsequent growing and ripening seasons has totally overcome the problem. For more details on how to erect and maintain an electric fence, we would recommend the reader to obtain a copy of the booklet 'Problems with Badgers?' (Harris *et al.* 1993) published by the RSPCA (Horsham).

THE PROBLEM OF TRAFFIC

As discussed in Chapter 9, road and rail traffic account for the deaths of a very large number of badgers and this is particularly true of main roads and motorways which cut through good badger country.

Michael Clark has been much concerned with the conservation of badgers in Hertfordshire. He suggested (Clark 1970) that because badgers used regular routes, some losses could be avoided by diverting the badgers into pipes underneath the roads. The Highways Department in Hertfordshire considered his detailed plans and general agreement on procedure was reached.

The first project to be completed in Hertfordshire involved the use of an Armco stream culvert which carried a steady flow in times of heavy rainfall. A concrete ledge was constructed along one wall of this culvert for the badgers to use when the water level was high. The fencing on either side of the culvert was fitted with galvanised netting as this not only

FIG 11.1   *Many badgers are killed crossing roads.*

prevented the badgers from crossing the road, but also guided them towards the culvert. However, it was found that where main badger paths had come to where the fence was erected, the badgers would dig underneath unless the netting was turned outwards at soil level and covered. Materials were paid for by the road construction unit, but all the work was done by volunteers including members of a Workers' Education Association group, Conservation Corps enthusiasts and local badger watchers. The project was a considerable success and badgers subsequently used the ledge regularly (Fig.11.2).

FIG 11.2   *Stream culvert of the Armco galvanised steel type under a by-pass in Hertfordshire, showing raised badger path (left). Water level nearly reaches the path when in flood. Photo M. Clark.*

Since Clark's original paper, Jane Ratcliffe, with the help of her husband (a civil engineer), put forward plans for a rather similar structure under the M53 motorway in Cheshire. This too used a culvert, towards which the badgers were directed by netting fastened to the wooden post-and-rail fencing. Specifications for this construction have been published and caused much interest (Ratcliffe 1974). Following the success of the initial ventures, several similar culverts have been installed under new roads.

Tom Wilton, a civil engineer concerned with the construction of the M5 motorway in Somerset, was also very keen to reduce the destruction of wildlife on the roads. He approached Ernest in 1973 about the possibility of putting in badger tunnels where these were appropriate. They surveyed the proposed route of a section of the M5 together, mapping out the position of badger setts and the main paths in relation to them. The most vulnerable places are undoubtedly where two setts are close to the road, but on different sides of it, or where the sett is on one side and a main feeding ground on the other. One such place was found west of Wellington, in Somerset and as the motorway was to be on an embankment at that point, it was a suitable place for a tunnel. The plans were passed, as it was accepted that this was not only for the benefit of the badgers, but that an adult badger knocked down by a light car travelling at 110 km⁻¹ was also a potential hazard to the motorist. Indeed, it may well be argued that the hazard posed by badgers to motorists is sufficient justification in itself for the Department of Transport to include such measures in new road schemes, even before one considers the conservation benefits. It would be interesting to know how many serious road traffic accidents are actually caused by badgers.

Unfortunately, there were long delays before work on this section of the motorway was started, but by the summer of 1976 the tunnel was in position at a place where a main path from the sett met the road. At this point a concrete drainage ditch ran parallel to the motorway, so wooden planking had to be erected to act as a bridge over which the badgers could pass. The tunnel consisted of a concrete pipe 600 mm in diameter and 50 m long. Sheep netting was fastened to the fencing for some distance on either side to help guide the badgers towards the entrance. At first the badgers were reluctant to use it so an aniseed scent trail was laid up to and through the tunnel to encourage them. But it was not until numbers increased in the sett nearby that they started to use it regularly. Finally they claimed it as part of their own territory by making latrines near both ends of the tunnel.

FIG 11.3   *Badger tunnel built under the M5 motorway in Somerset. The netting on the post-and-rail fence helps to guide the badgers to the entrance and stops them from crossing elsewhere.*

Kent County Council came up with an unusual solution to a problem where a sett had undermined a road on Romney Marsh. Having excluded the badgers, the sett was excavated and then reconstructed according to plans made of the original using concrete pipe and blocks. Although the badgers did not take immediately to their artificial home, they did subsequently move back in. In a relatively flat part of the country like this, a road embankment is obviously one of the few features in which a sett may be excavated.

In recent years the Department of Transport (DoT) has become increasingly aware of the environmental impact of new roads and has sought to minimise the effects on badgers as well as other protected species. It is estimated that between 1990 and 1994, the DoT spent in the region of £5 million on measures to mitigate the effects of new roads on badgers alone. Not surprisingly they are anxious to identify how effective these measures are and how they can be improved so that the highest level of success in reducing casualties is achieved for the money. Whilst one can give an instant subjective answer to the question of whether this expenditure can be justified, it is difficult to obtain hard evidence to enable an objective assessment to be made. We can expect this sort of expenditure to come under increasingly close scrutiny in the future as budgets are squeezed.

Attempts have been made to stop badgers crossing roads by the use of special badger-proof fencing. This involves long lengths of appropriate netting fixed to post-and-rail fencing. Certain manufacturers now make netting specifically for use against badgers (the reader is again referred to the booklet 'Problems with Badgers?' for details). This type of fencing is probably most successful when it is used to channel badgers into an underpass or other crossing point, but experience has shown that it is not actually 'badger-proof'. As a precaution netting is usually buried and turned at right angles towards badger territory, but badgers are determined creatures and are able to cross such barriers by digging or even climbing. In some circumstances badgers may become temporarily trapped on verges or carriageways and this could actually increase the risk of accident.

The electrification of certain parts of the rail network created a new hazard for badgers which had hitherto learned to live with the railway. On one notorious section of the Hastings to Tonbridge line a newly installed live conductor rail killed over 100 badgers in the first few weeks of operation. In order to alleviate the problem British Rail, in consultation with conservation organisations, introduced strategically placed 3-m gaps in the live rail to allow badgers to cross safely.

A special problem occurs when the route of a proposed road passes directly through a badger sett. The best method is to exclude the badgers, so that they move of their own accord to an alternative sett within their territory. Unfortunately, in some localities no alternative setts exist, in which case the only option is to provide an artificial one if the badgers are to have a chance of remaining in the area. The procedure for excluding badgers from a sett generally involves the installation of an electric fence incorporating one way gates. Sett occupancy can be checked by using sticks placed across the holes, combined with the examination of footprints left in a specially prepared fine tilth outside the sett entrances. The exclusion of badgers from a sett should not be practised when there is a likelihood that young cubs may be below.

Having said this, there are some circumstances where badger setts undermine roads or railways which require urgent remedial attention, with the danger of subsidence threatening the safety of cars or trains. In such circumstances the badgers have to be evicted from the sett as quickly as possible and measures taken to ensure that the sett is not reoccupied. There was one particular case where a sett had so badly undermined a section of railway embankment that the trains, which normally passed over that section of track at 200 km h^{-1} had to be slowed to a mere 48 km h^{-1} for safety. The line was closed over a whole day whilst the sett was excavated, the badgers having been excluded, and a mammoth operation took place to reinstate the line and lay chain link mesh along the embankment to stop the problem re-occurring. British Rail have employed some novel techniques to prevent further subsidence in such a situation, and at the same time stop badgers from reoccupying the sett. This has involved pumping either concrete or a special high-density foam into the empty tunnel system.

In another instance where a flood levee was being undermined, the water authority closed down the part of the sett nearest to the water course and drove in sheet piling to keep the badgers on the landward side. Thus the local farmers and householders had their flood protection preserved and the badgers continued to utilise the man-made structure for their sett.

Translocation

There are clearly some circumstances where there is no alternative than to move badgers from the location where they are causing a problem to a completely new location. This is usually where a main sett is threatened by building development, where there are no suitable alternative setts for the badgers to be encouraged to move, and where the provision of an artificial sett is not a practical proposition. In some cases a significant portion of the badgers' territory is also compromised by the development. Such cases leave the authorities with three options: (1) simply allow the development to proceed with the inevitable consequence that it will displace the badgers, as indeed must have happened many times in the past, and let the badgers fend for themselves, (2) catch the badgers and humanely destroy them, (3) catch and move the badgers elsewhere.

It is debatable which of these options is in the best interests of badgers. If badgers are simply displaced, some individuals may eventually integrate with other social groups, but the likelihood of mortality due to traffic accidents or aggressive encounters with other badgers is bound to increase. Assuming the surrounding badger population is in equilibrium with the environment, there will be no vacant niches and the population will eventually stabilise at whatever level the habitat will support, despite the addition of a few surplus badgers, and therefore nothing will be achieved. Humane destruction seems a poor solution if the badgers themselves have not caused any damage, which only leaves translocation.

The procedure of physically moving badgers around the country is not at all straightforward and should certainly only be considered as a last resort. The situation might be described as a 'Catch 22', because badgers should only be moved to areas of good habitat, for obvious reasons, and areas of good habitat should already contain a badger population. There are some exceptions to this last point, where, for example badger populations have suffered from persecution. If vacant setts and territory can be found, then provided the reason for the original population's demise no longer exists, these may make suitable translocation sites. There are other considerations, such as the risk of disease spread to different parts of the country, possible interference in the natural distribution of genetic races, and the potential costs and benefits. It may be better to allow an area temporarily depleted of badgers to be naturally recolonised, but there are some large tracts of country, such as parts of East Anglia for example, which could benefit from introductions to give nature a helping hand and speed up what would otherwise be a very prolonged process.

Therefore in certain circumstances where badgers are causing problems a potential solution is to translocate the animals responsible to another site. We would stress, however, that very little evidence exists as to the fate of translocated badgers. Apart from anecdotal information, scientific monitoring of animals after their release has rarely been carried out, and where this has been done observations have focused on survival rather than aspects such as movement behaviour and subsequent breeding success. There is a need for such translocation exercises that are licensed by MAFF and English Nature to be rigorously monitored as far as possible, and for the information accumulated to be collated and analysed so that proper guidance can be given on future translocations.

We do not propose here to give a lengthy account of the steps to be followed in a translocation exercise. Once again we would refer the reader to the booklet 'Problems with Badgers?' which contains comprehensive information on all aspects of this topic.

ARTIFICIAL SETTS

There are basically two types of situation where artificial badger setts are constructed: first, to provide alternative living accommodation where a natural sett has to be destroyed because it is in the way of a development, and second, to encourage badgers to take up residence in an area where the habitat is suitable in all other respects, but where sett sites are limiting badger distribution. As mentioned in Chapter 3, many setts are dug in man-made structures which itself is an indication that somewhere suitable to dig a sett is perhaps the most important habitat requirement. Providing they are well designed and constructed, artificial setts are readily taken to by badgers, but if the proper guidelines are not adhered to, an expensive failure will probably be the result. It is also worth emphasising that if artificial setts are being considered in order to encourage badgers to use an area, one must be certain that the habitat is suitable in all other respects, capable of sustaining badgers all year round, and not creating a potential threat to crops and livestock. With so many planners and developers now paying regard to the welfare of badgers, as indeed they are required to do under the legislation, the architecture and siting of artificial setts has become a highly refined procedure. Comprehensive details are contained in the booklet 'Problems with Badgers?'.

BADGERS AND FARMING

Under most circumstances, there is no conflict between the interests of farmers and badgers; the little harm they do is often more than balanced by their destruction of pest species. However, in a few places where population density has become unusually high or when weather conditions are exceptional, badgers may find it extremely difficult to get enough food and may cause some damage. To some extent this depends upon the type of farming.

The poultry farmer normally has little to fear from badgers, although poultry killing certainly occurs under exceptional circumstances. Hen houses and coops should be made strong enough to withstand the attentions of badgers where the risk occurs (see also Chapter 6).

For the arable farmer, the chief problem is when cereal crops are flattened and grain consumed. This may happen during the few weeks prior to harvesting oats and wheat. The matter has been discussed fully in a previous chapter (p. 127). However, it is worth emphasising that most damage occurs if a cereal crop is grown near to a wood or copse in which there is a sett. If the farmer has a choice, and grows barley in such a field, the badgers will usually avoid this and the crops of oats or wheat further away will receive far less attention. Even where this is not feasible, the extent of any damage caused by badgers is rarely serious enough to warrant action on the part of the farmer.

Occasionally, badgers will open up holes in fields which connect underground to setts in hedgerows or copses. This can be a hazard, especially with heavy machinery, as the roof of the connecting tunnel may collapse and the tractor sink into the ground. It is debatable whether it is worth a farmer going to the trouble and expense of applying for a licence from MAFF, excluding the badgers from the offending part of the sett, digging up the tunnel and reinstating the ground so that it may once again be cultivated. Perhaps the simpler solution would be to lift the plough and work round that part of the field, although this will depend on the tolerance of the individual farmer towards badgers.

A survey of farms in the county of Devon by the National Farmers Union in 1987 (cited in Symes 1989) found that of the 83% of farms where badgers were known to be present, 75% of these experienced badger related problems, and 30% perceived these as severe. In the NFU's survey structural damage (42%) was the most frequent complaint, followed by crop damage (39%) and predation (14%). Of course it is difficult to get a truly representative, unbiased sample in this type of survey. A different set of data was collated by the Agricultural Development and Advisory Service over the years 1985–1986. This covered England and Wales and consisted of requests for advice on badgers. Enquiries were dominated by behavioural problems, such as the digging of latrines and tunnelling under fences (25%), followed by feeding damage (18%), predation (13%) and structural damage (11%) (Symes 1989).

BADGERS AND GAME REARING

This is a subject about which there is much prejudice. It is understandable that a few gamekeepers take the line that it is better to be safe than sorry, so they kill the badgers near pheasant-rearing areas. As well as being illegal this attitude is not justified by the evidence (the matter is discussed in detail in Chapter 6). Here it is sufficient to reiterate that The Game Conservancy Trust considers that damage by badgers in relation to pheasant rearing is insignificant and calls for no repressive measures. Some losses do occur occasionally, but they are small. Damage can occur to the fences of pheasant release pens if care is not taken to position these away from badger runs. A further difficulty which has developed in the wake of the recent badger legislation is the growing problem of foxes laying up in badger setts and presenting keepers with a dilemma over fox control.

BADGERS AND FORESTRY

The Forestry Commission recognises that the badger is the friend of the forester. Badgers certainly play an important role in maintaining nature's balance, keeping in check certain species whose populations may reach pest proportions. Young rabbits are eaten in comparatively large numbers in districts where they are common, and nests of field voles and woodmice are also destroyed. In years when these rodents are abundant, large numbers are destroyed by badgers. As these mammals are the main enemies of natural regeneration, badgers are particularly helpful in this respect. Badgers also reduce the wasp menace, which is a constant irritation to foresters in autumn. The one action that is not appreciated is when a badger forces up the wire around a young plantation and lets rabbits in. This is now prevented by putting in badger gates whenever main badger paths leave a plantation. The gate was perfected by R.J. King (1964) and takes the form of a door which is free to swing both ways. It is made of heavy timber suspended from a stout wooden frame, and a wooden sill is placed below it so that rabbits do not burrow under and force an entrance. Badgers easily push through against the weight of the door,

FIG 11.4 *Badger using the type of swing gate recommended by the U.K. Forestry Commission. Photo G. Burness.*

but rabbits cannot enter. During erection the door is not hung in position until the badgers are using the opening regularly. The device works extremely well and the erection of badger gates is now normal forestry procedure in many parts. Details of construction are given in the booklet 'Problems with Badgers?'.

The Forestry Commission has also drawn up a code of practice for foresters when felling trees in the vicinity of badger setts. This seeks to minimise any disturbance in the immediate area of the sett, and to leave mature trees and other ground cover around the sett itself intact.

BADGER PRODUCTS

Not so very long ago in Britain, the best shaving brush that money could buy was made of badger bristles. Now of course it is illegal to sell, or even have in one's possession, any such badger products, unless they were obtained prior to the enactment of the present legislation. Historically, badgers have provided various items, including their flesh, which have been utilised by people.

There are plenty of people still alive today in parts of rural Britain who have eaten badger 'hams'; the meat is said to be rather like strong flavoured pork. Rendered down badger fat is reputed to be an excellent treatment for back and muscular pain, including rheumatism. In certain parts of Gloucestershire it is said to have almost magical properties, like being able to 'sweat through glass' — obviously an exaggeration, but indicative of its penetrating quality.

Badgers are still regarded as a commodity species in many countries and particularly in some areas of Eastern Europe, principally for their meat, fat, fur and leather, although practices such as the use of badger bits and pieces in cures for ailments probably represent the remnants of rapidly disappearing rural and ethnic cultures (Griffiths 1993).

BADGER HUNTING

A highly informative review of the status of the badger in Europe was carried out by Griffiths & Thomas (1993). This reported that the badger is currently a protected species in the UK, the Irish Republic, Spain, Portugal, Italy, Belgium, the Netherlands, Albania, Greece, Estonia, Luxembourg and Hungary. This leaves quite a considerable number of countries where the species is regarded either as small-game or as a pest, and legal hunting is regulated by closed seasons. Griffiths & Thomas gave a conservative estimate for the European badger population of 1 220 000. With an annual game-bag totalling about 118 000 badgers, it was concluded that populations appear to be either stable or increasing throughout much of Europe. Hunting was not regarded as posing a threat to harvested populations, providing it was properly regulated, although it was noted that few countries that allow hunting operate a robust game-management policy towards badgers. Griffiths & Thomas' comprehensive review highlighted the lack of reliable, comparative sources of information between countries, and while the overall picture was encouraging, there were some countries where badgers are rare or threatened.

BADGER BAITING

For historical completeness, this chapter on 'Badgers and Humans' should include reference to the old practice of badger-baiting; although having implied that this is a thing of the past, there are still reports of badger-baiting being carried out in the latter part of the 20th century, despite the activity having been outlawed in the middle of the 19th century. This unsavoury pastime was as much an excuse for gambling as for satisfying a blood-lust, as with bear-baiting and cock-fighting. A description of a badger pit is given by Sankey (1955) who prepared a detailed account of a pit which still existed at that time in the grounds of a house in Oxfordshire. Badgers were put into a circular pit, with walls about 2 m high and the same in diameter, with a door about 50 cm wide at one side. Opposite this was a small blind tunnel about 50 cm long and built entirely of brick with an arched roof. The tunnel entrance was about the size of a badger's burrow but slightly wider at the rear. This was intended to give the badger a place from which to take up its defence against the dogs, and wagers were made on how many times a dog — usually a bull terrier — would draw a badger in a given time, at which point badger and dog were separated with a spade or similar implement. Sankey was puzzled as to the purpose of a raised iron grid which covered the top of the pit, since neither badger nor dog could possibly climb or jump out of the structure. He came to the conclusion that it was to stop the demented onlookers from falling in!

BADGERS AS A DELIGHT

Having described some of the ways in which the interests of badgers and people may occasionally come into conflict, and the steps which may be taken to prevent or minimise any possible damage or annoyance that may result, it is appropriate in the final part of this chapter to refer to a further aspect which puts us greatly in the badgers' debt. This is the considerable amount of pleasure and satisfaction that badgers give to many people.

This has been brought home to Ernest in many ways, not least by the vast correspondence he has received about them over the past 50 years. In the last decade a huge number of badger groups (of the people kind!) have sprung up all over the country. There are now around 100 of them, representing it is estimated over 20 000 members. These groups not only provide the opportunity for people to share their common interest, but also perform an increasingly important policing role in the enforcement of the recent badger legislation.

It is no exaggeration to say that very large numbers of people have taken up badger watching and for many it has added a new dimension to their lives. Why do people from many walks of life and of all ages spend hours, often under uncomfortable conditions, watching for that black and white face to appear at the sett entrance — often without success? The reasons for doing so are no doubt mixed and varied. For some perhaps, the very fact of being in a wood at night is a thrilling adventure, for others what appeals most is the challenge of having to pit their wits against the animal's instincts and intelligence. Curiosity is one of our most obvious characteristics, so perhaps for some it is the desire to find out more about the lives of animals that makes them do it. For many, it may be a means of relaxation, an escape from the sophistication and materialism of our modern society, even an escape from boredom. Perhaps it also helps to satisfy that deeply ingrained desire to be one with nature, not apart from it.

But the appeal of badgers goes far beyond the magic circle of those who love to watch them in the wild. Badgers seem to typify the very essence of the countryside. They are part of our heritage.

CHAPTER 12

Studying Badgers in the Field

THE two authors of this book have spent a combined total of 80 years observing and studying badgers, with three quarters of this total belonging to Ernest! A large portion of Ernest's countless hours of observation have been spent watching at setts, while Chris, in his capacity as a professional biologist, has had the advantage of modern technology to assist his investigations. In this chapter we intend to give the reader a synthesis of our combined experience of studying badgers, including all the potentially useful tips and techniques which have been developed to make it easier to understand the lifestyle of shy, secretive animals like badgers. While it used to be true that the modern equipment used by the field biologist was beyond the means of most amateurs, this is no longer necessarily the case. However, armed with nothing more than our natural senses, enormous pleasure can be derived simply by observing badgers go about their business in the vicinity of their sett.

A good pair of binoculars is an invaluable aid to the badger watcher. Binoculars with wide objective lenses and moderate magnification, such as 7×50, are ideal, as in poor light they concentrate what light is available and you can see details which are quite invisible to the naked eye. In good moonlight, it is surprising how much can be seen. It is always worth getting the best binoculars that your budget will allow, although it has to be stated that some of those with the very finest optics are extremely expensive, whereas those with perhaps only slightly inferior performance are often considerably cheaper.

After dark a torch may be used successfully. Some of the modern high performance torches come with an optional red filter. Badgers take very little notice of the colour red and you can see most details with such a light from 10–20 m. However, it is always best not to focus directly on the badger immediately, but gradually bring the light towards it, avoiding concentrating the light on the head. However, if the badgers have already become suspicious, then the light can be the last straw and they may react with alarm. Ernest once used a lantern torch with a red filter which he placed on the ground so that its powerful red beam was directed on to the sett. This was to enable him to judge the right moment to take a photograph. To his surprise one badger came towards the light, which was about 1 m from where he was sitting, and sniffed it inquisitively before moving off. It showed no alarm even though the light was shining into its eyes. Infra-red light, which is sometimes used in filming and for night observation, is of course totally invisible but special optical equipment is required to see under infra-red illumination.

You can also use a normal torch if not too strong, but when first switched on it is best not to point it directly at the animal. Badgers take far less notice of torch light coming from above than from ground level. Perhaps they associate light from above with moonlight and so are less concerned. If a torch is used, it should be one with a silent switch.

Badger watching is not always easy. On some occasions everything goes marvellously, the badgers have no clue that you are there and you witness a wonderful uninhibited display of activity. But at other times the badgers are slightly suspicious and they go off quietly without doing much of interest. Every badger watcher has a few blank nights, and however much care is taken the badgers' suspicions are bound to be raised on some occasions, but by taking certain precautions disappointments can be minimised.

BADGER WATCHING BY A SETT

The choice of sett to watch is important; watching some setts can be extremely difficult. If you have a choice, choose one which is obviously well used, but has not too many entrances. There are some setts in the south-west of England, for example, where there are more than 50 entrances spread out over a large area. Such setts are very difficult to watch as it is not always easy to know which entrances will be used, and when the wind is right for one hole it is wrong for another, so you are likely to be discovered. Also, it does not always follow that there are more badgers living in a large sett than a small one. In the Cotswolds, Ernest once watched a sett which only had one entrance and out of it came 12 badgers in succession. It was like watching a conjurer producing rabbits from a hat!

Choose a sett where there is not too much undergrowth around the entrances so that you may obtain an uninterrupted view. The presence of bushes or trees within 5–10 m from the main entrances is a great help in giving you some cover.

Setts in some districts are much easier to watch than in others. This may be because the badgers are less disturbed by people or animals, but it may also be due to the terrain. In our experience, a sett is easier to watch when it is in a drier situation such as in chalk or limestone districts. In damp, ferny places where there are plenty of elders and nettles, your scent carries too well and watching is more difficult.

When going on a badger-watching expedition, some advanced planning is helpful. It is not wise to go on the spur of the moment to a sett you do not know well, but is far better to make a thorough reconnaissance first. This is best done in the morning, as this gives time for any scent you may leave around the sett to disperse before the badgers emerge in the evening. But to make quite sure, try to avoid standing in front of any of the used entrances or on any of the main badger paths.

First find out if the sett is occupied, because badgers often have more than one sett on their territory and a sett may be left unoccupied for weeks or months at a time. One way of establishing sett occupancy is to place small sticks over the entrances, spaced wide enough apart to allow a rabbit to pass through without disturbing them. If you make a fine tilth in the spoil outside the sett entrances, this will enable footprints to be identified and will help determine whether badgers or foxes are in residence.

Fresh earth thrown out of an entrance is a good sign of occupation, but badgers have been known to spend a night excavating a sett and then go back to sleep in an alternative one elsewhere; so you cannot be absolutely certain. Fresh pad marks around the sett are additional useful clues to occupation and if you can find fresh dung within 10 m or so from the sett, this is usually conclusive.

When a sett has many holes you need to find out which ones are likely to be used for emergence. You can usually eliminate entrances half filled with old leaves or which have cobwebs across. A well-used hole is often a large one with rather polished edges. Also the presence of flies going in and out is an excellent sign that badgers are not far below ground. The flies smell the badgers below and instinctively fly in that direction, but when they get into the semi-darkness of the tunnel another instinctive action causes them to fly towards the light, so they come out again. This shuttling to and fro can go on for a long time. It must be very frustrating for the flies, as they never quite make it!

Having decided which holes to watch, next choose your vantage point. This should finally be decided according to the direction of the wind when you arrive in the evening, so alternatives should be considered in case the wind should change. It is best to watch from a tree 5–7 m from the main entrances; then if the wind changes and you feel it on your back, your scent will probably blow over the heads of the badgers and you will not be detected. Trees have the additional advantage that badgers in their wanderings are unlikely to discover you, a hazard you have to reckon with if you are on the ground. The disadvantages of a tree are having to climb it in the first place, and then getting down again in the dark some time later when your limbs may be cold, stiff and cramped. It all depends on the tree! A short, light ladder may be used very successfully and it may even be possible to pull it up after you once you are in a good position. A ladder is well worth considering for regular watching. We have not yet discovered a tree which could be described as comfortable after the first quarter of an hour, but some are certainly better than others. Standing on a thin bough can give your instep agonies after a time; sitting on a foam cushion placed on a thick one is far better, unless you fall asleep! Some people have built platforms in trees suitable for regular badger watching, and even used old chairs either stood on a platform, or in some cases tied to the tree trunk and reached by a short ladder. If you go in for this style of elaborate badger watching in comfort, don't forget to get the permission of the landowner first, and remember that valuable timber trees can be seriously damaged by nails. The 'high seats' used by deer stalkers are useful in some difficult situations where natural vantage points are not available.

If a suitable climbing tree is not available you can sit or stand with your back to a large tree trunk or dense shrub. In this way you are not silhouetted against the sky. But choose a place which is not too near one of the main badger paths to minimise the risk of discovery.

A hide is not necessary in most situations, but some watchers have found one useful. If a hide is used it should be constructed from natural objects in the vicinity and built up gradually. Ernest has often used branches of elder to help camouflage his camera and to break up his own outline in case the badgers should emerge in good light. Elders are particularly recommended for this purpose as their scent is strong and familiar to the badgers and may disguise to some extent any human scent.

Having made a reconnaissance, the next thing to decide is when to watch. The easiest option is to go in the evening, but watching before dawn can be extremely rewarding, though you have to be either a poor sleeper or extremely good at getting up. For early morning watching, you should get into position a couple of hours before dawn. When you arrive the badgers will probably be away from the sett area, so watching from a tree is very desirable as this reduces the likelihood of discovery when they return. Badgers usually come back about an hour before dawn, but in summer it may be in good daylight (see p. 98).

For evening watching, you need to get there by sunset at the latest, unless you know very well the habits of the particular badgers you are intending to watch. At some setts they emerge much earlier than anticipated and if you leave your approach too late you are liable to disturb them on arrival.

It is always worthwhile approaching with the wind in your face, and as quietly as possible, and to pause some 50 m from the sett. If the sett can be seen from this distance, so much the better. If not, you can sometimes hear badgers, especially cubs, if they are out early. If they are already above ground, either wait for them to go down again, or make a slight clicking noise with your tongue. This is sometimes just enough to make them go underground without alarming them unduly. Then you can quickly reach your vantage point before they re-emerge.

When you arrive at your watching position check the wind direction carefully. Cloud movements can seldom be relied upon as they may not be related to the local wind currents at ground level. Watch the smoke from a blown-out match to make quite sure. Some native African trackers carry a small cotton pouch filled with fine wood ash. This can be shaken to make a small dust cloud which is sensitive even to the gentlest of breezes. If you find the wind is to any extent behind you when facing the sett, it is best to change to an alternative position as quickly as possible.

Some setts are particularly difficult to watch because of local wind conditions. If the entrances are at the base of a cliff or quarry face, the wind is nearly always wrong if your watching point is in front. This is because of the cyclic movements of air in such positions with an updraught from the base of the cliff. Local wind conditions also often change at dusk, especially in summer and in places where the sett is on the side of a valley. This can be exasperating, as when you arrive the wind may be slight and blowing in your face, but at dusk the warmer air in the valley rises and so there may be a complete reversal of direction for half an hour or more just when you may be expecting emergence.

It is important to wear suitable clothing. Badger watching even in summer can be a cold occupation when you have to be still for long periods; so clothes should be warm. They should also be drab in colour and not rustle when you move, or have a pronounced odour.

The most critical time for the watcher is when the badgers are about to emerge and just after. They often come near to an entrance and wait for a short time while scenting and listening. You may not be in a position to look right down the tunnel and see them, so it is always best to be as quiet as possible. When badgers are above ground it is also necessary to keep still as movement is quickly detected. If a mosquito settles on your face when a badger has just emerged, you should avoid making a quick movement to remove it, but it can be done in slow motion! Midges and mosquitoes can be a real menace in some areas and it is a useful precaution to cover up as much as possible of your anatomy except for your face. Two pairs of socks are better protection for your ankles than one. Some people anoint themselves with anti-midge cream; if the wind is right, this does no harm, but otherwise we prefer not to use it.

From these remarks it might be judged that watching badgers successfully is a most unlikely event. This is not so. On some occasions you seem to be able to get away with anything. The wind may be variable, but the badgers are not alarmed; you make noises and they take no notice; you may even wave your arms about and a cub may be so inquisitive that it comes right up to you to investigate this strange happening! But usually this does not happen, and if you wish to avoid disappointment it is far better to take as many precautions as possible, especially at setts which you have not watched previously. If you watch a sett regularly, the badgers may get used to your scent and become remarkably tolerant of your presence.

When leaving for home, it is advisable to wait until all the badgers have left and then go quietly, without passing too near the entrances or treading on main badger paths. This makes future watching more likely to be successful as the badgers will not have associated disturbance with any scent which may have lingered around the sett.

FOLLOWING BADGERS AFTER THEY HAVE LEFT THE SETT

Much can be discovered about badgers by watching regularly at a sett, but it is always rather frustrating to see them go off into the darkness and be unable to follow them. What they do for the rest of the night is more difficult to discover. You can find out a lot by tracking during the daytime, especially in snow; this may tell you where they went, and sometimes how and on what they fed, but most of their behaviour is never understood by this means and for most of the year any form of tracking is of limited use.

It is possible to follow them after they have left the sett, but it is difficult. You have one advantage; badgers do not usually wander about aimlessly but follow their main tracks for some distance before starting to feed, so you can follow these trails some way behind the badger until it starts hunting for food. Then it may become more difficult.

You need to walk very quietly along the path used by the badgers on leaving the sett. Soft-soled shoes are ideal for this. A weak torch will help you to avoid stepping on twigs. Stopping to listen at frequent intervals is a necessary precaution as you don't want to come upon the badgers unawares. They are often noisy in their movements, especially if there are stones or dry leaves about and if you cannot move quietly yourself, it is best to imitate the sort of noises the badgers are making. When badgers are moving quite quickly they do so in a series of short trots, stopping at frequent intervals to listen. It is not difficult to imitate this movement. If they become suspicious, it is a good idea to stop and make the scratching noise a badger makes so often after emergence from the sett. This can be done by rubbing your fingers rapidly against your neck or clothes. This often has a useful calming effect on badgers as they usually only scratch when in an unsuspicious state.

Once badgers are feeding they are not so alert, and it is possible with a torch to stand still and watch them catching earthworms, turning over cow-pats for beetles and searching elsewhere for other delicacies.

Following badgers is much easier when the ground is soft after rain and you can be more silent, and when the wind is right for following the badger you can approach closer. It is also a help when there is just enough moonlight for you to see where you are treading without using a torch, but is not too bright to make you conspicuous. You need some luck, but you improve with practice, and occasionally this technique can be very successful.

It is also possible, with experience, to go to particular places where badgers are likely to be seen and wait for them to arrive. Favourite feeding grounds are the most rewarding, but there is a considerable degree of chance with this method unless you know your particular badgers extremely well. Mild, damp autumn nights are the time when badgers are preoccupied with gorging on earthworms. A patch of permanent pasture near to a main sett will almost certainly be visited by the local badgers at this time of year, as indicated by the presence of well worn paths linking the feeding area with the sett. Other regularly visited feeding areas may be windfall fruit or cereal fields which may offer the opportunity to watch badgers away from their sett. Chris recalls badgers from one particular group in his study area which regularly visited a paddock in which there were several old apple trees. Competition for the fallen apples was fairly intense with cattle eating most of them before the badgers arrived. The badgers' strategy was to wait until they heard an apple fall, then rush quickly to the spot and devour it before any other animal arrived on the scene.

By far the best method of watching badgers going about their business is to habituate them to your presence so that they accept you as part of their world. This has been done with outstanding success by Chris Ferris who was the first person to our knowledge to exploit this technique with wild badgers. Night after night for many months she was 'just there'. At first the badgers avoided her, later they became curious but kept their distance, but finally they accepted her presence completely with remarkable trust. By setting scent on her they claimed her as one of their social group and came over to greet her when she appeared. In this way she was able to make unique close-up observations of their activities, some of which we are privileged to include in this book.

FIELD PROJECTS

An interest in badgers need not be confined to watching them around the sett or while they are foraging elsewhere. There are many aspects of badger biology and ecology which the amateur may pursue, such as studying feeding habits through dung analysis, monitoring road mortality in a given region or along a particular road, surveying setts — possibly as part of a nationally co-ordinated exercise — helping with the rehabilitation of injured or sick badgers, and mapping the territories of badger social groups.

Territorial studies can be fascinating. This usually involves the technique of bait marking, where a bait of peanuts and syrup is mixed with indigestible coloured plastic pellets and fed to badgers at their main sett (see also Chapter 7). Different coloured plastic markers are used for different setts, and by surveying badger latrines in the area it is possible to determine the location of the territorial boundaries of each social group. It is a labour-intensive procedure and only really successful when carried out during the peak of territorial activity in the spring. An enthusiastic badger watcher might, for example, use the technique of bait marking to discover the foraging areas which a particular group of badgers had access to. The method is fully described in the RSPCA booklet 'Problems with Badgers?'.

If the amateur badger biologist wishes to undertake other projects, such as sett surveys or dung analysis, there are two publications by The Mammal Society which cover most of the possibilities, giving useful advice on such important considerations as how to record data (Harris *et al.* 1989a, b). Details of dung and stomach content analysis are given in Chapter 6.

RESEARCH METHODS

The scientist has access to a variety of modern technology to aid the study of shy, nocturnal animals such as the badger, the chief one being radio telemetry. For this work, the badger has to be caught in a live trap, anaesthetised briefly and fitted with a collar carrying a minia-ture radio transmitter. This emits a continuous series of radio pulses which can be detected with an aerial and receiver tuned to the appropriate frequency. The electronics of the trans-mitter itself can be made from microscopically small components, so that the size of the electronic package is not a limiting factor. The bulky items are the battery, the capacity of which will determine the life and power of the transmitter, the transmitting aerial (larger being better in terms of effective range), and the protective encapsulation. Special epoxy resins are used both to waterproof the electronics and to protect them from abrasion whilst being carried by a badger. The final package is slightly bigger than a matchbox and weighs, complete with leather collar, around 100 g. Biologists have a general rule that animals should not be made to carry radio attachments which weigh more than 5% of their body weight, and since the average weight of an adult badger is 8–10 kg, the carrying of a radio collar does not pose a problem. Different individuals fitted with radio collars in the same area can be identified by the different radio frequencies of their transmitters.

The useful working range of these transmitters is up to about 500 m, often much more in open, flat country. Although much more powerful transmitters could be constructed, this range is perfectly adequate for most applications with badgers, and extra power can only be obtained at the expense of battery capacity, so it is necessary to adopt a compromise. An additional item which may be fitted to a radio collar is a 'Betalight'. This is a source of beta radiation, emitted by a glass bulb containing a phosphorus compound in tritium gas. These remarkable devices can be seen 150 m away at night with the naked eye, and at con-siderably greater distances with good light-gathering binoculars. As with the transmitter, the glass bulb needs protective encapsulation. In this case a clear epoxy resin is used, and the Betalight unit is fitted to the collar so that the heavier transmitter package keeps it sitting on top of the badger's neck. The great advantage of the Betalight is that it enables the observer to see precisely where the badger is, having located its approximate position by radio. The direction of travel and activity of the badger can then be quickly ascertained, thus enabling the observer to determine the best strategy to make a closer approach in order to make detailed observations with night viewing apparatus.

It is best not to approach a badger too closely whilst making field observations. About 50 m is near enough in most circumstances and it is important to maintain a safe distance to avoid the risk of disturbing the animal. The first and most obvious rule is to try to stay downwind of the badger. It is also a wise precaution to scan the field to see if other badgers are about. There is nothing more frustrating than peering intently at one badger, only to disturb another close by which had not been noticed, which then rushes off panicking every other animal in the vicinty. Observing badgers away from their sett is only really feasible in an open field situation. If a badger confines its activity to scrub or woodland it is usually impossible to approach the individual without disturbing it. When operating in the open, it is also important to avoid your silhouette being visible against the skyline by keeping trees, hedges or rising ground behind you. Although the badger's eyesight is not excellent, it is surprising how good they are at distinguishing between a human shape and, for example, those of cattle. Sometimes some slight noise causes a badger to look intently in the direction of the observer. If it is unable to decide whether the blob it can see poses a threat, it will often take a few tentative steps forward, sniffing the air, listening and watching, trying to get some further clue as to the blob's identity. The reaction to humans by badgers away from their sett is highly variable. It seems to depend more than anything else on whether they are used to seeing humans in a particular location. In the vicinity of gardens and farm buildings, for example, thay are far less concerned than when they are in a field a long way from human habitation.

Radio telemetry may be beyond the scope of most amateur badger watchers, not least because of Home Office regulations governing the use of radio equipment, and the need for a Home Office licence to catch badgers for the fitting of radio collars. There is also the fairly high cost of basic equipment. Night viewing equipment used to be

FIG 12.1   *Apparatus used by professional field biologists when studying badgers.*

prohibitively expensive but this is no longer the case. The demand for such products for security purposes has brought the cost down to the extent that a simple monocular image intensifier is not much more expensive than top-of-the-range binoculars. There are several makes on the market, some being advertised in magazines and journals which cater for the security market, and even sometimes in wildlife publications. The tremedous opportunity which night viewing equipment offers the amateur naturalist may make them a very worthwhile investment.

In good conditions, the clarity of the image seen through image intensifiers is remarkably sharp, so that even the items a badger is eating can be seen at close range. Chris has come extremely close to badgers on many occasions. In one particular instance, he was in a seated position observing a badger gleaning the wheat ears left on stubble after harvesting, when the badger wandered right up to his feet. It sniffed them, gave a loud snort and ran off, only to stop after a few metres, look round, and then carry on feeding again. Presumably, because Chris did not move a muscle during the encounter, the badger may have thought it was just a pile of human-scented clothes left in the field, and was not unduly perturbed.

A remarkably similar incident occurred when Chris was watching honey badgers in Africa. A group of these animals regularly visited the waste bins behind a safari camp kitchen after the tourists had gone to bed. Chris was sitting on the ground nearby with a log pile at his back, watching the badgers help themselves to tasty morsels from the bins with an image intensifier resting on his knees. One of the badgers looked inquisitively towards where he was sitting, walked over, sniffed between his legs, and then wandered off! On this occasion Chris remained totally motionless more out of abject fear than curiosity, because honey badgers have a reputation of being fearless predators, sometimes bringing down prey much larger than themselves, and often doing so by biting at the groin area . . .

We cannot leave the subject of research methods without describing in detail one of the latest novel techniques to be developed for studying badgers. This is the procedure of spool-and-line tracking. A badger fitted with a transmitter and Betalight is relatively easy to locate and watch for a while, but when the animal passes through dense cover it is difficult to stay in contact. Spool-and-line tracking has been used to study the behaviour of badgers in connection with their role in the transmission of bovine tuberculosis (Chapter 10) and in providing information on activity patterns (Chapter 5). A spool carrying up to 4 km of fine nylon thread is attached to the radio collar. The free end of thread is left trailing out of a hole in the end of the nylon container carrying the spool, and when the badger is mobile this simply pays out behind. The human tracker can thus follow the precise route a badger has taken, providing this is done fairly soon after the badger's activity, otherwise other animals will disturb and disperse the line. It is not uncommon for the line to be found passing through the branches of trees, presumably through the action of birds rather than unusually athletic badgers! It is fascinating to follow such a trail because signs of what the animal did when it passed are quite easy to interpret: a cow-pat turned over, small holes dug to excavate plant food or invertebrates, a visit to a latrine. A thread of 4 km is enough to monitor one complete night's activity, sometimes two nights. The spool is attached to the collar by means of a few turns of plastic tape which frays after a few days allowing the empty spool to drop off. When used in conjunction with biomarkers to make a badger's faeces and urine fluoresce under ultra-violet light, this technique has allowed a complete picture of individual animals' urinatory and defecatory behaviour to be obtained. In the course of this work badgers under observation sometimes visited the gardens of local residents, where they helped themselves to fruit and vegetables. The householders were remarkably tolerant, perhaps being somewhat intrigued by the evidence left behind of the badger's activity whilst in their garden. However, it was interesting that they were referred to as 'your' badgers, as if the innocent research worker was in some way responsible for the badger's behaviour!

CHAPTER 13

Badgers of the World

THE sub-family Melinae which contains the true badgers contains six genera: *Meles*, the Eurasian badgers; *Arctonyx*, the hog badgers of Asia; *Mydaus*, the Indonesian stink badgers; *Suillotaxus*, the stink badgers of Palawan and the Calamian Islands; *Taxidea*, the American badgers; and *Melogale*, the ferret badgers of Asia. In this chapter, the honey badger (ratel) will also be included, as although it belongs to the sub-family Mellivorinae, it shows many structural, behavioural and ecological similarities to the true badgers.

HOG BADGERS — GENUS *ARCTONYX*

There is only one species, *Arctonyx collaris*, which has a wide distribution in south-east Asia. It is found over most of China, Bhutan, Assam, Burma, Thailand, Vietnam and on the island of Sumatra. Thus its distribution is largely tropical and except in parts of China it overlaps very little with *Meles* which has a more northerly range.

Arctonyx resembles *Meles* in many ways, being comparable in size and build except in the northern and Sumatran subspecies which are smaller. The head and body length is 550–700 mm, but the tail is longer, up to 170 mm. Adult weights vary from 7 to 14 kg. It has the same heavy body as *Meles*, but the head is smaller and the snout more truncated and mobile with an area of pink, naked skin between the rhinarium and the upper lip. Typically there is a good deal of dark hair on the head including a conspicuous eye stripe, and a white stripe runs in the midline from the rhinarium to the nape. In some subspecies, particularly the one from Sumatra, the head is much whiter in the dorsal and anterior regions. The throat and ears are white in all subspecies. The body hair is coarse and in colder regions in winter the underfur becomes thick. Colour is variable, some having a yellowish appearance, others grey. The fore feet are broad and strong and have long, tough, light-coloured claws.

Hog badgers are found in a wide variety of habitats, but typically in forested areas. They occur in lowland jungles and the more wooded highlands up to at least 3000 m in northern China. No serious work has yet been done on their behaviour and ecology.

There are a number of subspecies which have been recognised. The most western one, *A. collaris collaris*, occurs in the south-eastern foothills of the Himalayas in Sikkim, Bhutan and into Assam. This is rather a small badger with a head–body length of around 600 mm. It is comparable in size to *A. c. leucolaemus* which is found at even higher altitudes in northern China. *A. c. albogularis* occurs throughout most of China south of the last-mentioned subspecies and is rather longer and darker. Another medium-sized hog badger, *A. c. consul*,

FIG 13.1   *Badgers of the world.*

FIG 13.2   *World distribution of six genera of badgers. For* Melogale *see Fig. 13.3.*

occurs in southern Assam and Burma. The largest, *A. c. dictator*, is found throughout
Thailand, Vietnam and northern Burma; it is yellowish brown. The Sumatran type, *A. c.
hoeveni*, is small and dark, but the top of the head, throat, front feet and tail are conspicuously white.

Hog badgers are shy and largely nocturnal lying up by day in deep burrows of their own
making or in natural fissures under boulders. Their eyesight is poor, but their olfactory
sense is extremely well developed; most food appears to be found by scent. They are truly
omnivorous, using their sensitive snouts for rooting in the manner of pigs. They dig up succulent roots and take many kinds of small invertebrates including earthworms. Like *Meles*,
they appear to be foragers rather than hunters. They are also fond of fruit, and in captivity
will eat meat, so it is probable that in the wild they will eat any small animal they can catch.

They are playful, especially when young. When attacked by a predator, they will fluff
out the guard hairs and display their white throats, defending themselves with teeth and
claws and making menacing growls. The skin is very loose and tough, making it very
difficult for another animal to get a grip without being bitten in return. Their anal
gland secretion is very pungent, but it is not known whether this is used in defence as in
the stink badger.

Little is known of their breeding habits except that the young are born in a burrow. There
is a record for the subspecies *A. c. leucolaemus* of a litter of four new-born young in April. It
was also reported by Parker (1979) that a captive pair from China brought up in Toronto
Zoo had two young in February 1977; later, various matings occurred that year and a litter
of four was born in February 1978. It is considered likely that delayed implantation occurs
in this species and that true gestation is not more than 6 weeks.

INDONESIAN STINK BADGER OR TELEDU — GENUS *MYDAUS*

There is only one species *Mydaus javensis* which is restricted in its distribution to Java, Sumatra, Borneo and the North Natuna Islands.

These are small badgers well adapted for burrowing and rooting. They have a head–body length of up to 510 mm plus a short tail. The head is small and rather pointed owing to the long flexible snout. The body is elongated and supported on very muscular short legs and the feet are armed with strong claws. The toes of the fore feet are united together as far as the roots of the claws — an adaptation for digging.

The general colour is dark brown, but the crown of the head is white and there may also be white patches along the back, but more often a white stripe takes the place of these patches and stretches from head to tail.

The teledu is mainly found in the mountains and is nocturnal. During the day it seeks refuge in a short simple burrow of its own making. There is little known about its diet, but it is said to feed mainly on invertebrates, particularly earthworms and insects.

This species is notorious for its anal gland secretion, which for its potency rivals that of the skunk. If molested, it will raise its tail and squirt from these glands a pale greenish fluid which is both nauseating and damaging. There are reports of dogs being asphyxiated by the secretion or even blinded if struck in the eye (Walker 1964). Like the anal gland secretion of civets, it has been used in great dilution as a basis for making perfumes.

PALAWAN OR CALAMIAN STINK BADGER — GENUS *SUILLOTAXUS*

The one species in this genus is *Suillotaxus marchei*. It closely resembles *Mydaus javensis* and is considered by Long & Killingley (1983) to merit only subspecific rank. It is found on two small islands of the Calamian group north and east of Borneo, Palawan and Busuanga.

It is a small animal with a head–body length of up to 460 mm plus a very short tail. Ian Grimwood (1976), who as far as we know is the only person to have studied the species in the wild, describes it as being:

> of a general chocolate-brown colour (lighter coloured specimens are not uncommon), with a yellowish cap and streak down the back which fades out at the shoulder, and a dirty white and almost bald muzzle which gives it an anaemic appearance. An enormous, hairless and pale-skinned anal region comprises (at least when the animal is alarmed) approximately one third of its total bulk, and stuck vertically on the extreme end of the anal bulge is a 40 mm stump of a tail, almost devoid of hair and cut square across the top, exactly like the funnel of a toy boat. It moves with a rather ponderous fussy walk, but when alarmed, can sustain a steady trot for up to 100 m; even then its speed is no more than that of a man walking.

Grimwood goes on to describe how it is capable of discharging its anal gland secretion with great accuracy. When photographing it, some of this yellowish oily fluid hit the lens of the camera from about 1 m! He describes the smell as pungent but not offensive and says it passes off after half an hour or so.

When one of these animals was first touched, it rolled over and shammed dead, but as Grimwood described 'it spoilt the act by continually swivelling its anal region to point in whatever direction its aggressor moved!' However, Grimwood believes that the secretion is not merely defensive as the tracks it uses are often permeated with its scent.

These stink badgers were found to be surprisingly common wherever they were found and were occasionally used as food by the local population.

THE FERRET BADGERS — GENUS *MELOGALE* (PREVIOUSLY *HELICTUS*)

These rather small badgers of tropical south-east Asia are more primitive than any other living badgers having four premolars in each jaw like the martens.

There are three (possibly four — see later) species: the short-toothed ferret badger *Melogale mosquata*, which ranges from Assam across China, the islands of Tainau and into North Vietnam; the large-toothed ferret badger *M. personata* with a more southerly distribution (but also overlaps the previous species over a wide area) including Assam, Burma, Thailand, Cambodia, Vietnam and Java; and *M. everetti*, which is endemic to Borneo.

They are small badgers with a head–body length of 330–430 mm with a pelage which can be fluffed up when alarmed. The head is pointed and ends on a pinkish snout and there are various whitish or yellowish markings on head and face including a short but conspicuous transverse band between the eyes which contrasts with a dark patch anterior to it. In addition, there is usually a pale stripe which runs in the mid-dorsal line from the back of the head. The underparts are white or yellow and the fore feet have strong digging claws.

Ferret badgers live mainly in tropical and sub-tropical forests and wooded hillsides, but also occur in grassy and more cultivated places. Patricia Marshall (1967) writing about *M. mosquata* says that their shy and secretive ways aided by acute senses of smell and hearing enable them to live undetected in close proximity with people. She describes them as 'omnivorous, feeding mainly on insects, worms, small birds, young rats and wild fruit. They are nocturnal and spend the day sleeping in a well-hidden burrow or natural shelter, or occasionally on the branches of a tree'. Although they can climb well, it is thought that they spend most of their time foraging on the ground and digging for worms.

Ferret badgers are fearless creatures which may defend themselves fiercely; they emit a pungent odour from their anal glands when attacked.

They have one to three young which are born in a burrow in May or June and are suckled for several months.

A male and female ferret badger were captured in sub-tropical mixed pine forest (1200–1500 m) in Manapur, India (Ramakantha 1992). It is not known whether this represents a new species or subspecies. It is described as 'a small animal with a flattened, almost snake-like head with a long snout that projects beyond, concealing lower lip and chin. The naked tip of the snout, along with the external and internal wings of the nostrils are pink and the upper lips have a row of rigid white whiskers. The colour of the coat varies from black to silvery grey with bleached tips of hair. The tail is sandy yellow throughout the year. The forked white stripes above and below the eyes extend down the throat to the belly as dirty white. The narrow whitish stripe on the crown of the head neither ends beyond the

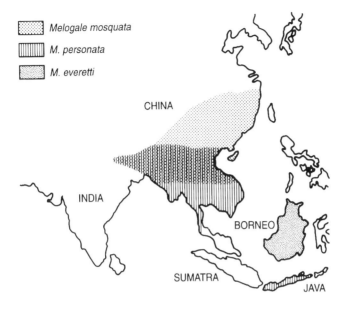

FIG 13.3   *General range of ferret badgers* (Melogale) *in south-east Asia.*

shoulders as in *M. mosquata* nor reaches up the rump as in *M. personata*. Unlike most ferret badgers, the Manipur specimens have a streamlined squirrel-like body'.

In captivity they were mainly active at night, had a highly developed sense of smell and an aptitude for climbing. Their choice of food was mainly carnivorous, eating frogs, toads, lizards, chopped meat and earthworms, avoiding fruits, tubers, cereals and honey. The female was pregnant when captured, and two blind and hairless cubs were born, but neither was reared successfully.

THE AMERICAN BADGER — GENUS *TAXIDEA*

Classification

There is a single species of American badger, *Taxidea taxus*, which is found as far north as southern Canada and ranges well into Mexico in the south. In the west it reaches the coast from Washington southwards into California and goes as far east as Illinois and Missouri and north-east as far as the Great Lakes. Four subspecies have been recognised by Long (1972):

(1) *Taxidea taxus taxus* from southern central Canada to the more northerly and central states of America;

(2) *Taxidea taxus jeffersonii* (formerly *neglecta*) from British Columbia down the west coast to California, into Nevada, Utah, Colorado and eastwards to central Montana and Wyoming;

(3) *Taxidea taxus jacksoni* south of the Great Lakes region in Wisconsin, northern Indiana and Ohio;

(4) *Taxidea taxus berlandieri* a smaller subspecies found in the southern states and Mexico.

These subspecies intergrade wherever they meet. There is considerable difference in size, the type species being comparable to *Meles*, but the southern badgers are much smaller, so the head–body length for the species as a whole varies from 420 to 720 mm and the tail, 100–150mm. Adult weights (4–12 kg) vary geographically and also seasonally as in areas which are cold in winter, stored fat can account for 30% of body weight. Females are distinctly smaller and lighter.

Structure and general characteristics

The colour of the upper parts varies from reddish-brown to greyish, but there is a conspicuous white median stripe which extends from the nose to neck or shoulders and may continue to the rump in the southern subspecies. Dark patches occur on cheeks and crown. The chin, throat and much of the ventral region are much lighter, varying from white to pale reddish-buff. The feet are dark brown. Young badgers are paler.

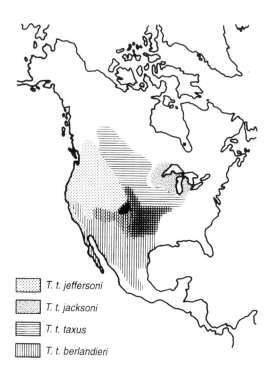

T. t. jeffersoni

T. t. jacksoni

T. t. taxus

T. t. berlandieri

FIG 13.4   *Distribution of the four subspecies of the American badger* (Taxidea). *Source: after Long and Killingley, 1983.*

Many of the badger's characteristics are associated with digging. The head is wedge-shaped, the body stocky and low-slung on short but very strong legs. The ears are rounded and protected from soil when digging by stiff bristles and the nictitating membrane is well developed so that it can cover and clean the whole eye surface. The fore feet are partially webbed, thus keeping the toes close together and making digging movements stronger and more effective. The claws of the fore feet are long and powerful and grow at a faster rate than the smaller ones of the hind feet, a compensation for greater wear.

The skull, 113–141 mm in length, is very robust with an exceptionally broad cranium and a high sagittal crest. The dental formula is:

$$\text{Incisors } \frac{3}{3} \quad \text{Canines } \frac{1}{1} \quad \text{Premolars } \frac{3}{3} \quad \text{Molars } \frac{1}{2} \ = 34$$

This shows a reduction in the number of premolars from four, as found in the more primitive ferret badgers, to three. *Meles* is intermediate having three functional but often a vestigial first premolar in addition (p. 25).

Although their eyes are small their sight appears to be better than *Meles*, perhaps because they are more diurnal. Senses of smell and hearing are acute and are of great importance in locating prey in their burrows. They hiss when confronted and sometimes make pig-like grunts but their vocalisation seems to be restricted.

The various subspecies inhabit a wide range of habitats, but the most usual are wide open plains and deciduous woodland. They may also occur in farmland, marshy areas and in the mountainous west on grassy slopes as high as 4260 m in the arctic–alpine zone. In contrast, the southern subspecies may live in hot, inhospitable deserts such as Death Valley and in the arid prairies of Mexico, but usually at low densities.

In the south they are active throughout the year, but where winters are cold they become semi-dormant and their temperature may drop as much as 9°C accompanied by a slower breathing and heart rate. However, during mild days they become active. Messick & Hornocker (1981) found that one female emerged only once during a 72-day period of severe cold. During semi-dormancy they feed on their stored fat.

They are normally active by night, but in secluded places they are more diurnal than *Meles*. However, in the hot arid regions of their range they are more strictly nocturnal, keeping to their burrows during the day to stay cool and avoid excessive loss of water.

Digging

Digging is a major activity. They excavate burrows as shelters and for breeding, but in particular they dig extensively during hunting operations. They may travel quite widely over their ranges during the summer, males travelling further than females; they may use a fresh burrow each day. In the autumn they tend to revert to previously used dens and occupy a single one for the winter.

Breeding dens tend to be bigger than those used as temporary refuges and so have larger spoil heaps outside. They may be 4–5 m long, reach a depth of 2 m and have one or two entrances. They are simple constructions, usually with a single large central chamber containing dry bedding. The main tunnel often bifurcates and joins up again and there may be several dead-end tunnels and smaller side pockets. Dung is usually deposited in the latter and is usually covered (Lindzey 1976).

FIG 13.5   *American badger. Photo P. Morris.*

The speed of digging is phenomenal. When caught in the open a badger can dig itself to safety and disappear within a minute or so leaving a plug of earth to block the burrow behind it.

Food and feeding habits

Taxidea is largely carnivorous although it will supplement its diet with plant food such as cereals. In contrast to *Meles* it is primarily a hunter, but above ground it will feed opportunistically on any small invertebrates it comes across.

There is often one species of small mammal, usually a rodent, which is its primary prey, the species varying according to region and habitat. In some places it is ground squirrels (*Spermophilus spilosoma*), in others mice (*Peromyscus maniculatus*), pocket gophers (*Geomys* sp.), kangaroo rats (*Dipodomys* sp.), prairie dogs (*Cynomys mexicanus*) or cottontails (*Sylvilagus floridanus*). Young skunks (*Mephites* sp.), marmots (*Marmota* sp.), chipmunks (*Eutamias* sp.), deer mice (*Peromyscus* sp.) voles (*Microtidae*) and rats are also taken when opportunities occur. Most of these mammals are caught below ground by rapid digging. The badger often makes numerous trial digs, smelling carefully at each to locate the position of the animal before digging after it. In a good rodent locality a badger may exploit this food source over many weeks and the whole area becomes riddled with excavated holes and extensive heaps of earth.

Occasionally a badger will make a quick dash at prey on the surface or follow for a short distance; cottontails and even hares are caught in this way. Like *Meles* the initial spurt is fast, but thereafter movement is relatively slow.

Insects form a significant part of the diet, particularly in the summer. These include crickets, grasshoppers, ground beetles and caterpillars. American badgers will dig for the larvae of cockchafers and ground-nesting bees and have been known to raid wasps' and hornets' nests.

Occasionally they take the eggs of ground-nesting birds, surprise a pheasant when incubating, or take poultry. When there is a surfeit of food the carcasses may be taken back to the burrow or buried and eaten later. Rattlesnakes, garter snakes, lizards, frogs and toads are all taken occasionally but perhaps more at times when their favourite rodent prey is scarce.

Social life and organisation of living space

Unlike *Meles* their social life is limited to mating and rearing their young. The males live solitary lives for most of the year and females and young are only together until shortly after weaning. Occasionally there are fights between males over females but there are no signs of territorial behaviour such as perimeter marking or defence of an area.

This comparative lack of social contact is reflected in the use of the scent glands. There are no sub-caudal glands as in *Meles*, but anal glands are present which produce a pungent and somewhat disagreable odour used in defence. The dung would be somewhat contaminated by anal gland secretion, but as the faeces are normally placed in pits and covered with earth it seems likely that they are not important scent signals.

It was found by radio-tracking that in good badger country in Idaho the population density could be as much as five adults per km² (Messick & Hornocker 1981). Males had home ranges of 2.4 km² and females 1.6 km². Some male ranges overlapped up to three female ranges and the latter also overlapped. Within these large ranges the badgers lived solitary lives except when breeding. In Minnesota a female used a range of 752 ha in summer and had 50 dens within that area, but in autumn she used a much smaller adjacent area of 52 ha which in winter was further reduced to 2 ha (Sargeant & Warner 1972).

Reproduction

Mating occurs in summer and autumn and appears to be of long duration although sightings have been few. There is no sign of pair bonding and the sparse evidence available suggests that a male will mate with any female in contiguous ranges. There is a period of delay before implantation which occurs between December and February — significantly during the period of semi-dormancy as in *Meles*. The young are born after about 6 weeks of true gestation in March–early April in a nest of dry bedding in an underground chamber. Litters are usually of two or three (range 1–5). The young at birth are covered in short, soft, silky hair and are blind and helpless. The eyes open 4–6 weeks later. Lactation lasts 6–8 weeks, possibly longer, after which the mother will bring back dead rodents to the burrow. The young may disperse quite soon after being weaned, or remain until the approach of the mating season.

In Idaho, it was found that 30% of the young females became mature and were mated in their first year, the remainder as yearlings (Messick & Hornocker 1981). Males do not breed until their second year (Wright 1969).

The young are playful and will romp near the entrance of the den while their mother is away hunting. If disturbed they will quickly return to the shelter of the den. Females will defend their young with great ferocity and their bites are strong and capable of inflicting serious damage.

American badgers can live a long time. The record in the wild is 14 years, but in San Diego Zoo a badger lived for 26 years. Greatest mortality occurs during the first 2 years. Starvation, especially after weaning, is one important reason (Messick 1987).

Status and economic importance

The American badger is considered beneficial owing to its predatory habits, especially in controlling rodent populations which destroy crops. Other benefits include their effect on the soil, providing ready-made dens for other fur-bearers, killing venomous snaks and eating carrion and insects (Long & Killingley 1983, Messick 1987). On the other hand, limited damage is done to cereal fields in some districts and their extensive burrowings can be a hazard to domestic animals.

In many states badgers have been hunted for sport and trapped for their fur which, as in *Meles*, is not very valuable but may be used as trimmings to clothing and the tanned hides as mats or wall hangings. Trapping for coyotes has also accounted for many badger deaths and they have been poisoned in predator control programmes both intentionally and incidentally. These factors have resulted in much lower densities in some regions. On the other hand, in certain states hunting is prohibited in some seasons and licenced at other times so that numbers killed do not exceed replacements by breeding. One thing in their favour has been the increase in suitable habitat provided for them by changes in land use such as clearing of forests and increasing areas of meadowland in consequence, leaving fields fallow and the abandonment of small holdings (Long & Killingley 1983, Messick 1987).

Long & Killingley conclude that over much of its range, the badger is holding its own quite well, but in Mexico in particular its status is precarious, and much needs to be done to improve conditions for it in such states as British Columbia, New Mexico and California.

For a more detailed account of the American badger the book by Long & Killingley, *The Badgers of the World* (1983), is recommended.

HONEY BADGER OR RATEL — GENUS *MELLIVORA*

The honey badger is classified in the sub-family Mellivorinae, partly because it differs from members of the Melinae in having only one molar on each side in both jaws. However, it is very badger-like in form and behaviour. There is one species, *Mellivora capensis*. It occurs over the greater part of Africa south of the Sahara and its range extends through the Middle East and Arabia as far as India.

They are immensely strong, stocky animals about the size of the Eurasian badger and similar to it in build (head–body length 600–770 mm, with a tail of 250–300 mm). They weigh up to 12 kg. They have strong warning colours — a contrast of dark and light. All the upper parts are silvery grey or whitish, but the sides and underparts are black or dark brown. When you see them in poor light you notice only the silvery portions so they appear to float along in a most uncanny manner. However, in some forest areas in Zaire they may be darker dorsally. The neck and limbs are very muscular and the fore feet are armed with formidable claws. There are no external ears but the aperture can be closed by muscles which bring the margins together. This happens when digging, keeping the ear free of soil; it may also prevent access of bees or termites when raiding their nests.

The skin is extremely loose and as tough and hard as rubber — an effective protection against many stinging insects, porcupine quills and the bites of other animals. The skin of the throat is particularly thick — up to 6 mm. Kingdon (1977) considers this to be a special protection during fights with other honey badgers. They can also defend themselves with their extremely strong jaws and by secreting a vile-smelling substance from the anal glands. Consequently, they have no other enemies apart from humans. But we too have reason to be cautious of the honey badger as there are a number of records of people being viciously attacked and badly bitten. This warning has to be taken seriously as there are a number of safari lodges where honey badgers regularly come to eat scraps; at close quarters, they should be treated with respect (p. 233).

Honey badgers show no fear and will attack even the largest and most ferocious animals when defending their young, making most menacing grunting growls. M. Cowie (pers. comm.) related how three honey badgers saw off four half-grown and three sub-adult lions from a wildebeest kill and they have been known to attack sheep and horses. In Kruger National Park an adult buffalo, wildebeest and waterbuck were found dead from loss of blood after honey badgers had attacked them in the scrotum. They have a considerable reputation as castrators, even of humans.

A honey badger was raised in captivity by Sylvia Sykes (1964). She recounts how, when fighting a dog, once it got a grip, it held on regardless of being tossed about, jerking and twisting inside its loose skin until the dog collapsed with exhaustion. It is this tenacity and endurance which makes them such formidable opponents and allows them to overcome large prey.

They feed largely at night although they may be seen occasionally by day near the dens and when travelling. Characteristically, using their nose, they will investigate any hole or cranny for potential prey. They usually hunt on their own or in pairs; however, on one occasion, Ernest saw three of about the same size together, and there are accounts of larger numbers, but usually these are when a good regular food source attracts them from a wider area. When you see them on their travels they seem to amble along quite slowly, but they can keep up this pace for long periods. Their home range appears to be large.

They are mainly carnivorous but will eat fruits and other vegetable material. They kill many kinds of mammal such as porcupines, hares, rodents and the young of larger antelopes. Large prey is taken exceptionally. They will also eat ground-nesting birds and their eggs, raid crocodile nests and kill snakes, lizards, tortoises and turtles; the latter may be caught under water as honey badgers are good swimmers. They often eat carrion and visit refuse heaps.

However, in spite of all this diversity it is insects that provide a major source of food at certain times of the year. These include dung beetles, wood-boring beetles, ants, termites and the contents of bees' nests; termites and bees are of special importance.

The honey badger has a highly specialised technique for raiding bees' nests. When faced with the fury of a disturbed colony and the probability of a host of stings, it uses its anal gland secretion to subdue the bees. The anal gland can be everted through the anus and used to expel a nauseating fluid which acts rather like an anaesthetic, causing some bees to flee and others to become moribund. The badger then tears away the bark to expose the nest and devours the comb containing honey and larvae. Honey badgers are not immune to stings

FIG 13.6   *Honey badgers, Kenya.*

and occasionally they have been found dead within hives having been killed by the bees. Raiding hives can be a major problem in some regions. During a single year in Tanzania, 2700 hives out of a total of 24 000 were damaged by honey badgers (Kingdon 1977).

When hunting for bees' nests there is a well authenticated association between the greater honey guide (*Indicator indicator*), a bird of the African bush, and the honey badger. When one of these birds finds a bees' nest it is usually unable to get at the larvae and bees' wax on which it feeds, so it may seek out a honey badger. It attracts its attention by repeatedly calling and swooping near, displaying the white on its tail. The badger then follows the bird to the tree which contains the bees' nest. If out of reach, the badger may even climb to reach it. When the nest is exposed the badger takes its fill, but there is always sufficient left for the bird to feed upon.

Honey badgers will also attack termites' nests and eat vast numbers of these insects. In some species those of the soldier caste are very aggressive and will inflict painful bites and stings. Kingdon (1977) relates how, if attacked in this way, the badger will roll on the ground to dislodge the attackers and at the same time emit much anal gland secretion as a defence.

Anal gland secretion is not only used when attacking the nests of bees and termites. As in all mustelids it also has an important function in marking out features in the home range. The honey badger has been seen marking tree roots, holes, crevices, tufts of grass and patches of bare ground whilst foraging, particularly near its den. Young raised in captivity regularly set scent on their owners, so in the wild this may happen within families. They often drop their faeces into crevices or holes which they may have dug themselves. These may act as scent messages, for as Kingdon remarks, 'these are just the places where other honey badgers would visit'.

They can live in very diverse habitats from dense forests to extremely arid scrub although they seem to have a preference for hilly and boulder-strewn country where natural refuges are easier to find. They may also hide up in old termite mounds or aardvark dens particularly during the dry season, using more temporary refuges during the rains.

Mating has been observed in various months of the year and gestation is said to be about 5–6 months according to data from zoos. If this is correct they must exhibit delayed implantation, a phenomenon more often associated with mammals which have become adapted to a more northerly distribution. As this is not so in the honey badger, it is possible that it could be an adaptation to well-marked wet and dry seasons. It is said that birth is seasonal in Turkmenia in what was southern USSR, mating occurring in the autumn with births in the spring. However, in captivity there is much greater variability. In Africa, the pattern is less clear although births appear to be associated with the rains, a time when honey is at an optimum. There is no oestrus following birth as in *Meles* and *Taxidea*.

They usually have two young (range 1–4) which are born in a den lined with grassy bedding. Young born in captivity were blind and naked except for a few facial hairs. One weighed 212 g. The eyes opened around 5 weeks and by this time they had the markings of adults. By 2 months they could walk normally and by 3 months were about half grown. In the wild they probably come above ground when 2–3 months old.

In recent years honey badgers in some areas have suffered much persecution because of their habit of attacking bee hives, poultry and other livestock and their numbers have declined markedly. In Tanzania it has been shown that preventative measures, including chemical deterrents, can be effective and by suspending bee hives by wires from trees, attacks can be avoided. So it is hoped these techniques may take the place of extermination policies.

THE ORIGIN OF BADGERS

The fossil record shows that badgers may be traced back to primitive marten-like ancestors and that way back in the Tertiary, 2–65 million years ago, the ancestors of badgers showed a change in dentition which reflected the evolution from a carnivorous to a more omnivorous diet; shearing teeth became reduced and the molars more flattened. There was also a reduction in the number of teeth from 38 to 34, although the oriental badgers of today still have the more primitive number and *Meles* retains in some specimens vestigial remains of the first premolars.

The *Meles* line appears to have evolved in the temperate forests of Asia, spreading west into Europe. Rather primitive forms, but recognisable as badgers, were present some 4 million years ago; they may have originated from the Pliocene genus *Melodon* in China (Kurten 1968). Thoral's badger, *Meles thorali*, was the earliest fossil of the genus *Meles* in Europe. It was found in France at Saint-Vallier, near Lyons, of mid-Villafranchian date — perhaps 2 million years old. Other very similar fossils of the same period were found in China, so this species was probably very widespread. By the early to middle Pleistocene, Europe was inhabited by badgers similar to the modern species; these are now referred to as the subspecies *Meles meles atavus* Kormos. *Meles* is a common fossil in the middle and late Pleistocene, their bones having been found along with those of extinct species such as the cave bear. The earliest record for Britain is a fossil from Barrington in Cambridgeshire estimated at about 250 000 years old.

The fossil badger, *Arctomeles*, from the late Pliocene, may have evolved from ancient *Meles* stock and given rise to the modern hog badgers, *Arctonyx*. *Meles* did not spread into the more tropical parts of Asia, possibly because *Arctonyx* filled that niche (Petter 1971).

The ancestors of the American badger, *Taxidea*, must have crossed the land bridge between Siberia and Alaska and spread south and west. It is probable that they had their remote origins in forms inhabiting the more tropical parts of Asia which also gave rise to present-day ferret badgers, *Melogale*. An intermediate form found in North America is the fossil *Pliotaxidea*, leading to *Taxidea* with its present four distinctive subspecies.

Ferret badgers, *Melogale*, have remained more like the ancestral stock than other badgers, occupying the same tropical habitats. The line of evolution of the honey badger, *Mellivora*, is unknown, but from their teeth it would appear that they are nearer the Mustelinae (martens, etc.) than the Melinae (true badgers), but sufficiently different from both to be put into a subfamily, the Mellivorinae. The remarkable similarities in form, behaviour and ecology are due to parallel evolution resulting from a comparable mode of life.

To sum up, we cannot do better than quote from Long and Killingley (1983) who have studied the evidence in depth: 'a picture emerges of long-ago carnivores, slender and quick marten-like climbers, leaving the forests to wander through open woods and over the plains and steppes, digging for shelter, the rearing of young and eventually for food, specialising in fossorial form, generalising in diet and dentition and differentiating into the distinctive genera of today'.

THE FUTURE

There is still much to be discovered about many of the badger species. Badgers have been a very successful group, exploiting a great number of habitats on four continents. So far they have held their own with tenacity and have adapted to changes forced upon them by human activities. In Britain, they have survived human persecution for many centuries. Today they need our tolerance and understanding if they are to survive along with us. 'It is their world too.' This philosophy of course applies even more to wildlife in general and one is reminded of those words of wisdom from Charles Elton when he defined conservation as 'some wise co-existence between man and nature, even if it means a modified type of man and a modified kind of nature'.

Badgers and the Law in Britain

BADGERS were first given some legal protection under the Badger Act (1973) which was amended by the Wildlife and Countryside Act (1981) and further amended (1985). These were all primarily concerned with ill-treatment, particularly against the practice of badger digging with the aid of dogs (badger baiting had been made illegal in 1835).

These Acts gave good protection to badgers, but not to their setts unless damage to the latter could be proved to cause ill-treatment to the badger such as preventing lactating sows feeding their cubs. Hence it could only be applied to an agreed season from 1 December to 30 June and in practice cases were difficult to prove.

The Badgers Act (1991) greatly stregthened previous legislation as it gave formal year-round protection of setts and made the introduction of dogs to setts illegal. A separate Act, The Badgers (Further protection) Act (1991), made provision for the removal, disposal or destruction of any dogs used illegally for badger digging.

These various separate Acts produced a confusing legal situation which made it necessary to bring together all the relevant legislation in a single Act. This was done with the passing of The Protection of Badgers Act (1992) and the repealing of all previous Badger Acts. The present provisions are summarised as follows.

The following actions are illegal.

(1) Wilfully to kill, injure or take any badger or attempt to do so. This applies to anybody, including the landowner, unless he has a licence for so doing.

(2) To dig for a badger.
   If there is reasonable evidence that the accused was attempting to achieve any of the above in (1) and (2), the defendant will be presumed to have committed the offence unless he can prove otherwise.

(3) To possess a dead badger, or any part of one (such as a skin) or an object derived from one (such as a sporran) if that badger was taken in contravention of the Act in operation at the time of death. It is also an offence to offer for sale, or have in possession or under control a live badger, or to mark, or attach any ring, tag, or other marking device. However, small tags implanted subcutaneously in a badger that is due to be released is not an offence because they can be inserted without the use of anaesthetics.

(4) Intentionally or recklessly to damage, destroy or obstruct access to any part of a badger sett; to cause a dog to enter one or to disturb a badger whilst it is occupying a sett. The legal definition of a 'badger sett' is 'any structure or place which displays signs indicating current use by a badger'. Interpretation of 'current use' is open to slightly

different meanings according to the views of English Nature and MAFF; however, both agree that a sett is protected whether or not there is a badger in that sett. Hence a licence is needed *before* it is interfered with.

The following actions are not illegal.

A number of the above illegal acts are allowable under licence (see later) for certain purposes and under particular circumstances:

If a badger is killed or injured in an unavoidable traffic accident.

If a badger is killed *when caught in the act* of causing serious damage e.g. killing livestock or domestic animals.

If a sett is damaged *unwittingly* during a lawful action. However, if it is known in advance that a sett may be damaged or the badgers within it harmed, this is an offence.

Mercy killing, i.e. in an emergency, such as a road accident, a seriously injured badger may be killed to put it out of pain.

A badger may be taken, if picked up by hand, when disabled by another person, but only for the purpose of tending it. No licence is required for looking after it so long as it is returned to the wild *when no longer incapacitated*, preferably at the place where it was found. This also applies to rearing an orphan cub for the purpose of later release. In both cases a licence is needed to keep it in captivity longer than the above mentioned period.

The body of a badger recently killed on the road may be legally kept but the onus is on the person concerned to be able to prove that the badger was killed legally. This is also the case for mounted skins when being bought or sold.

Watching badgers at a sett or using indicators of usage, such as putting a stick across an entrance, is not an offence but it is wise to use an accepted code of practice to avoid undue disturbance.

If a pet dog enters a sett *under its own volition* when out with its owner this is not an offence, but when near known badger setts a dog should be kept on a lead.

PROVISIONS RELATED TO FOX HUNTING AND GAMEKEEPING

Earth stopping is legal under certain conditions: the top and sides of an entrance must not be damaged by digging and the entrance only lightly blocked with (1) such material as untainted straw, hay, bracken or loose soil, or (2) bundles of small sticks or paper sacks containing such substances.

This blocking may only be done on the day of the hunt (or after mid-day on the day preceding it) with items under (1) and have to be removed the same day if composed of items under (2). The 'stopper' must be authorised to do so by the landowner or occupier of the land and by a recognised hunt, which must keep a register of all such persons.

If hounds, during a hunt, 'mark' a fox at a sett; this is not an offence provided the hounds are called off as soon as possible.

Under very exceptional circumstances, a sett may be dug out to release a dog or remove a fox, *but a licence has to be obtained first.*

PENALTIES

A person found guilty of any of the illegal actions listed previously (1–4) is liable on summary conviction to imprisonment for a term not exceeding 6 months and/or a fine not exceeding £5000 (as for 1994) for each badger (and presumably, sett). In addition, any weapon or article (including vehicles) used in committing an offence can be seized and ordered to be forfeited. Where a dog has been used, the court may also make an order destroying or otherwise disposing of the dog and/or disqualifying the offender from having control of any dog for a defined period.

LICENSING

A licence is normally only granted *in advance* for specific situations, although general licences may be issued to certain individuals e.g. when carrying out research. The applicants will need to provide a good case *each time* to convince the authority of the necessity of the proposed action.

Licences may be obtained from (1) Statutory Nature Conservation Agencies: English Nature, Scottish Natural Heritage or the Countryside Council for Wales according to the country in which the proposed action is to take place, (2) Ministries: Ministry of Agriculture, Fisheries and Food in England and the Secretaries of State (Scottish Office and Welsh Office) in Scotland and Wales. The choice between (1) and (2) depends on the type of situation; these are listed below.

Statutory Conservation Agency

For licences to kill, take or keep in captivity, display in zoos, conservation measures including translocation. For permission to interfere with a sett for scientific research, any form of land development, the preservation or archaeological investigation of a scheduled monument and for investigating or gathering evidence about an offence. For fox control in order to protect game being reared, or wildlife on a Nature Reserve.

The ministries

For licences to kill or take badgers or interfere with setts for the prevention or spread of disease. For prevention of damage to land, crops, poultry or property. For permission to interfere with a sett for the purpose of any agricultural or forestry operation, to maintain, construct or improve watercourses, draining works, and sea or tidal defence systems.

In many of the above, Statutory Conservation Agencies will also be consulted before a licence is issued.

Note. Anybody holding a licence should carry that licence with them when carrying out any authorised operation. It is a form of proof and will contain exact details of what is allowed and the conditions attached.

Further details and discussion regarding the 1992 Act including legislation for Northern Ireland and the Republic of Ireland are contained in a booklet, *Badgers and the Law*, published by the Mammal Society, Unit 15, Cloisters House, Cloisters Business Centre, 8 Battersea Park Road, London SW8 4BG. The text of the Act may be obtained from Her Majesty's Stationery Office, London.

APPENDIX 2

Methods of Ageing Badgers

THERE is no doubt that the ability to age individual animals, whether dead or alive, is an extremely important part of many biological studies. With some species the methods available are relatively straightforward and reliable, but regrettably with badgers this is not the case. There are several reports in the literature of various methods being used with differing degrees of success on badgers (for examples see van Bree *et al.* 1974, Graf & Wandeler 1982, Hancox 1988b, da Silva & Macdonald 1989, Page 1993). Techniques have included measuring tooth wear, which has the advantage of being applicable to both live and dead animals; sectioning teeth and counting the annuli which appear in the dentine and less obviously in the cementum; examining the ossification of the epiphyseal cartilage in the long bones (this can be done by X-ray on live animals), but the technique is only useful for badgers up to about 2 years of age, when the epiphyses are fully closed; measuring the weight and length of the baculum (obviously only of use for males).

The skulls of badgers in their first year of life pass through fairly easily recognised stages (Fig. 2.14), so that it is possible to place specimens into an age category with a reasonable degree of accuracy. After they have reached 1 year of age the practice of ageing individuals becomes rather more difficult.

Four reviews on methods of ageing badgers have been published (Ahnlund 1976, Lups *et al.* 1987, Hancox 1988a, Harris *et al.* 1992). The reader is referred to the most recent of these by Harris *et al.* which recommends a pragmatic approach. Probably the most convenient method is the assessment of tooth wear. Harris *et al.* using known age material to compare with their sample of unknown age, found that this can also be a surprisingly accurate technique, contrary to the findings of some earlier workers. The accuracy of the age assessment was enhanced when the month of death was known, such that when assigning each badger to a year class it was possible to be within 1 year of the correct age in about 90% of cases.

Of course there are certain limitations to the method of assessing the pattern of tooth wear. Diet, soil type, disease and other factors will affect the pattern and rate of tooth wear, and animals in the older age classes become increasingly difficult to age accurately because tooth wear occurs at a negative exponential rate. Thus while it is relatively easy to separate a 2 year old from a 3 year old, it is very much more difficult to distinguish between a 7 and 8 year old. The limitations of the tooth wear technique make it difficult to compare material from different sources or geographical locations. Therefore the tooth wear categories should be regarded as a guide to the various degrees of wear seen on badger teeth, rather than a reference source for the accurate ageing of individuals.

If a large enough, unbiased sample is obtained, and age specific mortality rates are known, the pattern of tooth wear can be used to study the age structure of badger populations, as well as just giving the age of individuals, so there is no doubt that the technique can have great potential in the study of population dynamics.

A combination of methods will be more reliable than just one. Here it is worth sounding a note of caution regarding the sectioning of teeth in order to count annuli in the dentine. In some mammalian studies this technique has proved to be remarkably effective, but in badgers the problem seems to be that the number of annuli observed does not necessarily correspond to the number of years the animal has lived. Annuli may be likened to the growth rings of a tree, with one wide light band and one narrow dark band for each year of growth. Thus animals living in areas of seasonal change, where periods of food shortage occur, show light and dark bands in their teeth which correspond to periods when there is a cessation on the deposition of dentine. Unfortunately this pattern is probably affected by other factors as well as the seasons, so that some known age individuals have a greater number of rings than their age in years would account for.

References

Ahnlund, H. (1976) Age determination in the European badger, *Meles meles* L. *Säugetierkunde* **41:** 119–125.

Ahnlund, H. (1980) Sexual maturity and breeding season of the badger, *Meles meles*, in Sweden. *J. Zool. Lond.* **190:** 77–95.

Andersen, J. (1955) The food of the Danish badger, *Meles meles danicus*, with special reference to the summer months. *Dan. Rev. Game Biol.* **3:** 1–75.

Anderson, R.M. & Trewhella, W. (1985) Population dynamics of the badger (*Meles meles*) and the epidemiology of bovine tuberculosis (*Mycobacterium bovis*). *Phil. Trans. Roy. Soc.* **B310:** 327–381.

Arthur, D.R. (1963) *British Ticks*, London: Butterworths.

Aune, V.A. & Myberget, S. (1969) The present distribution of the badger (*Meles meles*) in Norway. *Fauna* **22:** 27–33.

Barker, G.M.A. (1969) Wytham badger survey . . . diet, unpublished.

Bateman, J.A. (1970) Supernumerary incisors in mustelids. *Mamm. Rev.* **1:** 81–86.

Batten, H.M. (1923) *The Badger Afield and Underground*, London: Witherby.

Batty, A. & Cowlin, R.A.D. (1969) Notes on some Essex badger mortalities. *Essex Nat.* **32:** 240–241.

Baty, F.W. (1952) Letter in *The Field*, 24 October.

Benham, P. (1985) The inter-relationships between cattle and badger behaviour and farm husbandry practices and their relevance to the transmission of *Mycobacterium bovis*. MAFF.

Bere, R. (1970) The status and distribution of badgers in Cornwall, unpublished.

Blakeborough, J.F. & Pease, A.E. (1914) *The Life and Habits of the Badger*, London: Foxhound.

Bobrinskii, N.A., Kuzelzov, B.A., and Kuzyakin, A.P. (1944) *Key to the Mammals of the USSR*, Moscow: State Publishing House Soviet Science.

Bock, W.F. (1988). Untersuchungen zur Lage und Zum Mikrolima von Dachsbauen (*Meles meles*). *Jagdwiss.* **34:** 141–152.

Bonnin-Laffargue, M. & Canivenc, R. (1961) Étude de l'activité du blaireau européen (*Meles meles*). *Mammalia* **25:** 476–484.

Bradbury, K. (1974) The badger's diet. In *Badgers of Yorkshire and Humberside*, R.J. Paget & A.L.V. Middleton (eds.), pp. 113–125. York: Ebor.

Brown, C. The status of badgers in Hampshire. In press.

Brown, C.A.J. (1981) Prey abundance of the European badger (*Meles meles*) in north-east Scotland, *Mammalia* **47:** 81–86.

Brown, C. (1993) The status of the badger in Hampshire. *Proc. Hampsh. Field Club Archaeol.* Soc. **49:** 5–18.

Brown, J.A. (1993) Transmission of bovine tuberculosis (*Mycobacterium bovis*) from badgers (*Meles meles*) to cattle. Ph.D. Thesis, University of Bristol.

Brown, J.A., Harris, S. & Cheeseman, C.L. (1993). The development of field techniques for studying potential modes of transmission of bovine tuberculosis from badgers to cattle. In Hayden, T.J. (ed.), 1993 *The Badger*, 139–153. Dublin Royal Irish Academy.

Budgett, H.M. (1933) *Hunting by Scent*, London: Eyre and Spottiswood.

Bunce, R.C.H., Barr, C.J. & Whittaker, H.A. (1981) Preliminary descriptions for users of the Merlewood Method of land classification. Merlewood Research & Development paper 86.

Burke, N. (1963) *King Todd. The True Story of a Badger*, London: Putnam.

Burke, N. (1964) Some observations on the badger (*Meles meles*). *Trans. Suffolk Nat. Soc.* **12**: 437–442.

Burness, G. (1970a) *The White Badger*, London: Harrap.

Burghess, G (1970b) Seven year watch on a white badger, *Animals* Jan., 404–411.

Burrows, R. (1968) *Wild Fox*, Newton Abbot: David and Charles.

Burton, M. (1957) Badgers' warnings. *Ill. Lond. News*, 23 Nov., 900.

Butterworth, W.C.J.R (1905) *Victoria History of the County of Sussex*, London: Constable.

Canivenc, R. & Bonnin-Laffargue, M. (1966) A study of progestation in the European badger (*Meles meles*). *Symp. Zool. Soc.* **15**: 15–25.

Canivenc, R. & Bonnin-Laffargue, M. (1979) Delayed implantation is under environmental control in the badger (*Meles meles*). *Nature* **278**: 849–850.

Canivenc, R., Bonnin, R. & Ribes, C. (1981) Décleohement de l'ovoimplantation allongement de la phase sombre de la photoperiode chez le blaireau européen, *Meles meles*. Comptes Rendue Hebd. des séances de l'acad. des sci. Paris, **292**: 1009–1012.

Cheeseman, C.L. (1979) The behaviour of badgers, *Applied An. Ethology* **5**: 193.

Cheeseman, C.L. & Mallinson, P.J. (1979) Radiotracking in the study of tuberculosis in badgers, in Amlaner, C.J. & Macdonald, D. *A Handbook of Biotelemetry and Radiotracking*, pp. 649–656, Oxford: Pergamon Press.

Cheeseman, C.L. & Mallinson, P.J. (1981) Behaviour of badgers (*Meles meles*) infected with bovine tuberculosis. *J. Zool.* **194**: 284–289.

Cheeseman, C.L., Jones, G.W., Gallagher, J. & Mallinson, P.J. (1981) The population structure, density and prevalence of tuberculosis (*M. bovis*) in badgers (*Meles meles*) from four areas of south-west England., *J. Appl. Biol.* **18**: 795–804.

Cheeseman, C.L., Wilesmith, J.W., Ryan, J. & Mallinson, P.J. (1987). Badger population dynamics in a high-density area. *Symp. Zool. Soc. Lond.* **58**: 279–294.

Cheeseman, C.L., Cresswell, W.J., Harris, S. & Mallinson, P.J. (1988a). Comparison of dispersal and other movements in two badger (*Meles meles*) populations. *Mamm. Rev.* **18**: 51–59.

Cheeseman, C.L., Wilesmith, J.W., Stuart, F.A. & Mallinson, P.J. (1988b). Dynamics of tuberculosis in a naturally infected badger population. *Mamm. Rev.* **18**: 61–72.

Cheeseman, C.L., Wilesmith, J.W. & Stuart, F.A. (1989). Tuberculosis: the disease and its epidemiology in the badger, a review. *Epidem. Inf.* **103**: 113–125.

Cheeseman, C.L., Mallinson, P.J., Ryan, J. & Wilesmith, J.W. (1993). Recolonisation by badgers in Gloucestershire. In Hayden, T.J. (ed.) 1993 *The Badger* 78–93. Dublin Royal Irish Academy.

Clark, M. (1970) Conservation of badgers in Hertfordshire, *Trans. Herts. Nat. Hist. Soc* **27**: 1–9.

Clark, M. (1981) *Mammal Watching*, London: Severn House Publishers.

Clements, E.D. (1974) National survey in Sussex. *Sussex Trust for Nat. Cons. Mamm. Rep.* for 1970/1.

Clements, E.D. (1995) Percentage of setts in various habitats in selected counties of Great Britain. From Mammal Society Survey (Clements, E.D. in Neal 1986 up-dated). Pers. comm.

Clements, E.D., Neal, E. & Walden, D.W. (1988). The national badger sett survey. *Mamm Rev.* **18**: 1–19.

Cocks, A.H. (1903) The gestation of the badger, *The Zoologist* **7**: 441–443; **8**: 108–114.

Cowland, C.M. (1953) Badger v Fox Letter, in *Countryside*, 19 Nov.

Cowlin, R.A.D. (1977) An excavation of a badger sett in Southend. *Essex Nat.* **39**: 70–72.

Cox, N. (1721) *The Gentleman's Recreation*, London.

Cresswell, P., Harris, S. & Jefferies, D.J. (1990). The history, distribution, status and habitat requirements of the badger in Britain. Nature Conservancy Council, Peterborough.

Cresswell, W.J. & Harris, S. (1988). The effect of weather conditions on the movements and activities of badgers (*Meles meles*) in a suburban environment. *J. Zool. Lond.* **216**: 187–194.

Cresswell, W.J., Harris, S., Cheeseman, C.L. & Mallinson, P.J. (1992) To breed or not to breed: an analysis of the social and density-dependent constraints on the fecundity of female badgers, *Meles meles*. *Phil. Trans. R. Soc. Lond.* **B: 338**, 393–407.

Crossland, J.R. (1934) *Britain's Wonderland of Nature*, London: Odhams.

Cuthbert, J.A. (1973) Some observations on scavenging of salmon carrion. *Western Naturalist* **2**: 71–74.

da Silva, J. & Macdonald, D.W. (1989) Limitations to the use of tooth wear as a means of ageing Eurasian badgers (*Meles meles*). *Rev. Ecol.* (*Terre Vie*), **44**: 275–278.

Dahl, H. (1954) Der Norske Grevling. *Univ. Bergen. Arbon. Nat. Renne* **16**: 5–55.

Darling, F. (1937) *A Herd of Red Deer*. Oxford: Oxford Univ. Press.

Davies, J.M., Roper, T.J. & Shepherdson, D.J. (1987) Seasonal distribution of road kills in the European badger (*Meles meles*). *J. Zool. Lond.* **211**: 525–529.

Dines, A.M. (1981) Phantom vandals. *Beecraft* **11**: 263–265.

Doncaster, C.P. & Woodroffe, R. (1993) Den site can determine shape and size of badger territories: implications for group-living. *Oikos* **66**: 88–93.

Drabble, P. (1969) *Badgers at my Window*, London: Pelham.

Drabble, P. (1970) Aural evidence of spring mating in badgers (*Meles meles*). *J. Zool. London* **162**: 547–548.

Drabble, P. (1971) The function of mutual grooming in badgers (*Meles meles*) *J. Zool. London* **164**: 260.

Dunwell, M.R. & Killingley, A. (1969) The distribution of badger setts in relation to the geology of the Chilterns. *J. Zool. Lond* **158**: 204–208.

Edwards, M. (1966) *The Badgers of Punchbowl Farm,* London: Michael Joseph.

Edwards, M. (1971) *The Valley and the Farm*, London: Michael Joseph.

Ellerman, J.R. & Scott, T.C.S. (1961) Checklist of Palaearctic and Indian Mammals. *Museum (Nat. Hist.)* Lond.

Evans, H.T.J. & Thompson, H.V. (1981) Bovine tuberculosis in cattle in Great Britain. Eradication of the disease from cattle and the role of the badger. (*Meles meles*) as a source of *M.bovis* for cattle. *Anim Regul Stud.* **3**: 191–216.

Evans, P.G.H., Macdonald, D.W. & Cheeseman, C.L. (1989) Social structure of the Eurasian badger (*Meles meles*): genetic evidence. *J. Zool. Lond.* **218**: 587–595.

Ewer, R.F. *The Carnivores*, London: Weidenfeld Nicolson.

Fairley, J.S. (1975) *An Irish Beast book*, Belfast: Blackstaff.

Fargher, S & Morris, P. (1975) An investigation into age determination in the badger, *Meles meles*. M.Sc. thesis, unpub.

Ferris, C. (1986) Mating and early maturity of badgers in Kent. *J. Zool. Lond.* **209**: 282.

Findlay, D.C. (1973) in Clark, R.S. *et. al.*, Bovine tuberculosis in badgers. *PICL Triennial Rev.* 1971–1973.

Fischer, E. (1931) Early stages in the embryology of the badger. *Verv. Anat. Ges. Jena* **40**: 22–34.

Fletcher, M.K., Hunter, K. and Barnett, E.A. (1994) Pesticide poisoning of animals 1993: investigations of suspected incidents in the United Kingdom. Environmental Panel Report, MAFF, London.

Fowler, P.A. & Racey, P.A. (1988) Overwintering strategies of the badger (*Meles meles*) at 57°N *J. Zool. Lond.* **214**: 635–651.

Frank, H.R. (1940) Die Biologie des Dachs. *Z. Jadgk.* **2**: 1–25.

Frewin, B.C. (1976). The excavation of badger setts at Stantonbury and Milton Keynes village. *Milton Keynes Nat. Hist. Soc.* **2**: 20–28.

Frisch, R.E. (1988) Fatness and fertility. *Scientific American* **258**: March, 70–77.

Fries, S. (1880). Uber die Fortpflanzung von *Meles taxus*. *Zool. Anz.* **3**: 486–492.

Fullagher, P.J., Rogers, T.H. & Mansfield, D. (1960) Supernumerary teeth in the badger. *J. Zool.* **133**: 494.

Gallagher, J. & Nelson, J. (1979) Causes of ill health or natural death in badgers in Gloucestershire. *Vet. Rec.*, **105**: 546–551.

Gillam, B. (1967) The distribution of the badger in Wiltshire. *Arch.*, **62**: 143–153.

Göransson, G. (1974) Automatisk registering av grävlingens ak twitet vid grytet. *Fauna och Flora*, **5**: 165–170.

Gorman, M.L., Kruuk, H. & Leitch, A. (1984) Social functions of the sub-caudal scent glands secretions of the European badger (*Meles meles*). *J. Zool. Lond.*, **204**: 549–559.

Graf, M. & Wandeler, A.I. (1982a) The reproductive cycle of male badgers (*Meles meles*) in Switzerland. *Revue suisse Zool*, **89**: 1005–1008.

Graf, M. & Wandeler, A.I. (1982b) Altersbestimmung bei Dachsen (*Meles meles*). *Revue suisse Zool*, **83**: 1017–1023.

Graf, M. & Wandeler, A.I. (1982c) Age determination in badgers (*Meles meles*). *Revue suisse Zool*, **89**: Pt 4: 1017–1023.

Griffiths, H.I. (1993). The Eurasian badger (*Meles meles*) (L. 1758) as a commodity species. *J. Zool. Lond.* **230**: 340–342.

Griffiths, H.I. & Thomas D.H. (1993). The status of the badger (*Meles meles*) (L. 1758) (Carnivora, Mustelidae) in Europe. *Mamm. Rev.* **23**: 17–58.

Grimwood, I. (1976) The Palawan stink badger. *J. Fauna Pres. Soc.* **13**: 279.

Hager, P.D. (1957) Badgers in the south-west Herts/Bucks area of the Chilterns. *Trans. Herts. Nat. His. Soc.* **24**: 201–208.

Hainard, R. (1961) *Mammifères sauvages d'Europe* Delachause et Niestlé, Neuchatel.

Hampton, C. (1947) The badger's funeral. *Field Sports* 7: 24.

Hancox, M.K. (1973) Studies in the ecology of the Eurasian badger (*Meles meles*). Unpublished.

Hancox, M.K. (1980) Parasites and infectious diseases of the Eurasian badger (*Meles meles*): a review. *Mammal Review* **10**: 151–162.

Hancox, M.K. (1988a). A review of age determination criteria in the Eurasian badger. *Lynx.* **24**: 77–86.

Hancox, M.K. (1988b) Field age determination in the European badger. *Rev. Ecol. (Terre Vie)* **43**: 399–404.

Hancox, M. (1988c). Dental anomalies in the Eurasian badger. *J. Zool. Lond.* **216**: 606–608.

Hancox, M. (1988d) The nidicolous fauna of badger setts. *Entomologist Mag.* **124**: 93–95.

Hancox, M. (1991). Badger predation on bumblebees and wasps. *Am. Ent. Soc.* **50**: 35–36.

Harris, S. (1982) Activity patterns and habitat utilisation of badgers (*Meles meles*) in suburban Bristol: a radio-tracking study. *Symp. Zool. Soc. Lond.* **49**: 301–323.

Harris, S. (1984a) Bristol badgers, an urban success, *Living Countryside* 137: 2721–2723.

Harris, S. (1984b) Ecology of urban badgers (*Meles meles*): distribution in Britain and habitat selection, persecution, food and damage in the City of Bristol. *Biol. Conserv.* **28**: 349–375.

Harris, S. & Cresswell, W.J. (1991) Bristol's badgers. In Frey, A.E. (ed.) *Bristol's urban ecology, Bristol Nat. Soc.* special issue, 17–30.

Harris, S., Cresswell, P. & Jefferies, D. (1989a) Surveying badgers. *Mamm. Soc. occasional publn. no: 9.*

Harris, S., Jefferies, D., Cheeseman, C. & Bright, P. (1989b) Projects on badgers. *Mamm. Soc. occasional publn. no 12.*

Harris, S., Cresswell, W.J. & Cheeseman, C.L. (1992) Age determination of badgers (*Meles meles*) from tooth wear: the need for a pragmatic approach. *J. Zool. Lond.* **228**: 679–684.

Harris, S., Jeffries, D., Cheeseman, C. & Booty, C. (1994) Problems with badgers? Report RSPCA, Horsham.

Harting, J.E. (1888) The badger, *Meles taxus. Zoologist* 3: 2.

Henshaw, R.R. (1952) Letter in *Country Life*, 9 May.

Hewer, H.R. & Neal, E.G. (1954) Filming badgers at night, *Discovery*, March 121–124.

Hofer, H. (1988). Variation in resource presence, utilisation and reproductive success within a population of European badgers. *Mammal. Rev.* **18**: 25–36.

Howard, R.W. (1951) Observations on the sexual behaviour of the badger, unpublished.

Howard, R.W. and Bradbury, K. (1979) Feeding by regurgitation in the badger, *J. Zool. Lond.* **188**: 299.

Humphries, D.A. (1958) Badgers in the Cheltenham area. *School Sc. Rev.* **139**: 416–425.

Hunford, D. (1960) Friendly with badgers. *Countryman*, 57: 59–66.

Jackson, H.H.T. (1961) Mammals of Wisconsin. *Univ. Wisconsin Press*, Madison.

Jefferies, D.J. (1968) Causes of badger mortality in eastern counties of England. *J. Zool.* 157: 429–436.

Jefferies, D.J. (1975) 'Different activity patterns of male and female badgers as shown by road mortality. *J. Zool.* 177: 505–506.

Jense, G.K. & Linder, R.L. (1970) Food habits of badgers in eastern South Dakota. *Proc. S.D. Acad. Sci.* 49: 37–41.

Jensen, P.V. (1959) Lidt om gravlingen. *Naturens Verden* 11: 289–320.

Johnson, P.N. (1989) Latrine training of a badger cub. *The Naturalist* 114: 137.

Jones, G.W., Neal, C. & Harris, E.A. (1980) The helminth parasites of the badger (*Meles meles*) in Cornwall. *Mammal Rev.* 10: 163–164.

King, N. & Barker, G.M.A. (1964) Badgers of Old Winchester Hill, Hampshire. Report to Nature Conservancy, unpublished.

King, R.J. (1964) The badger gate, *Q.J. Forestry* 58: 505–506.

Kingdon, J. (1977) *East African Mammals. An Atlas of Evolution in Africa*, London: Academic Press.

Kock, le D. (1965) Ringa the honey badger, *Animals* 7: 333–335.

Kruisinga, D. (1965) Enige winterwaarnemingen aan Dassen en andere Masterachtigen te St Michielsgestel. *De Levende Natuur* 68: 73–83.

Kruuk, H. (1978) Spatial organisation and territorial behaviour of the European badger (*Meles meles*). *J. Zool. Lond.* 184: 1–19.

Kruuk, H. (1989) The Social Badger. Oxford: Oxford University Press.

Kruuk, H. & Macdonald, D. (1985) Group territories of carnivores: empires and enclaves. *Symp. British Ecol. Soc.* 25: 521–536.

Kruuk, H. & de Kock, L. (1981) Food and habitats of badgers (*meles meles*) on Monte Baldo, Northern Italy. *Z. Saugetierk.* 48: 45–50.

Kruuk, H. & Parish, T. (1977) Behaviour of badgers. *ITE Env. Res. Council* 1–16.

Kruuk, H. & Parish, T. (1981) Feeding specialisation of the European badger, *Meles meles*, in Scotland. *J. Anim. Ecol.* 50: 773–788.

Kruuk, H. & Parish, T. (1982) Factors affecting population density, group size and territory size of the European badger (*Meles meles*). *J. Zool. Lond.* 196: 31–39.

Kruuk, H. & Parish, T. (1987) Changes in the size of groups and ranges of the European badger (*Meles meles L.*) in an area in Scotland. *J. Anim. Ecol.* 56: 351–364.

Kruuk, H. & Parish, T. (1985) Food, food availability and weight of badgers, *Meles meles*, in relation to agricultural change. *J. App. Ecol.* 22: 705–715.

Kruuk, H., Parish, T., Brown, C.A.J. & Carera, J. (1979) The use of pasture by the European badger (*Meles meles*). *J. App. Ecol.* 16: 453–459.

Kruuk, H., Gorman, M. & Parish, T. (1980) The use of ^{65}Zn for estimating populations of carnivores. *Oikos* 34: 206–208.

Kruuk, H., Gorman, M. & Leitch, A. (1984) Scent marking with the sub-caudal gland by the European badger (*Meles meles*). *Anim. Behav.* 32: 899–907.

Kurten, B. (1968) *Pleistocene Mammals of Europe*, London: Weidenfeld & Nicolson.

Lampe, R.P. (1976) Aspects of the predatory strategy of the North American badger (*Taxidea taxus*). Ph.D. Thesis, University of Minnesota.

Lancum, F.H. (1954) *Badgers' Year*, London: Crosby and Lockwood.

Lawrence, M.J. & Brown, R.W. (1973) *Mammals of Britain, their Tracks, Trails and Signs*, Poole: Blandford Press.

Leeson, R.C. & Mills, B.M.C. (1977) Survey of excavated badger setts in the county of Avon. ADAS, MAFF.

Likhachev, G.N. (1956) Some ecological traits of the badger of the Tula Abatis broadleaf forest. Studies on mammals in Govt. Reserves. Min. of Ag. Moscow.

Lindsay, I.M. & Macdonald, D.J. (1985) The effect of disturbance on the emergence times of Eurasian badgers in winter. *Biol. Conserv.* **34**: 289–306.

Lindzey, F.G. (1976) Characteristics of the natal den of the badger (*Taxidea taxus*). *Northwest Science* **50**: 178–180.

Little, T.W.A., Naylor, P.F. & Wilesmith, J.W. (1982) Laboratory studies of *Mycobacterium bovis* infection in badgers and cattle. *Vet. Rec.* **111**: 550–557.

Lloyd, J.R. (1968) Factors affecting the emergence time of badgers (*Meles meles*) in Britain. *J. Zool.* **155**: 223–227.

Long, C.A. (1972) Taxonomic revision of the North American badger (*Taxidea taxus*). *J. Mammal.* **53**: 725–759.

Long, C.A. & Killingley, C.A. (1983) *The Badgers of the World*, Charles C. Thomas, Springfield, Illinois.

Lups, P. (1990) Untersuchungen am P1 im Gebib des Europäischen Dachses, *Meles meles*. *Z. Saugetierk.* **55**: 16–27.

Lups, P., & Roper, T.J. (1990) Cannibalism in a female badger: infanticide or predation? *J. Zool. Lond.* **221**: 314–315.

Lups, P., Graf, M. & Kappeler, A. (1987) Möglichkeiten der Altersbestimmung beim Dachs *Meles meles (L). Jb. naturh. Mus. Bern.* **9**: 185–200.

Lynch, J.M., O'Corry-Crowe, G., Cheeseman, C.L., Harris, S. & Hayden, T.J. (1993) Morphogenetic variation among badger populations. In Hayden, T.J. (Ed.), pp. 94–107. *The Badger*, Royal Irish Academy, Dublin.

Macdonald, D.W. (1980) Patterns of scent marking with urine and faeces amongst carnivore communities. *Symp. Zool. Soc. Lond.* **45**: 107–139.

Macdonald, D. (1985) Badgers and bovine tuberculosis — case not proven. *New Scientist*, 25 October.

Macdonald, D. (1993) It's tough at the top. *Natural World* **37**: 26–28.

MacNally, J. (1970) *Highland Deer Forest*, London: Dent.

Madge, G. (1982) Badgers move to a better hole. *The Countryman* **87**: 87–92.

MAFF (1976–1994) Bovine Tuberculosis in badgers. London: MAFF.

MAFF (Ministry of Agriculture, Fisheries and Food) (1984) *A review of bovine tuberculosis in Great Britain*, London: HMSO.

Malins, C.W. (1974) *Bully and the Badger*, London: Yeatman.

Mallinson, R.H. (1954) *The Field*, 25 March 1954.

Marshall, P. (1967) The Chinese Ferret badger. *Animals* **10**: 357.

Martin-Franquelo, R. & Delibes, M. (1985) Biology of the badger (*Meles meles*) in Doñana, Mediterranean Spain. 4th International Theriological Congress, Edmonton, 1985.

Maurel, D. (1981) Variations saisonnieres des fonctions testiculaire et thyroidienne en relation avec l'utilisation de l'espace et du temps chez le blaireau europèen *Meles meles* et le renard roux, *Vulpes vulpes*, These Doct. es Sciences, Université Montpellier.

Maurel, D. & Boissin (1979) Seasonal variations of thyroid gland activity in the male badger (*Meles meles*). *Gen. Comp. Endocr.* **38**: 207–214.

Maurel, D. & Boissin (1983) Seasonal rhythms of locomotor activity and thyroid function in male badgers (*Meles meles*). *J. Interdiscipl. Cycle Res.* **14**: 285–303.

Melgren, R.I. & Roper, T.J. (1986) Spatial learning and discrimination of food patches in the European badger. *Anim. Behav.* **34**: 1129–1134.

Messick, J.P. (1987) North American Badger. In *Wild furbearer management and conservation in North America* (Ed. Nooak *et al.*). Ministry Nat. Resources, Ontario, Canada.

Messick, J.P. & Hornocker, M.G. (1981) Ecology of the badger in south-western Idaho. *Wildlife Monographs* **76**: 1–53.

Middleton, A.D. (1935) The food of the badger, *Meles meles*. *J. Anim. Ecol.* **4**: 291.

Milner, C. (1967) Badger damage to upland pasture. *J. Zool.* **153**: 554–556.

Moysey, G.F. (1959) Badger activity automatically recorded. *Bull. Mamm. Soc.* **12**: 19–23.

Muirhead, R.A., Gallagher, J. & Burn, K.S. (1974) Tuberculosis in wild badgers in Gloucestershire: epidemiology. *Vet. Rev.* **95**: 525–555.

Murray, R.R. (1968) Concern for the badger. *Animals* **11**: 302–304.

Neal, E.G. (1948) *The Badger* (4th edn, 1975), London: Collins.

Neal, E.G. (1962) The reproductive cycle of the badger. *Bull. Mamm. Soc.* **10**: 15–17.

Neal, E.G. (1964) The breeding behaviour of badgers. *Animals* **5**: 302–306.

Neal, E.G. (1965) Implantation in the badger. *Bull. Mamm. Soc.* **24**: 6–8.

Neal, E.G. (1966) Ecology of the badger in Somerset. *Proc. Som. Arch. Nat. Hist. Soc.* **110**: 17–23.

Neal, E.G. (1969) Badger nests above ground. In *Countryman Wildlife Book*, Bruce Campbell (ed), pp. 122–127. Newton Abbot: David and Charles.

Neal, E.G. (1972a) The National Badger Survey, *Mamm. Rev.* **2**: 55–64.

Neal, E.G. (1972b) Conservation of badgers. In *Everyman's Nature Reserve*, Newton Abbot: David and Charles.

Neal, E.G. (1977) *Badgers*, Poole: Blandford Press.

Neal, E.G. (1982) Badgers make hay. In *The Countryman* **87**: 102–106.

Neal, E.G. (1986). *The Natural History of Badgers.* Beckenham, Kent: Croom Helm.

Neal, E.G. (1987). A litter of five badger cubs in an overground nest. *J. Zool. Lond.* **212**: 349–350.

Neal, E.G. (1988). Status of badgers in Somerset. 24th Annual Report, Somerset Trust for Nature Conservation.

Neal, E.G. (1988). The stomach contents of badgers. *J. Zool. Lond.* **215**: 367–369.

Neal, E.G. & Harrison, R. (1958) Reproduction in the European badger (*Meles meles*). *Trans. Zool. Soc. Lond.* **29**: 67–131.

Neal, E. & Roper, T.J. (1991). The environmental impact of badgers (*Meles meles*) and their setts. *Symp. Zool. Soc. Lond.* **63**: 89–106.

Neal, K.R.C. & Avery, R.A. (1956) Observations on badgers in the Quantocks, unpublished.

Newcombe, M.J. (1982) Some observations on the badger in Kent. *Trans. Kent Field Club* **9**: 16–30.

Notini, G. (1948) Biologiska undersökningar över gravlingen, *Meles meles. Svenska Jägareförbundet Meddelande*, **13** (Uppsala) 1–256.

Novikov, G.A. (1956) 'Carnivorous mammals of the fauna of the USSR. In *Key to the Fauna of the USSR 62. Trans. Israel Prog. Sci. Trans* (1962), Jerusalem.

Nowak, R.M. & Paradiso, J.L. (1983) *Walker's Mammals of the World Vol. 2*, Baltimore: Johns Hopkins.

O'Kelly, J.H. (1969) Funeral of a badger. In *The Field*, 31 July.

Ognev, S.I. (1935) Mammals of the USSR and adjacent countries. *Trans. Israel Prog. Sci. Trans III* (1962), Jerusalem.

Orchard, J. (1958) Wildlife and tame. In *Countryman* **55**: 437–438.

Page, R.J.C. (1993) X-ray method for determination of the age of live badgers (*Meles meles*) in the field. *Mammalia* **57**: 123–126.

Page, R.J.C., Ross, J, & Langton, S.G. (1994) Seasonality of reproduction in the European badger, *Meles meles*, in south-west England. *J. Zool. Lond.* **233**: 60–91.

Paget, R.J. (1980) Dormancy of a badger outside the sett entrance. *J. Zool. Soc. Lond.* **192**: 558.

Paget, R.J. & Middleton, A.L.F. (1974a) Some observations on the sexual activities of badgers in Yorkshire in the months December–April. *J. Zool.*, **173**: 256–260.

Paget, R.J. Middleton, A.L.F. (1974b) *Badgers of Yorkshire and Humberside*, York: Ebor.

Palmer, N.B. (1959) Effect of isolation on behaviour of badgers. *Chelt. Grammar Sc. Biology Report*, **3**.

Parker, C. (1979) Birth, care and development of Chinese hog badgers (*Arctonyx collaris albogularis*) at Metro Toronto Zoo, *Int. Zoo Year Book* **19**: 182–185.

Pearson, O.P. & Enders, R.K. (1944) Distribution of pregnancy in certain Mustelids. *J. Exp. Zool.* **95**: 21.

Pease, A.E. (1898) *The Badger*, London: Lawrence and Bullen.

Petter, G. (1971) Origine, phylogenie et systematiquie des blaireaux. *Mammalia* **35**: 567–597.

Pickvance, T.J. & Babb, H.E.E. (1960) Badgers and badger setts on Bredon Hill, Worcestershire. *Proc. Birmingham Nat. Hist. Soc.* **20**: 41–47.

Pigozzi, G. (1988) Diet of the European badger (*Meles meles*) in the Maremma National Park, Central Italy. *Mamm. Rev.* **18**: 73–75.

Pitt, F. (1935) The increase in the badger (*Meles meles*) in Great Britain during the period 1900–1934, with special reference to the Wheatland area of Shropshire. *J. Anim. Ecol.* **4**: 1–6.

Pitt F. (1941) The badger in Britain, *J. Soc. Faun. Pres. Emp.* **42**: 17–21.

Pocock, R.I. (1911) Some probable and possible instances of warning characteristics amongst insectivorous and carnivorous mammals *Ann. Mag. N.H.* **8**: 750–757.

Pocock, R.I. (1940) Hog Badgers (*Arctonyx*) of British India. *J. Bombay N.H. Soc.* **41**: 46

Popescu, A. & Sin, G. (1968) Le terrier et la nourriture du blaireau (*Meles meles*) dans les conditions de la steppe de Dobrouja, *Centen. vol. Mus. Nat. Hist. Grigore Antiopa* **8**: 1003–1012.

Ramakantha, V. Ferret badgers (Melogale spp) in Manipur and a report on the birth of badger cubs in captivity. Zoo's Print, Feb. 1992, 16–17.

Ransome, R.D. (1958) Badger expansion around Cheltenham and factors affecting emergence. *Cheltenham Grammar School Report*, **2**: 5–9.

Ratcliffe, E.G. (1974) Wildlife consideration for the highway designer. *J. Inst. Mun. Engineer* **101**: 289–294.

Ringberg, T. & Oen, E. (1978). Hormonal aspects of winter dormancy in the European badger. *Proc. Alaska Sci. Conf.* **29**: 637.

Roberts, T.V. (1893) *Trans. Herts. Nat. Hist. Soc.* **57**: 160–161.

Rodriguez, A. & Delibes, M. (1992) Food habits of badgers (*Meles meles*) in an arid habitat. *J. Zool. Lond.* **227**: 347–350.

Roper, T.J. (1992). Badger (*Meles meles*) setts – architectural, internal environment and function. *Mamm. Rev.* **22**: 43–53.

Roper, T.J. (1994). Do badgers (*Meles meles*) bury their dead? *J. Zool. Lond.* **234**: 677–680.

Roper, T.J. & Mickevicius, E. Badger (*Meles meles*) diet: a review of literature from the former Soviet Union, *Mamm. Rev.* (in press).

Roper, T.J. & Mickevicius, E. Badger, *Meles meles*, diet: a review of literature from the former Soviet Union. *Mammal Review*, (in press).

Roper, T.J. Shepherdson, D.J. & Davies, J.M. (1986) Secret marking with faeces and anal secretion in the European badger (*Meles meles*): seasonal and spatial characteristics of latrine use in relation to territoriality. *Behaviour* **97**: 94–117.

Roper, T.J., Tait, A.I. & Christian, S. (1991). Internal structure and contents of three badger (*Meles meles*) setts. *J. Zool. Lond.* **225**: 115–124.

Roper, T.J., Christian, S., Fee, D. & Tait, A.I. (1992). Structure and contents of four badger (*Meles meles*) setts. *Mammalia* **56**: A65–70.

Russell, C. (1967) National badger survey – Shropshire. *Bull. Shropshire Trust for Nature Conservation*, 16–18.

Sankey, J.H.P. (1955) Observations on the European badger (*Meles meles*). *South-eastern Naturalist and Antiquary* **60**: 20–34.

Sargeant, A.B. & Warner, D.W. (1972) Movements and denning habits of a badger (*Taxidea taxus*). *J. Mamm.* **53**: 207–210.

Satchell, J.E. (1967) Lumbricidae. In Burgess, A. and Raw, F. (eds.), *Soil Biology*, Academic Press, London and New York, 259–322.

Schlegel, M. (1933) Die Lungenwormeuche beim Dachs. *Berlin Terarztl. Wschr* **341**: 344.

Schmidt, P. & Lups, P. (1988) Zur Bedeutung von Vespen (Vespidae) als Nähring des Dachses, *Meles meles Bonn Zool. Beitr.* **39**: 43–47.

Scott, D.R. (1960) The badger in Essex. *Essex Nat.* **30**: 272–275.

Shaw, P. (1994). Orchid woods and floating islands – the ecology of fly ash. *British Wildlife* **5**: 149–157.

Shepherd, S. (1964) *Brocky*, London: Longmans.

Shepherdson, D.A., Roper, T.J. & Lups, P. (1990) Diet, food availability and foraging behaviour of badgers (*Meles meles*) in Southern England. *Z. Saugetierk.* **55**: 81–93.

Skinner, C., Skinner, P. & Harris, S. (1991) An analysis of some of the factors affecting the current distribution of badger setts in Essex. *Mamm. Rev.* **21**: 51–67.

Skoog, P. (1970) *The Food of the Swedish badger*, Svenska Jagareforb, Vitrevy 7.

Soper, E.A. (1955) *When Badgers Wake*, London: Routledge and Kegan Paul.

Soper, E.A.(1957) *Wild Encounters*, London: Routledge and Kegan Paul.

Southern, H.N. (ed). (1964) *The Handbook of British Mammals*, Oxford: Blackwell.

Speakman, F.J. (1965) *A Forest by Night,*, London: Bell.

Steck, F. (1982) Rabies in wildlife. In Edwards, M.A. and MacDaniel (eds). *Animal diseases in relation to animal conservation*. London: Academic Press.

Stocker, G. & Lups (1984) Qualitative and quantitative aspects of food consumption of badgers, *Meles meles*, in Swiss Midlands. *Rev. Suisse Zool.* **92**: 1007–1015 (In German with English and French summaries).

Stubbe, M. (1970) Population biology of the badger (*Meles meles*). *Trans. Internat. Cong. Game Biologist*, Moscow **9**: 544.

Stubbe, M. (1971) Die Analen Markierungsorgane der Dachses (*Meles meles*). *Zool. Gart. N.F. Keipsig* **40**: 125–135.

Stubbe, M. (1973) Schutz und Hege des Dachses (*Meles meles*), in *Buch der hege, Bd 1: Haarwild*, VEB Deutscher Landwirtschaftsverlag, Berlin, pp. 227–249.

Stubbe, M. (1980) Biometrie und Morphologie des Mitteleuropäischen Dachses (*Meles meles*). *Saugetierk, Inform 1*, 3026.

Sykes, S.K. (1964) The ratel or honey badger. *Afr. Wildlife* **18**: 29–37.

Symes, R.G. (1989) Badger damage: fact or fiction? In *Mammals as pests*, Putnam, R. (ed.), pp. 196–206. London: Chapman & Hall.

Teagle, W.G. (1969) The badger in the London area. *Lond. Nat.* **48**: 48–75.

Thompson, G.B. (1961) The ectoparasites of the badger (*Meles meles*). *Eng. Mon. Mag.* **97**: 156–158.

Thornton, P. (1988) Density and distribution of badgers in South-West England – a predictive model. *Mamm. Rev.* **18**: 1–23.

Tinelli, A. & Tinelli, P. (1980) Le tane di istrice e di tasso. *Proc. La Reserva Presidenziale di Castelporziane*, Segretariat (Generale Della Presidinza Della Republica), Nr Roma, Italy.

Tischler, W. (1965) *Agrarokologie*, Fischer, Jenja.

Tregarthhen, J.C. (1925) *The Life Story of a Badger*, London: Murray.

van Bree, P.J.H., van Soest, R.W.M. & Stroman, L. (1974) Tooth wear as an indication of age in badgers (*Meles meles*) and red foxes (*Vulpes vulpes*). *Z. Saugetierk* **39**: 243–248.

Vesey-Fitzerald, B. (1942) *A Country Chronicle*, London: Chapman and Hall.

Walker, E.P. (1964) *Mammals of the World* (4th edn, 1983), Baltimore: Johns Hopkins.

Wandeler, A.I. & Graf, M. (1982) The reproductive cycle of female badgers (*Meles meles*) in Switzerland. *Revue suisse Zool.* **89**: 1009–1016.

Weber, J.M. & Aubry, S. (1994) Dietary response of the European badger (*Meles meles*) during a population outbreak of water voles (*Arvicola terrestris*). *J. Zool. Lond.* **234**: 687–690.

White, P.C.L., Brown, J.A. & Harris, S. (1993) Badgers (*Meles meles*), cattle and bovine tuberculosis (*Mycobacterium bovis*): a hypothesis to explain the influence of habitat on the risk of disease transmission in Southwest England. *Proc. R. Soc. Lond.* **253**: 277–284.

Wiertz, J. (1976) De voedsel-ecologie van de das (*Meles meles*) in Nederland. *Rijks Instituut voor Natuurbeheer Report*, 79/9, Leersum, Netherlands.

Wiertz, J. (1993) Fluctuations in the Dutch badger (*Meles meles*) population between 1960 and 1990. *Mamm. Rev.* **23**: 58–64.

Wijngaarden, A. van & Peppel, J. van de (1964) The badger (*Meles meles*) in the Netherlands. *Lutra* **6**: 1–60.

Wilesmith, J.W., Little, T.W.A., Thompson, H.V. & Swan, C. (1982) Bovine tuberculosis in domestic and wild mammals in an area of Dorset. I. Tuberculosis in cattle. *J. Hyg.* **89**: 37–48.

Wilesmith, J.W., Sayers, P.E., Little, T.W.A., Brewer, J.I., Bode, R., Hillman, G.D.B., Pritchard, D.G. & Stuart, F.A. (1986) Tuberculosis in East Sussex. IV: A systematic examination of wild animals other than badgers for tuberculosis. *J. Hyg.* **97**: 37–48.

Willan, R.L. (1963) Unwelcome squatters and their hosts. *Ill. Lond. News*, 3 December, 867.

Wilson, C.J. (1993) Badger damage to growing oats and an assessment of electric fencing as a means of its reduction. *J. Zool. Lond.* **231**: 668–675.

Winsatt, W.A. (1963) Delayed implantation in the Ursidae. In Enders, A.C. (ed.), pp. 49–73, *Delayed Implantation*, Chicago: Chicago University Press.

Wood, J.E. (1958) Age structure and reproductivity of a grey fox population. *J. Mamm.* **39**: 74–86.

Woodroffe, R. (1993) Alloparental behaviour in the European badger, *Meles meles, J. Anim. Beh.* **46**: 413–415.

Woodroffe, R. Body condition affects implantation date in the European badger, *Meles meles. J. Zool. Lond.* (in press).

Woodroffe, R. & Macdonald, D. Female/female competition in European badgers, *Meles meles*, and effect on breeding success. *J. Anim. Ecol.* (in press).

Woodroffe, R., Macdonald, D. & da Silva, J. Dispersal and philopatry in the European badger, *Meles meles*, (in press).

World Wildlife Fund (1984) *Wildlife Link Report: badgers, cattle and bovine tuberculosis*, Godalming, Surrey.

Wright, P.L. (1969) The reproductive cycle of the American badger *(Taxidea taxus) J. Reprod. Fert. Suppl.* 435–445.

Wright, P.L. (1984) The reproductive cycle of the male American badger (*Taxidea taxus*). *J. Reprod. Fert. Suppl.* **6**: 435–445.

Yamamoto, Y. (1991) Food habits of *Meles meles anakuma* in Mt. Nyugasi, Nagano, Pref., Japan. *Nat. Envir. Sci. Res.* **4**: 73–83.

Zunker, M. (1954) L'importance des renards dans le propagation de la rage en allemagne. *Bull. Office Internal. Epizooties* **42**: 83–93.

Index